D0948165

palgrave advances in thomas hardy studies

Palgrave Advances

Titles include:

Phillip Mallett (*editor*)
THOMAS HARDY STUDIES

Lois Oppenheim (*editor*)
SAMUEL BECKETT STUDIES

Jean-Michel Rabaté (*editor*)
JAMES JOYCE STUDIES

Forthcoming:

Patrick Finney (*editor*)
INTERNATIONAL HISTORY

Robert Patten and John Bowen (*editors*)
CHARLES DICKENS STUDIES

Frederick S. Roden (*editor*)
OSCAR WILDE STUDIES

Anna Snaith (*editor*)
VIRGINIA WOOLF STUDIES

Nicholas Williams (*editor*)
WILLIAM BLAKE STUDIES

Jonathan Woolfson (*editor*)
RENAISSANCE HISTORIOGRAPHY

Palgrave Advances
Series Standing Order ISBN 1–4039–3512–2 (Hardback) 1–4039–35⌐3–0 (Paperback)
(*outside North America only*)

You can receive future titles in this series as they are published by placing a standing order.
Please contact your bookseller or, in the case of difficulty, write to us at the address below
with your name and address, the title of the series and the ISBN quoted above.

Customer Services Department, Macmillan Distribution Ltd, Houndmills, Basingstoke,
Hampshire RG21 6XS, England

palgrave advances in
thomas hardy studies

edited by
phillip mallett
university of st andrews

palgrave
macmillan

First published 2004 by
PALGRAVE MACMILLAN
Houndmills, Basingstoke, Hampshire RG21 6XS and
175 Fifth Avenue, New York, N.Y. 10010
Companies and representatives throughout the world

PALGRAVE MACMILLAN is the global academic imprint of the
Palgrave Macmillan division of St Martin's Press LLC and of
Palgrave Macmillan Ltd.
Macmillan® is a registered trademark in the United States,
United Kingdom and other countries. Palgrave is a registered
trademark in the European Union and other countries.

ISBN 1–4039–0257–7 hardback
ISBN 1–4039–0258–5 paperback

This book is printed on paper suitable for recycling and
made from fully managed and sustained forest sources.

A catalogue record for this book is available
from the British Library.

Library of Congress Cataloging-in-Publication Data
Palgrave advances in Thomas Hardy studies / edited by Phillip Mallett.
p. cm.
Includes bibliographical references (p.) and index.
ISBN 1–4039–0257–7 (cloth) —ISBN 1–4039–0258–5 (paper)
1. Hardy, Thomas, 1840–1928—Criticism and interpretation. 2. Wessex
(England)—In literature. I. Mallett, Phillip, 1946–

PR4754.P35 2004
823'.8—dc22   2004044365

10 9 8 7 6 5 4 3 2 1
13 12 11 10 09 08 07 06 05 04

Printed and bound in Great Britain by
Antony Rowe Ltd, Chippenham, Wiltshire

notes on the contributors

Professor Roger Ebbatson teaches English at Loughborough University. His work on Hardy includes editions of *A Pair of Blue Eyes* and *The Trumpet-Major* for Penguin Classics, as well as *The Evolutionary Self* (1982) and *Hardy: The Margin of the Unexpressed* (1993). He is currently working on a study of literary Englishness.

John Hughes is Lecturer in English at Cheltenham and Gloucester College of Higher Education. He is the author of *Lines of Flight* (1997) and *'Ecstatic Sound': Music and Individuality in the Work of Thomas Hardy* (2001).

Charles Lock is Professor of English at the University of Copenhagen, and has also held teaching appointments at the Universities of Karlstadt and Toronto. In addition to essays and articles on John Cowper Powys, Hopkins, Dostoevsky and Bakhtin, among others, he is the author of *Thomas Hardy: Criticism in Focus* (1992).

Phillip Mallett is Senior Lecturer in English at the University of St Andrews. He has edited *The Return of the Native* and *The Mayor of Casterbridge* for Norton, as well as several collections of essays on Hardy, including *The Achievement of Thomas Hardy* (2000) and *Thomas Hardy: Texts and Contexts* (2002) for Palgrave Macmillan. His most recent work, *Rudyard Kipling: A Literary Life*, was published in 2003.

Rosemarie Morgan teaches English at Yale. Her work on Hardy includes *Women and Sexuality in the Novels of Thomas Hardy* (1988) and *Cancelled Words: Rediscovering Thomas Hardy* (1992), several collections of edited essays, including *Editing Hardy* (1999), and an edition for Penguin of *Far from the Madding Crowd*. She is President of the Thomas Hardy Association.

Richard Nemesvari teaches at St Francis Xavier University. His published work includes editions of *Jane Eyre* and Mrs Braddon's *Aurora Floyd*, as well as Hardy's *The Trumpet-Major*. He is the co-editor, with Rosemarie Morgan, of *Human Shows: Essays in Honour of Michael Millgate* (2000).

Ralph Pite is Senior lecturer in English at Liverpool University. His published work includes *The Circle of Our Vision: Dante's Presence in English Romantic Poetry* (1994), and more recently *Hardy's Geography: Wessex and the Regional Novel* (2002). He is currently working on *The Guarded Life*, a biography of Hardy.

Angelique Richardson is Senior Lecturer in Victorian Culture at Exeter University. She is the author of *Love and Eugenics in the Late Nineteenth Century: Rational Reproduction and the New Woman* (2003), editor of *Women Who Did: Stories by Men and Women, 1890–1914* (2002), and co-editor of *The New Woman in Fiction and in Fact: Fin-de-Siècle Feminisms* (2001). She is currently working on a study of Hardy and the unconscious.

Mary Rimmer teaches English at the University of New Brunswick, Canada. In addition to numerous articles and chapters, her work on Hardy includes the recent Penguin edition of *Desperate Remedies*. She is currently working on a study of allusions in Hardy's writing.

Professor Linda Shires teaches English at Syracuse University. She is the author of a study of *British Poetry of the Second World War* (1985), and editor of a collection of essays, *Rewriting the Victorians: History, Theory, and the Politics of Gender* (1992). In addition to a number of essays, her work on Hardy includes editions of *The Trumpet-Major* and *Far from the Madding Crowd*.

John Powell Ward taught English at the University of Wales, Swansea. He is the author of critical studies of Wordsworth, Raymond Williams, and R. S. Thomas, as well as volumes of poetry, including *The Clearing* (1985). His study of *The English Line: Poetry of the Unpoetic from Wordsworth to Larkin* was published in 1991.

contents

chronology

1840 *2 June*   Born at Higher Bockhampton, near Dorchester, the first of four children of Thomas Hardy, builder, and his wife Jemima, née Hand. Three other children follow: Mary (1841–1915), Henry (1851–1928), and Katharine, usually called Kate (1856–1940).

1848   Attends the newly established National School in Lower Bockhampton; one of the founders of the school, Mrs Julia Augusta Martin, takes a special interest in him.

1850   Moves to the British School in Dorchester, run on Nonconformist lines by Isaac Last; begins to learn Latin.

1853   Last starts an independent academy in Dorchester; Hardy's studies with him continue until 1856.

1856 *July*   Joins the Dorchester office of the architect, John Hicks, as an apprentice. About this time forms friendship with Horace Moule, son of the Rev. Henry Moule, Vicar of Fordington, who encourages his studies.

1858   The poem 'Domicilium' probably written about this time, after the death of his grandmother, Mary Hardy, in January 1857.

1860   Completes his apprenticeship; stays on as Hicks's assistant.

1862 *April*   Moves to London, where he works in the office of Arthur (later Sir Arthur) Blomfield, an architect specialising in church restoration and design. Hardy makes regular visits to the National Gallery, and soon begins his 'Schools of Painting' notebook.

James Whitehead teaches English at Radley College in Oxfordshire. The author of a number of articles on Hardy, he is currently working on a study of *Hardy and the Poetry of Empire*.

1863		Forms a close relationship with Eliza Bright Nicholls, its course possibly reflected in the 'She, to Him' sonnets. The relationship founders around 1867, when Hardy comes to prefer her younger sister Mary.
1865	*March*	Hardy's sketch 'How I Built Myself a House' is published in *Chamber's Journal*.
1867		Leaves London to resume work with Hicks in Dorchester. Begins his first novel, *The Poor Man and the Lady*.
1868		Submits manuscript of *The Poor Man and the Lady* to Chapman & Hall in December; it is rejected in February 1869.
1869	*March*	Hardy meets George Meredith in the London office of Chapman & Hall, and is encouraged by him to continue writing.
	April	Invited to join the architectural practice of G. R. Crickmay in Weymouth. Further efforts to place *The Poor Man and the Lady* are unsuccessful; begins work on *Desperate Remedies*.
1870	*March*	Sent by Crickmay to examine the church at St Juliot, Cornwall, where he meets and falls in love with Emma Lavinia Gifford.
1871	*March*	*Desperate Remedies* published by Tinsley Brothers, at Hardy's expense; at work on his next novel, *Under the Greenwood Tree*, completed by the summer.
1872	*June*	*Under the Greenwood Tree* published by Tinsley (to whom Hardy has sold the copyright); it is moderately successful.
	August	*A Pair of Blue Eyes* begins publication in *Tinsley's Magazine*, in eleven monthly instalments; it appears in volume form in May 1873.
1873	*September*	Horace Moule commits suicide.
1874	*January*	Serialisation of *Far from the Madding Crowd* begins in the *Cornhill Magazine*, under the editorship of Leslie Stephen. The volume publication, in November, brings Hardy his first major success.
	September	Marries Emma Gifford at St Peter's, Paddington. After a honeymoon in France, they settle in the Paddington district.
1875		Moves to Swanage, Dorset; works on *The Hand of Ethelberta*, which begins serial publication in the *Cornhill* in July.

1876		Moves first to Yeovil, later to Sturminster Newton (in July); Hardy and Emma visit Holland and Germany in May.
1878	*January*	*The Return of the Native* begins serialisation in *Belgravia*, after being rejected by both Leslie Stephen and John Blackwood as unsuitable for family reading.
	March	The Hardys move to London; Hardy begins work on *The Trumpet-Major*. He is elected to the Savile Club.
1879		Hardy reviews William Barnes's *Poems of Rural Life*.
1880	*January*	Serialisation begins of *The Trumpet-Major*, published in volume form in October.
	October	Hardy falls ill, and is unable to leave the house until April the following year. Much of *A Laodicean*, which begins serialisation in December, is dictated to Emma.
1881	*June*	The Hardys leave London for Wimborne in Dorset. *A Laodicean* appears in volume form in November.
1882		Serialisation begins of *Two on a Tower*, with volume publication in October.
1883		The Hardys move to Dorchester; construction of Max Gate begins in November.
1885		*The Mayor of Casterbridge* is completed in April, ready for serial and volume publication in 1886. In June the Hardys move into Max Gate.
1887		*The Woodlanders* is published in volume form in March, when the Hardys take a holiday in Italy.
1888		*Wessex Tales* is published. The Hardys visit Paris.
1890		*A Group of Noble Dames* begins serialisation in December, with volume publication in May 1891.
1891		*Tess of the d'Urbervilles* begins serial publication in July; volume publication follows in December.
1892	*July*	Death of Hardy's father.
	October	Serial publication of *The Pursuit of the Well-Beloved* begins.
1893		While on a visit to Dublin with Emma, Hardy meets Florence Henniker for the first time.
1894		*Life's Little Ironies* published in February. Serial publication of *Jude the Obscure* begins in December.
1895		*Jude* comes out in volume form in November. The first collected edition of Hardy's work, published by Osgood, McIlvaine, begins to appear.

1896	The Hardys visit the site of the Battle of Waterloo.
1897	*The Well-Beloved* published in volume form in March. The Hardys holiday in Switzerland.
1898 *December*	Hardy publishes his first poetry collection, *Wessex Poems*.
1899	Hardy's dismay at the outbreak of the South African war is reflected in a number of poems.
1901	*Poems of the Past and the Present* published in November.
1904	Part First of *The Dynasts* is published. Hardy's mother dies in April.
1905 *April*	Hardy receives his first honorary degree, from Aberdeen University. Probably meets Florence Dugdale during this year.
1906	Part Second of *The Dynasts* is published.
1908	Part Third of *The Dynasts* is published in February.
1909	*Time's Laughingstocks* published in December. Hardy becomes President of the Society of Authors.
1910 *July*	Hardy awarded the Order of Merit by King George V; receives Freedom of Dorchester in November.
1911	Emma Hardy completes her *Some Recollections*.
1912	The Wessex Edition (Macmillan) begins to appear. In June Hardy receives the Gold Medal of the Royal Society of Literature.
November	Emma Hardy dies on 27 November; Hardy begins the sequence of 'Poems of 1912–13'.
1913 *March*	Hardy visits scenes of his courtship of Emma in Cornwall. During the spring Florence Dugdale moves in to Max Gate; in July Hardy accepts an honorary fellowship at Magdalene College, Cambridge. *A Changed Man* published in October.
1914 *February*	Hardy marries Florence Dugdale (10 February). *Satires of Circumstance* published in November.
1915	Death of Hardy's sister Mary (24 November).
1916	Publication of *Selected Poems of Thomas Hardy*.
1917	Hardy begins sifting papers in preparation for his autobiography, to be published after his death over the name of Florence Hardy. *Moments of Vision* appears in November.

1919	*Collected Poems* published. In October Hardy receives a 'Poet's Tribute', a bound volume of holograph poems by 50 contemporary poets, each one signed.
1920	Hardy receives message of congratulation on his 80th birthday from King George V.
1922	Hardy receives honorary degree from University of St Andrews, and is made an honorary fellow of Queen's College, Oxford; *Late Lyrics and Earlier* published in May.
1923	Prince of Wales (later Edward VIII) visits Hardy at Max Gate.
	The Famous Tragedy of the Queen of Cornwall performed by the Hardy Players (28 December).
1924	Stage adaptation of *Tess* performed in Dorchester.
1925	*Human Shows* published in November.
1928 11 *January*	Hardy, who has been ill since mid-December, dies in the evening of 11 January. On 16 January, in a double ceremony, his ashes are interred in Westminster Abbey, and his heart in the churchyard at Stinsford.
October	*Winter Words* is published. The first volume of his autobiography, *The Early Life of Thomas Hardy*, appears over his widow's name in this year; the second volume, *The Later Years of Thomas Hardy*, follows in 1930.

introduction

phillip mallett

Hardy's first career, the one 'practical wisdom dictated' as a route away from the world of village artisans which was his birthright, towards the professional middle class which was his goal, was that of architect.[1] His career as a published writer began in 1865, with a short sketch entitled 'How I Built Myself a House', and ended more than 60 years later with his eighth volume of poems, *Winter Words*, published posthumously in October 1928. Midway through this second career, signalled by the appearance in 1897 of his last novel, *The Well-Beloved*, and in 1898 of his first volume of verse, *Wessex Poems*, there was another change of direction, from novelist to poet – though in fact some of the *Wessex Poems* date from the 1860s, and in 1912 he took the opportunity afforded by the publication of the Wessex Edition to revisit, and revise, the novels which had earned him his reputation. It is, then, an oversimplification to think of him as a Victorian novelist and a twentieth-century poet, the literary contemporary of first George Eliot and then T. S. Eliot. Yet George Eliot's name was invoked, somewhat to Hardy's chagrin, in reviews of his first truly successful novel, *Far from the Madding Crowd*; and as Christopher Ricks has shown, in an essay comparing Hardy's poem 'A Spellbound Palace' with T. S. Eliot's 'Sweeney Agonistes', Thomas Hardy, O.M., the Grand Old Man of English letters, was willing to be influenced by the younger American.[2]

The essays collected in this volume attend to Hardy as both novelist and poet. Critical inquiry, in the past ten or twenty years especially, has often been directed to the disruptions and discontinuities in Hardy's writings: the intermingling of realist and non-realist elements in the fiction, the evident respect for the traditions of English verse, and the no less evident readiness to break with them, in the poetry. Yet across both of his writing careers, there are characteristic emphases, motifs, moods,

1

concerns, techniques – an imaginative coherence, so to speak, which justifies the use of such adjectives as 'Hardyan', or 'Hardyesque'. Indeed, a recurring concern of these essays, though not one contributors were directly asked to address, is the way Hardy himself, his Victorian reviewers and editors, his twentieth-century readers – both the general reader and the academic critic – as well as the later writers whose work seems to reflect his influence, have constructed different notions of 'Hardy' and the 'Hardyan'.

This is one of the issues raised by Rosemarie Morgan in her chapter on 'Editing Hardy'. The General Preface to the 1912 Wessex Edition describes it, oddly, as the 'definite edition'. Most readers have taken this to mean that it was the definitive edition, as did Richard L. Purdy in his influential *Thomas Hardy: A Bibliographical Study* (1954), and 'definitive' has been taken to mean authoritative – authoritative enough to provide the base text for most of the many editions currently available. But after *Desperate Remedies* and *Under the Greenwood Tree*, all of Hardy's novels had a complicated publishing history, with significant changes made at a series of points. These include a serial version, often substantially revised from the manuscript to comply with the demands of editors, or Hardy's guesses as to what those demands might be; a first volume edition, in which, typically, the text was revised back towards its pre-serial form; and the two collected editions, from Osgood, McIlvaine in 1895, and from Macmillan in 1912. There are at least three orders of change here: those which were forced on Hardy, and which he increasingly came to resent; those made by his own decision, most of them for the 1895 or 1912 editions, in an effort to impose, retrospectively, a unified idea of 'Wessex', which had in fact developed in piecemeal fashion; and those which reflect a refuelling of his creative energies as he worked his way through the texts, and felt compelled to reimagine and rewrite characters and situations. As Rosemarie Morgan points out, chapter XXII of the *Life* is entitled 'Another Novel, Finished, Mutilated, and Restored', the novel in question being *Jude*; but as Hardy knew from his experience as an architect, while 'restoration' ideally described the process of returning something to its original condition, it might also mean, as it did with the chancel screen at St Juliot's, the replacing of the original with 'a new and highly varnished travesty' in keeping with the taste of a later age (*Life*, p. 82) – or, as Morgan suggests, with the 1895 and 1912 editions in mind, the taste of the author at a later age.[3] This suggests an argument for taking the first volume edition as the base text (in the absence of a complete manuscript), rather than the supposedly definitive one of

1912. That this was the edition Hardy's reviewers had to deal with adds support to the case.

There are of course countervailing arguments. For a variety of reasons, Hardy did not always return to his original conception in the first volume edition. In the serial version of *The Mayor of Casterbridge*, for example, Henchard and Lucetta marry on the mistaken assumption that Henchard is a widower; in the first book versions (both English and American), they have a non-sexual relationship; and it was not until the Osgood, McIlvaine edition of 1895 that they have the irregular sexual liaison Hardy seems to have planned for them. To use the first volume edition here would be to challenge the form in which the novel has been read, adapted, discussed, loved and hated, for more than a century. Similar arguments might be made about other of the novels, in particular, as Morgan points out, *Tess of the d'Urbervilles*. More generally, one might argue that the word 'restoration' is tendentious; the title of Patricia Ingham's indispensable study of 'The Evolution of *Jude the Obscure*' offers a more sympathetic alternative, with the suggestion that textual change is an organic if also potentially unending process.[4] Fortunately, unlike church restoration, revisions to the text of a novel do not involve the destruction of its earlier forms. Ruskin argued that restoration, where it was necessary to preserve a building from collapse, should be unmistakable – using a plain white block, say, rather than one carved in imitation of earlier work – so that the spectator could at once tell which was the old and which the new part of the structure. Professor Morgan makes a compelling case for a similar clarity in the work of Hardy's editors.

Richard Nemesvari also examines the pressures brought to bear on Hardy by publishers, editors and reviewers. When Leslie Stephen accepted *Far from the Madding Crowd* for the *Cornhill*, Hardy told him that he was 'willing, and indeed anxious' to make any changes required of him for the sake of magazine publication (*Life*, p. 102). This often-quoted letter has been variously interpreted as timid and self-doubting, even a sign of Hardy's class and cultural insecurity; as sensible and pragmatic, as befitted a man recently married, and with a chance to publish in one of the most prestigious of Victorian journals; or as early evidence that, as Hardy insists in the *Life*, his true interest was always in poetry, and not in fiction. On the face of it, Hardy was fortunate to find a number of literary men – Stephen, George Meredith, John Morley – who even this early in his career recognised his talent and urged him to continue. But none of them encouraged him to follow his own creative instincts. Rather, they advised him to play safe, to conform to the market, and to adopt standards and values they themselves professed to doubt or deplore. Often, it seems, Hardy tried to do so; the increasing attention given to the Wessex topography and landscape as he revised the novels may be an instance. But there remained that irreducible idiosyncrasy, to use his word, which increasingly compelled him to go his own road. So, for example, his first volume of verse, *Wessex Poems*, had a reassuring title, but there was more than a hint of defiance in his decision that the first poem should be 'The Temporary the All', written in unfamiliar sapphics rather than the nineteenth century's preferred iambics.

In tracing the way Hardy both internalised and resisted the opinions of the reviewers, Nemesvari draws on modern reception theory, in particular Hans Robert Jauss's concept of a 'horizon of expectation', as well as the three essays on fiction Hardy wrote between 1888 and 1891 – the period, of course, of *Tess*, when Hardy's negotiations with the publishers were still more fraught and protracted than usual. Hardy, in Nemesvari's analysis, was deliberately concerned to instruct his readers in the proper way to read his fiction, and later his poetry: not quite Henry James – Hardy's arguments are tactical rather than theoretically refined – but not content either to stay within the framework prescribed for him by the reviewers. Virginia Woolf's placing of Hardy among the 'unconscious' writers, who are never quite in control of what they are doing, is on one level suggestive and astute; but is only a small step away from the patronising view of him as a naive and clumsy artist who sometimes stumbled, unawares, into greatness. Nemesvari's chapter is a useful corrective to such readings. Hardy may have been a recalcitrant writer, but he was not an uninformed one.

One product of Hardy's determination to control the way he was read was the two-volume biography published shortly after his death over the name of his second wife, but since 1940 recognised as substantially an autobiography. It is a partial, selective and at times deliberately misleading account, but as Ralph Pite argues, it has continued to shape the work of Hardy's biographers. Literary biography, in recent years, has often challenged the Victorian 'three-decker' in both length and popularity. It also seems to have usurped its ideological role. Both are drawn towards a notion of 'character' which has been largely displaced from the postmodern novel; both offer to re-present the world in a manner which confirms both the truth of the text, and the reader's existence as a knowing, autonomous subject. *The Life of Thomas Hardy* is less easily contained, not least because of the frequent but typically brief references to poems introduced with some such phrase as 'probably written around this time'. These invite the reader away from the *Life* towards the poems, and the question – unanswerable as it may be – why these were mentioned and not others. So, after quoting a series of diary entries made over the previous three or four months, Hardy records that in December 1894 he 'ran up to London alone on publishing business, and stayed at a temporary room off Piccadilly', when, he continues, 'there seems to have occurred ... some incident of the kind possibly adumbrated in the verses called "At Mayfair Lodgings", in *Moments of Vision*' (*Life*, p. 284). He left it there, though when revising the text after his death Florence Hardy chose to round out the story, explaining that Hardy's attention had been drawn to a lighted window, behind which, he later discovered, a woman he had once cared for lay dying (*Life*, p. 513).[5] But this does not answer the questions raised by the admission that the poem was ('possibly') autobiographical: why the woman dies 'Unpardon'd', what her offence might have been, or why her death 'need not have come due / Had she been less unbending'. The poem, itself oblique, and here obliquely foregrounded, briefly suggests the passionate emotional or erotic life which the third-person narrative of the *Life* seems designed to damp down, if not quite to deny, but then draws a veil over it. What Pite nicely describes as the 'self-distance' of Hardy's text both invites and frustrates speculation. There is more than one sense in which his biographers have to see through the Hardy presented in the *Life*.

This is certainly true of Hardy's account of his class origins, which was, as Roger Ebbatson notes, sympathetically, a deviation from the truth. Hardy's sensitivity is understandable. He was deeply loyal to his own class fraction – arguably to the extent of allowing it to skew his reading of social conditions in early and mid-Victorian Dorset – but at the same time he traded on his knowledge of it in fictions written to amuse the middle class he aspired to join: 'Wessex' was both his home, and what he had to sell. As Andrew Lang put it in a review of *Far from the Madding Crowd*, he was 'telling clever people about unlettered people', and inevitably adopted 'a sort of patronizing voice'.[6] Part of the debt Hardy owed to his social and family background was precisely that it gave him the will and the encouragement to leave it. His recognition of the cost of doing so is apparent throughout the novels: in *The Woodlanders*, for example, it is there in the conflict in Grace between her loyalty to Giles and her ambition for the wider life which seems to be promised by Fitzpiers and Mrs Charmond, but also, and more disturbingly, in Melbury's willingness to abase himself before his daughter, seeking her disdain as the measure of her success, and proof of the canniness of his investment in her education. Social ascent, Hardy understood, meant that others were left behind.

In his discussion of *The Mayor of Casterbridge* Ebbatson points out that this is a novel where issues of class predominate over questions of sexual relationship. Elsewhere in Hardy's work, however, class and gender issues are often closely linked. Victorian marriage law, including the Divorce and Matrimonial Causes Act of 1857, which made adultery sufficient grounds for the divorce of a wife but not of a husband, was framed with regard to the transmission of property, and not the happiness of men and women – a point not lost on Hardy's Jude and Sue. The interconnection of class and gender is signalled more subtly in the way each draws on the same pool of vocabulary, so that words like 'propriety', 'refined', or 'gross', refer simultaneously to social status and sexual behaviour: both contexts are present, for example, when Sue tells Jude that she has always longed 'to ennoble some man to high aims'. Correspondingly, Elizabeth-Jane, who is said to be almost 'vicious' in her concern for respectability, distinguishes herself from the 'fallen women' in *The Mayor* – Lucetta, but also Susan Henchard – by acquiring the 'masculine' elements of a classical education. Class, in Hardy's fiction, infiltrates every area of experience: how to hold a chess piece, and the choice of bonnet or curls, as well as decisions about marriage, or aspirations towards a Christminster education – even, as Ebbatson suggests, Hardy's tendency in the *Life* to slight his work as a novelist, which had been the means of his escape from, but also bore the signs of, his class origins, in favour of the culturally privileged role of the poet.

Cultural authority, and Hardy's relationship to it, is the subject of Mary Rimmer's chapter. The key figure here is Matthew Arnold, and a key issue Arnold's critique of 'provincialism' in his 1864 essay on 'The Literary Influence of Academies'. In the *Life* Hardy remarks that 'Arnold is wrong about provinciality … A certain provincialism of feeling is invaluable. It is of the essence of individuality, and is largely made up of that crude enthusiasm without which no great thoughts are thought, no great deeds done' (*Life*, p. 151). The word 'crude' here is unwarranted, and revealingly defensive. Arnold *was* wrong about provincialism, or at least he was wrong about what was happening in the provinces: Oxford did no more for science, art and design, even philosophical debate, than was achieved in the provincial cities. But Arnold would have been a less troubling figure if he had merely asserted the need for a cultural centre to define standards of taste and judgement. What he also insisted on, especially in *Culture and Anarchy*, was the ideal of a culture which was not the property of a class but of a temperament, open to all who were led by the 'love of perfection'. Yet while he seemed to beckon to those like Hardy or Jude who aspired to something more than a strictly utilitarian education, the style and manner in which he did so dismissed their eagerness as crude and provincial. The young Jude is more right than he knows when he thinks of Christminster as both 'a city of light' and 'what you may call a castle, manned by scholarship and religion': at once a centre of illumination, and a fortress built to defend the interest of a select, and self-selecting group. Culture as the harmonious study of perfection is reserved for those, like Arnold, who claim ownership of the castle; for Ethelberta, Elizabeth-Jane or Jude, the interlopers within its walls, it is fragmentary and elusive, won if at all only by hard and secret struggle, and never wholly possessed. Unlike Arnold, as Mary Rimmer points out, Hardy is alert to the ways in which culture is contingent on class, gender, and family ties.

Angelique Richardson's chapter on Hardy and science suggests further reasons why the idea of culture, for Hardy, was contested ground; Darwin's vision of endless struggle in a world without purpose left little room for harmony and perfection. That Hardy's imagination was stirred by scientific writing is evident throughout the fiction: witness Knight's confrontation with the trilobite in *A Pair of Blue Eyes*, the 'voids and waste places of the sky' in *Two on a Tower*, or the theories of chance in *A Laodicean*, and of degeneration in *Jude the Obscure*. Nor was this an uninformed interest: his conversation with Leslie Stephen in 1875, on 'the constitution of matter, the unreality of time, and kindred subjects' (*Life*, p. 109), suggests that both had been thinking about John Tyndall's Belfast Address, given a year earlier, which argued that there was no sharp distinction between organic and inorganic matter, or between matter and consciousness – ideas which have a place in *The Dynasts*. But while Hardy admired the intellectual fearlessness of men like Tyndall, Darwin and Huxley, and was in no doubt that the novelist's account of human behaviour had to acknowledge the work of the scientists, he also doubted their claim to authority. *Nescience*, for Hardy, was ineluctably part of the human condition; he professed himself baffled that anyone could dispute Herbert Spencer's doctrine that 'beyond the known, there must always be an unknown' (*Life*, p. 400). The great scientific discoveries of the nineteenth century – Lyell in geology, Herschel in astronomy, Darwin in biology – had, paradoxically, diminished the status of humanity. Yet the late poem 'Drinking Song' treats our limitations comically. Darwin's 'strange message' that 'We are all one with creeping things', and Einstein's still stranger idea that 'there's no time, no space, no motion', are met with equanimity: 'Fill full your cups: feel no distress; / 'Tis only one great thought the less!'

Angelique Richardson quotes a sentence Hardy copied into his notebooks: 'The very ground-thought of Science is to treat man as part of the natural order.'[7] To do so, however, as Hardy recognised, might be to set limits to human freedom. Theories of heredity, for example, construed as a system of inevitable laws, could easily substitute for older notions of Destiny or Necessity. Everybody, wrote the psychologist Henry Maudsley, in another passage copied by Hardy, 'in the main lines of his thought, feelings & conduct, really recalls the experiences of his forefathers'.[8] For the most part, Hardy resisted ideas of biological and evolutionary determinism. Human behaviour and identity, as I argue in my own chapter on Hardy and sexuality, is shaped by cultural as much as by natural factors – though cultural pressures too could be overwhelming. The Men and Women's Club which gathered around Karl Pearson in the 1880s included many free spirits – Olive Schreiner was one – who wanted to rethink the relations between men and women. But Pearson, while ready to argue for 'complete freedom in the sex-relationship', was already teasing out the implications of hereditarian thought. Not only might the less fit members of society be denied the right to reproduce, but the more fit, including 'the best women', might have parenthood required of them as a national duty, at the expense, if need be, of their own personal development: 'If child-bearing women must be intellectually handicapped, then the penalty to be paid for race-predominance is the subjection of women.'[9] The New Women of the 1890s might reasonably have wondered whether they would escape the traps set by Nature only to fall into others set by the state. Hardy, a lifelong admirer of Mill's essay *On Liberty*, preferred to cherish whatever space could be found for individual freedom.

Hardy was sufficiently interested to attend at least one meeting of the Eugenics Education Society, but 'race-predominance' was not an idea that appealed to him. His engagement with concepts of national identity was shaped in part, as James Whitehead shows, by his misgivings about the New Imperialism, and his dismay at the war in South Africa. When, he asked in his sonnet 'Departure' (1899), will patriotism 'scorn to stand / Bondslave to realms, but circle earth and seas?' To raise such a question at such a time was to be criticised as 'one shaped awry [who] disturbs the order here' ('In Tenebris II'). This at least was the view taken by the *Daily Chronicle*, which objected to his poem 'A Christmas Ghost-Story' on the grounds that Hardy's soldier-ghost, who asks why the Christian message of peace has been ignored, lacked the heroism of the Dublin fusiliers who had cried 'Let us make a name for ourselves!' at the battle of Colenso ten days earlier. Hardy's carefully crafted reply, that to such a ghost 'nations are all one … ; his country is not bounded by seas, but is co-extensive with the globe itself', was, as Whitehead suggests, as much a political act as a poet's defence of the 'artistic propriety' of his poem.[10] There are anecdotes of soldiers in both world wars carrying a volume of Hardy in their packs, as a reminder of the national character they were fighting to defend, but Hardy himself was wary of national stereotypes and suspicious of those who spoke most loudly of 'England'. Whitehead's chapter, as well as exploring the way Hardy has been co-opted for various accounts of 'Englishness', also suggests that he embraced a clear-sighted internationalism, which has too often been disparaged (as it is by Donald Davie) as a modest, even quiescent liberalism.

The other four chapters in this volume all raise questions about the aesthetics of Hardy's work. John Hughes discusses the importance of the visual in Hardy's fiction. Typically, a Hardy novel begins by observing a character, often unnamed, as if, Hughes suggests, Hardy is waiting to discover how the qualities gradually revealed will set the story in motion. Narrator, reader and, often, an observing character are drawn together by an interpretive curiosity, as if the tale exists independently of Hardy's construction of it. Even the more confident descriptions often carry a note of provisionality. The narrator devotes four leisurely paragraphs to introducing Gabriel Oak, only to speculate in the fifth that 'some thoughtful persons' might have seen him differently. The scene which follows, as Bathsheba gazes into her mirror, and smiles at her own blushing reflection, is witnessed by the narrator and Oak alike, and both seem to come to the same conclusion, that she is motivated by what the narrator calls 'Women's prescriptive infirmity', and Gabriel, more shortly, terms 'Vanity'. But the narrator withdraws as much as is offered: 'the whole series of actions were so idly put forth as to make it rash to assert that intention had any part in them at all'. The scene is left open, indeterminate, waiting on what Hughes describes as those 'physically produced moments of becoming' which mark Hardy's fiction; '[t]hese people of Wessex,' as D. H. Lawrence remarked, 'are always bursting suddenly out of bud and taking a wild flight into flower'.[11] The self in Hardy – it was this as much as anything else that drew Lawrence to his work – is not stable, but in process. Hardy's characters, one might suggest, are surprised into being; their spiritual life exists through the body and the emotions, revealing itself to itself, and to others, above all through moments of eye contact.[12] The visual in Hardy, as Hughes shows, is bound up with metaphysical as well as aesthetic questions.

Charles Lock also comments on Hardy's interest in the visual, quoting Judith Wittenberg's remark that Hardy's is a 'spectatorial narrator'. But his concern is to distinguish Hardy's monological narrative approach from that of writers like Flaubert and Henry James, who make extensive use of free indirect speech. Rather than effacing himself, Hardy's narrator typically retains the telling voice of the traditional story – the story, as Walter Benjamin observed, of the oral tradition and not of print culture. Hardy's fiction, Lock suggests, shows no interest in the method to which Flaubert, James and Turgenev were slowly finding their way: in Bakhtin's terms, he employs 'prose' rather than 'novelistic discourse', is a teller of tales rather than a novelist. Rather than from the use of *style indirect libre*, where a word or phrase can potentially be voiced by more than one speaker, the complexity of the narrative voice in Hardy's fiction comes from shifts of perspective and authorial distance, and the kind of spatial and temporal discontinuities Lock examines in the opening pages of *The Mayor of Casterbridge*. Novelistic discourse, in Bakhtin's analysis, enables the novelist to break the rules of prose; in Hardy's fiction, Lock argues, it is the optics that do so. In Hardy's novels, we see things that no other novelist can show us; we also see 'things that cannot be shown in prose'.

Linda Shires's concern is with Hardy's poetry, particularly in relation to his Victorian and Romantic predecessors. Studies of Victorian poetics have for the most part had little to say on Hardy, yet while Hardy's standing as a novelist is secure, his own view of himself as primarily a poet is becoming more widely accepted in critical discussion: readers who came for the novels, as it were, have stayed on for the poems. Even so, Hardy is, as Shires suggests, difficult to 'place'. He begins the 'Apology' to *Late Lyrics and Earlier* (1922) with the thought that a volume launched 'in neo-Georgian days by one who began writing in mid-Victorian' may need some excuse; the text which follows cites or quotes Wordsworth, Coleridge, Shelley, Tennyson and Arnold, all heirs to the high Romantic claim for poetry as 'the breath and finer spirit of all knowledge'. Yet even as he situates himself in this line, Hardy admits that his (unlike theirs) is 'a book of various character', with poems of a 'humorous intention' mixed with those 'in graver voice', so that readers may find themselves baffled by the 'consecutive piping of vocal reeds in jarring tonics'. Hardy's volume, presumably, will not bind together by passion and knowledge the vast empire of human society.

The keynote of Hardy's verse, as Linda Shires notes, may be the line 'No answerer I ... ', from 'Nature's Questioning' – a poem published alongside an illustration of a broken key. Rather than the Wordsworthian epiphany, Hardy's is 'a poetry of unknowing and of belated awareness'. The point is extended through a reading of 'During Wind and Rain' as a double poem – the characteristic mode of Victorian poetry, as Isobel Armstrong has argued, in which the lyric expression contains a counter voice to itself, an internal self-critique. Hardy's poetry, like that of Robert and Elizabeth Barrett Browning, Christina Rossetti and Hopkins, traces the recoil of the mind upon itself. The plot, as Clough put it, has 'counterplot': ' It may be, and yet be not.'

Like Linda Shires, John Ward draws attention to Hardy's interest in the Gothic and the grotesque, but his aim is to emphasise Ruskin's insistence that to demand perfection is always to mistake the nature of art. 'A man's reach', as Browning's Andrea del Sarto comes to realise, too late, 'should exceed his grasp'. The wholly achieved is always inferior, because the artist has drawn back on approaching the point of failure; it is also morally offensive, because it proudly denies, or seeks to deny, its human origin – as, in Ruskin's analysis, Renaissance architecture sought to do by following a series of supposed 'rules'. Imperfection, in the Ruskinian sense, and with the full range of Ruskinian implications, is, Ward argues, the basis of Hardy's aesthetics. This imperfection is variously manifested in the poetry. It is there in what are sometimes described as Hardy's 'philosophical' poems, for example, in the sense of the world as incomplete, badly made, or neglected by its creator, as well as in dramatic and lyrical poems dealing with the 'too late' theme, or with human unknowing, or with the failure within human sexual relationships. More significantly, Ward relates this aesthetic of imperfection to Hardy's social-democrat sympathies. Much as Ruskin welcomed the signs in Gothic art of the individual workman, with all his failings, so Hardy admits into his poetry speakers whose remarks are humdrum, clumsy, yet oddly touching. And though Ward turns for theoretical support to the work of Isobel Armstrong and Gillian Rose, his further argument, that Hardy's poems often leave the middle ground between two offered views open for the reader's own entry, might also be linked to Ruskin's account of the highest kinds of grotesque art, which similarly call on the mind of the beholder.

It was the licensed imperfectness of Hardy's poetry, Ward suggests, that attracted later writers like Auden and Larkin. Hardy gave him hope, Auden remembered, where a flawless poet might have made him despair.

Larkin thought that, like himself, John Betjeman and C. Day Lewis may have learned from Hardy to feel confidence in their own way. In his influential study, *Thomas Hardy and British Poetry*, Donald Davie both applauds Hardy for his modesty and criticises him for selling short the vocation of a poet. Ward's essay invites a closer look at Hardy's 'modesty' as not merely a quirk of temperament, but a deeply considered and aesthetically grounded position.

These essays included here have all been written specifically for this volume. It would, of course, have been possible to gather a group of essays which systematically covered the range of Hardy's work – early fiction, the 'tragic novels', the short stories, and so on – or to work through the approaches suggested by a series of 'isms' – Marxism, feminism, New Historicism, and the like. Neither route has been taken here, though the volume does reflect a variety of approaches, and a wide range of Hardy's work is explicitly discussed. Contributors were asked instead to address the areas which seem likely to be the growth points for future Hardy studies. Inevitably, because of the limitations of space, some topics have not been given the attention they merit; there is, for example, no chapter devoted to 'Hardy and Film', nor to 'Hardy's Language', nor to 'Hardy and the Victorian Family', nor to 'Hardy and Victorian Psychology', though individual essayists have offered thoughts about these and many other issues not identified in the chapter titles. None of the pieces included takes the form of a review essay, though each, in different ways, takes note of previous work: contributors were invited to look towards future work rather than to consolidate work already done.

It remains to add that in the experience of this editor, Hardy scholars are a lively and generous group, as well as (quite properly) obstinate, questioning and occasionally obsessive. I am grateful to the contributors for exhibiting all these qualities, and for their patience and tolerance when I have been, in turn, obstinate or questioning.

a note on editions

All but the two earliest of Hardy's novels, *Desperate Remedies* and *Under the Greenwood Tree*, were published first as serials, then in volume form – typically with changes between first, second and later volume forms – and then, after further changes, in the collected editions of 1895 and 1912. This last, the Wessex Edition, has been the starting point for most modern editions, but critics have offered good arguments for using other versions, usually the first volume edition, as the base text. For this reason, there has been no attempt made here to regularise the choice of editions referred to in different chapters. In most cases, however, these are either the Wessex Edition, or editions based on it, or the first volume editions, usually citing the new Penguin series under the editorship of Patricia Ingham.

References to Hardy's ghosted autobiography, first published over the name of Florence Hardy as *The Early Life of Thomas Hardy* (1928) and *The Later Years of Thomas Hardy* (1930), are to the edition prepared by Michael Millgate as *The Life and Work of Thomas Hardy, by Thomas Hardy* (London: Macmillan, 1984).

notes

1. Michael Millgate, ed., *The Life and Work of Thomas Hardy, by Thomas Hardy* (London, 1984), p. 61: henceforth throughout this volume cited parenthetically as *Life*.
2. Christopher Ricks, *Essays in Appreciation* (Oxford, 1996).
3. In 1909 Hardy advised the Stinsford church restoration committee to concentrate on preservation, and 'never to indulge in alterations'; it was not a principle he followed in his own revisions. *The Collected Letters of Thomas Hardy*, 7 vols (Oxford, 1978–88), eds Richard Little Purdy and Michael Millgate, IV, p. 1: henceforth cited as *Letters*.
4. *Review of English Studies*, 1976.
5. She was probably Cassie (Catherine) Pole, to whom Hardy was supposed to have given a ring.
6. *Thomas Hardy: The Critical Heritage*, ed. R. G. Cox (London and New York, 1979), p. 36; henceforth cited as *Critical Heritage*.
7. *The Literary Notebooks of Thomas Hardy*, 2 vols, ed. Lennart Björk (London, 1985), I, p. 65: henceforth cited as *Literary Notebooks*.
8. *Literary Notebooks*, I, p. 201.
9. Karl Pearson, *The Ethic of Freethought* (London, 1888), p. 389. Pearson later became Britain's first professor of Eugenics.
10. *Thomas Hardy's Public Voice: The Essays, Speeches, and Miscellaneous Prose*, ed. Michael Millgate (Oxford, 2001), p. 157. In the first version of the poem, the nationality of the speaker is not disclosed ('be he or not your countryman'); in revising it, Hardy made him 'your countryman': a man, that is, sent out to fight, and to die, by those who are reading the poem.
11. *Study of Thomas Hardy*, in *Lawrence on Hardy & Painting*, ed. J. V. Davies (London, 1973), p. 22.
12. Perhaps for this reason Hardy, like Darwin in his study of *The Expression of the Emotions*, was fascinated by the blush.

1
hardy and the critics
charles lock

Thomas Hardy and Henry James seem to have shadowed each other throughout their careers, and the critical tradition has extended the rivalry. Theirs was a rivalry not over who was to be regarded as the greatest English novelist of their generation: rather, what was being contested was the status of the novel.[1] In critical writings Henry James constructed an extraordinarily elaborate apparatus, in which he explained what he was attempting in his novels, and by which he instructed his readers in the proper approach to his fiction. Hardy, by contrast, made minimal claims for the literary or aesthetic value of his novels, or indeed for the novel as a genre. He showed little interest in his novels as works of art, and it would not have occurred to him that his readers might stand in need of any assistance or guidance. Hardy's fiction attempts nothing new, not at any rate new in a challenging way; it is merely the modern form in which traditional matter is best conveyed. Good 'fiction' will be, in Hardy's view, that which most closely resembles the classical or traditional genres:

> Good fiction may be defined here as that kind of imaginative writing which lies nearest to the epic, dramatic, or narrative masterpieces of the past. One fact is certain: in fiction there can be no intrinsically new thing at this stage of the world's history.[2]

However, that extreme claim is modified by Hardy himself, just three paragraphs later:

> the two hundred years or so of the modern novel's development have not left the world so full of fine examples ... The conclusion cannot be

resisted ... that the scarcity of perfect novels in any language is because the art of writing them is as yet in its youth, if not in its infancy.[3]

In other words, it is not this late stage in the world's history that precludes innovation, but the youthfulness of the novelistic genre. On renouncing the genre in 1897, after the publication of *Jude the Obscure* and *The Well-Beloved*, Hardy wrote no more essays about fiction, nor addressed the question of the novel. His prefaces to later editions of his novels (notably the Wessex Edition of 1912) are, with the exception of that to *Jude the Obscure*, perfunctory.

Not even the later novels of Henry James could persuade Hardy of the value of fiction, let alone that something close to an 'intrinsically new thing' had arisen in the world. Suffering from a bout of rheumatism in 1903, Hardy reports to a friend:

> In my enforced idleness I have been reading H. James's 'Wings of the Dove' – the first of his that I have looked into for years & years. I read it with a fair amount of care – as much as one would wish to expend on any novel, certainly, seeing what there is to read besides novels. At the same time James is almost the only living novelist I can read, & taken in small doses I like him exceedingly, being as he is a real man of letters.[4]

Which is to say that James's novels are readable because he is not only a novelist, or despite the fact that they are novels. The disdain is palpable, yet the tone is also defensive. For Henry James left others in no doubt that he believed that what he had achieved, especially in his late novels, was something truly unprecedented: he had contributed some salient instances to what was now a distinguished genre, as he famously concludes his preface of 1909 to *The Ambassadors*:

> ... not that the particular production before us exhausts the interesting questions it raises, but that the Novel remains still, under the right persuasion, the most independent, most elastic, most prodigious of literary forms.[5]

What Henry James had elaborated, though not quite knowingly, is what later literary analysts would term *style indirect libre* or free indirect discourse. Ian Watt could write his celebrated essay on the opening paragraph of *The Ambassadors* precisely because the linguistic texture is so dense, so overlaid and interpenetrated with discursive and evaluative resonances, that every paragraph repays limitless attention. Yet Ian Watt himself displays no awareness of *style indirect libre* nor of its implications for the concept of 'prose'. Watt can see only that the way in which *The Ambassadors* is written has the effect of conflating physical and mental phenomena, things and the perception of things, and that 'it involves, in fact, both Strether's mind and the narrator's'.[6]

No comparable essay has been devoted to any one paragraph in a novel by Thomas Hardy. This is partly because, unlike James – and deliberately so, we might suppose – Hardy himself did nothing to encourage 'close reading' or in any way to draw attention to the manner in which his novels were written. Furthermore, in his few comments on fiction, Hardy stressed the elements of storytelling and narrative, of those aspects which are not necessarily written at all. When he renounced fiction, so he tells us in the autobiographical third person,

> It was not as if he had been a writer of novels proper, and as more specifically understood, that is, stories of modern artificial life and manners showing a certain smartness of treatment. He had mostly aimed, and mostly succeeded, to keep his narratives close to natural life, and as near to poetry as the conditions would allow, and had often regretted that those conditions would not let him keep them nearer still. (*Life*, pp. 309–10)

Insofar as he had troubled to prepare his readers at all, Hardy would not have protested at Donald Davidson in 1940 explaining 'The Traditional Basis of Thomas Hardy's Fiction'. Indeed he might even have approved of Davidson asserting that Hardy 'wrote as a ballad-maker would write if a ballad-maker were to have to write novels'. 'My thesis', Davidson states, 'is that the characteristic Hardy novel is conceived as a *told* (or *sung*) story, or at least not as a literary story.'[7] Indeed Davidson even argues that the best of Hardy's novels are those which appear to be told, while the worst – he names *The Hand of Ethelberta* and *A Laodicean* – represent 'Hardy's attempt to be a fully modern – and literary – novelist.'

Much in Davidson's argument corresponds (quite independently and without influence in either direction) to Walter Benjamin's nostalgic yearning for the art of oral narrative. In his essay 'The Storyteller' of 1936 Benjamin points to the Russian Nikolai Leskov (1831–1895: Hardy's near-contemporary) as an instance of a writer who, in spite of writing, was able to maintain the traditions of oral storytelling

The earliest symptom of the process whose end is the decline of storytelling is the rise of the novel at the beginning of modern times. What distinguishes the novel from the story (and from the epic in the narrower sense) is its essential dependence on the book ... What differentiates the novel from all other forms of prose literature – the fairy-tale, the legend, even the novella – is that it neither comes from the oral tradition nor goes back into it.[8]

Benjamin wrote this essay in 1936, at the same time (again, without possible interference in either direction) that Mikhail Bakhtin was making a similar point, in 'Epic and Novel', though with a quite contrary evaluation:

Of all the major genres only the novel is younger than writing and the book: it alone is organically receptive to new forms of mute perception, that is, to reading.[9]

Where Bakhtin celebrates the novel for the linguistic innovations opened up by silent reading, Benjamin mourns the loss of voice. And what Benjamin does with Leskov in 1936 is remarkably similar to the sort of uses to which in 1940 Davidson puts Hardy. Here is Benjamin:

... no event any longer comes to us without being shot through with explanations ... Actually, it is half the art of story-telling to keep the story free from explanation as one reproduces it ... The most extraordinary things, marvellous things, are related with the greatest accuracy ...

And Davidson:

The logic of the traditional story is not the logic of modern literary fiction. The traditional story admits, and even cherishes, the improbable and unpredictable. The miraculous, or nearly miraculous, is what makes a story a story, in the old way.

Benjamin:

A man listening to a story is in the company of the storyteller; even a man reading one shares this companionship. The reader of a novel, however, is isolated, more so than any other reader.

Davidson:

> [Hardy] wrote like a creator of tales and poems who is a little embarrassed at having to adapt the creation of tales and poems to the conditions of a written, or printed, literature.

Benjamin:

> To be sure, only a few have ventured into the depths of inanimate nature, and in modern narrative literature there is not much in which the voice of the anonymous storyteller, who was prior to all literature, responds so clearly as it does in Leskov's story.

Davidson:

> There is surely no other example in modern English fiction of an author who ... comes bringing the tradition with him, not only the mechanics of the tradition but the inner conception ... He did what the modern critic ... is always implying to be impossible. That is, Hardy accepted the assumptions of a society which in England was already being condemned to death, and he wrote in terms of those assumptions, almost as if Wessex, and perhaps Wessex only, would understand.[10]

It has been easy to ignore Davidson, to ascribe his position merely to that bookish indulgence in rural nostalgia with which an enthusiasm for Hardy has long been complicit. And it is tempting to treat Benjamin's essay as something of an aberration in the work of a brilliant and apparently progressive intellectual.

I would propose, however, that neither of these essays is motivated by nostalgia as such: rather, each is concerned to defend and explain an admiration for fictional prose which does not conform to the expectations or canons of the novel. Why are Hardy's novels so unlike those of James, or of Hardy's early mentor and editor, George Meredith, whose work has recently been recuperated under the flag of Bakhtin?[11] Can Hardy fail to measure up to the criteria of 'good fiction', and yet be acknowledged as a major novelist? To suggest, as Davidson does, not without sanction from Hardy's own comments on fiction, that Hardy is something other than a novelist, a storyteller perhaps, is not necessarily a reactive move. It may be thought to address, with unusual honesty, the peculiar texture

of Hardy's novels. And what we have learnt about the novel from Bakhtin
and others, since Ian Watt's essay on *The Ambassadors*, may help to clarify
what it was that troubled Davidson, and Benjamin.

Bakhtin is famous for celebrating the novel, for making claims for
the genre that exceed even those advanced by Henry James. In the term
'dialogical', indeed, Bakhtin describes (in Hardy's phrase) an intrinsically
new thing. Free indirect discourse names that linguistic phenomenon
which occurs only in writing, when one word or phrase can be potentially
voiced by two or more speakers.[12] And that possibility arises only because
the phrase is not actually voiced at all, but will be read in silence. Thus
the novel, the literary genre that established mass literacy, and created
a silent reading public, manifests a peculiar and entirely unprecedented
linguistic feature. In Benjamin's lament for the storyteller, it is the absence
of the telling voice that is mourned, and the presence of the alienating
technology of print that is resented. By contrast, Bakhtin celebrates in the
novel the absence of the single authorial voice, the 'monological'; and he
points to writing and printing as providing the technological conditions
under which 'new forms of mute perception' have emerged.

Hardy's novels are full of incident and action, and have often been
judged by his detractors to have been contaminated by 'sensation novels'
and other popular forms. Nobody would thus accuse Henry James, who
can keep his readers waiting ten pages before one person speaks: action
is altogether too vulgar a concept for whatever his characters might, after
deliberation and still with much circumspection, perform. Davidson,
attentive to the opposition, defends Hardy against those critics who find
his novels sensational, packed with incidents and coincidences:

> The logic of the traditional story is not the logic of modern literary
> fiction. The traditional story admits, and even cherishes, the improbable
> and unpredictable. The miraculous, or nearly miraculous, is what makes
> a story a story, in the old way. Unless a story has some strange and
> unusual features it will hardly be told and will not be remembered ...
> Thus coincidence in Hardy's narratives represents a conviction about
> the nature of story as such.[13]

Davidson is among the first of many critics to have cited Hardy's own
note to the effect that

> A story must be exceptional enough to justify its telling. We taletellers
> are all Ancient Mariners, and none of us is warranted in stopping

Wedding Guests (in other words, the hurrying public) unless he has something more unusual to relate than the ordinary experience of every average man and woman. (*Life*, p. 268)

The implication of this, and of all such terms as 'storyteller' or 'taleteller', is that the story already exists, in oral tradition, and that the telling now is presumed to be carried by a voice. Thus the necessary condition of writing, by which the reader is, as it were, buttonholed, is treated as a representation of the speaking voice. This is, after all, the usual understanding of the conventions of prose.

Hardy's novels are relentlessly monological, and for a reader with Bakhtinian expectations, inordinately frustrating. In Hardy's narratives there is none of that confusion of voice that characterises the texture of a novel by James or Meredith, or by Virginia Woolf. Free indirect discourse is the linguistic realisation, the syntactical enactment, of the permeating of the border that separates inner from outer, speech from thought, address from description, or, in Aristotle's terms, dialogue from diegesis. It seems to be brought about through indirect or reported speech.[14] Ian Watt is attentive to the means, even while oblivious to the ends, when he explains the frequency of the word *that* in James's paragraph:

> The number of 'thats' follows from two habits already noted ... 'That' characteristically introduces relative clauses dealing not with persons but with objects, including abstractions; and it is also used to introduce reported speech – 'on his learning that Waymarsh' ... Reported rather than direct speech also increases the pressure towards elegant variation ...[15]

In a brief survey of the opening *two* paragraphs of some of Hardy's novels we find a quite remarkable paucity of *thats*. In *Far from the Madding Crowd*, just one demonstrative: 'that vast middle space of Laodicean neutrality'. In *The Return of the Native*, none; in *The Mayor of Casterbridge*, none. In *Tess of the d'Urbervilles*, just one *that*, relative to objects: 'The pair of legs that carried him'. In *Jude the Obscure*, another solitary *that*, also relative to an object: 'a cottage piano that he had bought at an auction'. In *The Woodlanders* alone do we find a respectable frequency of *thats*:

> ... the blistered soles that have trod it, and the tears that have wetted it, return upon the mind of the loiterer.

The physiognomy of a deserted highway expresses solitude to a degree that is not reached by mere dales or downs, and bespeaks a tomb-like stillness more emphatic than that of glades and pools.

We should note that of these four *thats*, three are relative to objects and one is antecedently demonstrative: none is the particle that introduces the reporting of speech or thought.

It is worth recalling that two of the most famous and characteristic opening sentences in English fiction contain *that*: 'It is a truth universally acknowledged, that a single man ... ' (*Pride and Prejudice*) and (from *Jane Eyre*) 'There was no possibility of taking a walk that day.' In the first of these, the *that* introduces a reported claim of such ill-placed assurance that the reader is instantly forced to inquire as to whether this is the narrator's own voice or the narrator's representation of another voice. In the second case, we are confronted with a non-antecedent demonstrative, unlike either the antecedent demonstrative of 'that [stillness] of glades and pools' in *The Woodlanders* or the assumed familiarity of 'that vast middle space of Laodicean neutrality' in *Far from the Madding Crowd*. The non-antecedent *that* is most characteristic of novelistic discourse when it involves time or space, for only then does it exclude the possibility of prior or deducible reference. Such a *that* as *Jane Eyre*'s breaks the rules of prose. As does, for merest example (Christopher Isherwood, *The World in the Evening*): 'The party, that evening, was at the Novotnys.' The rules of prose are broken because the voice of the narrator is rendered insufficient; another voice, no longer heard, or not clearly separable from the narrator's, is necessarily implicated.

The initiating demonstrative is the most obvious linguistic marker of free indirect discourse, though no sign in itself is ever a sufficient marker: free indirect discourse cannot be 'marked'. Once the narrative has begun, context is likely to do the work of vocal disruption. In *To the Lighthouse* we read: 'Never did anybody look so sad.' In his celebrated analysis of this passage in *Mimesis* Erich Auerbach asks: 'Who is speaking in this paragraph? Who is looking at Mrs. Ramsay here, who concludes that never did anybody look so sad? Who is expressing these doubtful, obscure suppositions?'[16] Auerbach is himself unaware of *style indirect libre*, though his readings are of such sensitivity that he can register precisely the shock to be felt. One may recall that over ten years later, in 1968, Roland Barthes would pose the very same question of Balzac: 'Who is speaking thus?'[17] Yet in 'The Death of the Author' Barthes astonishingly, and by this date inexplicably, remains in ignorance, and ascribes the effect achieved by Balzac not to *style indirect libre* but to writing itself. This is to mistake, somewhat elementarily, the necessary condition for the explanation itself.

Free indirect discourse, or dialogism, is present whenever we are prompted to ask, with Auerbach: 'Who is speaking?' And that occurs whenever we are unable to keep apart the voice of the one reporting and the voice reported. Auerbach's enquiry into that one sentence continues:

> 'Never did anybody look so sad' is not an objective statement. In rendering the shock received by one looking at Mrs. Ramsay's face, it verges upon a realm beyond reality. And in the ensuing passage the speakers no longer seem to be human beings at all but spirits between heaven and earth, nameless spirits capable of penetrating the depths of the human soul ...[18]

Through a curious similarity one is reminded of a second occasion on which Hardy wrote about the novel as a genre with a future, in a note supposedly jotted down on 4 March 1886:

> Novel-writing as an art cannot go backward. Having reached the analytic stage it must transcend it by going still further in the same direction. Why not by rendering as visible essences, spectres, etc., the abstract thoughts of the analytic school?

On which a retrospective Hardy comments:

> This notion was approximately carried out, not in a novel, but through the much more appropriate medium of poetry, in the supernatural framework of *The Dynasts* as also in smaller poems. (*Life*, p. 177)

As long as one refuses – reasonably enough – to recognise free indirect discourse as a linguistic innovation, an 'intrinsically new thing', one must ascribe its effects to psychological and philosophical motivations. Rather than acknowledge that language is behaving in an unprecedented fashion, one would suppose that viewers, persons, subjects, are seeing, experiencing and analysing the world in entirely new ways. Hence this remarkable confluence of speculation by Hardy and Auerbach: both are aware of what the novel is doing, of the effects it is creating, and both are unable to explain them except in terms of new and somewhat 'spectral' analytic skills.

It is usually not difficult to tell apart the two voices at work in reported speech. In listening to a speaker we can hear a modulation of tone and sometimes a shift in linguistic register when the other's words are being reported. In prose, properly speaking, there are clear syntactic markers of person and tense that keep the reporting voice distinct from the voice reported. As soon as there is the slightest confusion, the reader will be exasperated, for to cause the reader to ask of an essay, 'Who is speaking now?' is to have dissolved the contract of the voice on which prose relies. In politics or ethics or scholarship it is a prerequisite that we know at all times who is speaking, and who bears responsibility for every single word. Prose has developed in order to preserve in writing the identity of voices.

Bakhtin's radical recognition was that the medium of fiction is not 'prose' at all; lacking a sanctioned term in the presence of an intrinsically new thing, he offers the label 'novelistic discourse'. It is not 'prose' precisely because the safeguards by which voices are held separate and distinct no longer obtain. They break down when reported speech merges with the reporting voice. This is likely to become evident when such explanatory frontier posts as 'he said that ... ' and 'she thought that ... ' are omitted. And the confusion becomes acute when the linguistic register, the idioms and vocabulary of the two speakers, are much alike. The narrative voice used by Virginia Woolf is hardly to be distinguished from the voices (as represented in direct speech) of Mrs Ramsay or Mrs Dalloway; nor is that of Henry James from Strether's. It is often objected that novelists such as Jane Austen, Henry James and Virginia Woolf (with Elizabeth Bowen and Iris Murdoch as more recent instances) write only about people of their own class and background, characters who share the cultural and social assumptions of their creators. This tends to be presented as a political or ethical complaint. Yet it is precisely in the works of such novelists as these that free indirect discourse emerges and becomes most intriguing. Such social restrictiveness may be less a political choice than a necessary condition of free indirect discourse.

In contrast to Henry James and Virginia Woolf, Hardy's narrative voice is quite distinct from those of his characters. The class difference, with the consequent differentiation in register, tone and lexicon, often indicated by irregular orthography in direct speech, is highly marked. And accusations levelled at Hardy on grounds of snobbery sometimes advert to this feature of his novels. Yet such a discursive distance – presented as over a social divide – is probably the necessary condition of fictional representation without confusion of voices. We have already noted the absence of *that* in Hardy's novels, relative to *The Ambassadors*, at least in opening paragraphs: Hardy appears deliberately to restrict the use of reported speech, and even of reported thought. The reader is left on the outside of things, and of persons.

An extreme manifestation of this resistance is to be found in the assimilation of Hardy's protagonists to animals. Tess, Henchard, Mrs Yeobright are all figured as animals; under that figure persons are silenced, rendered inarticulate, dumb as beasts. This was noticed as long ago as 1922, the year in which a novel appeared whose characters, Stephen Dedalus and Leopold Bloom, shared the register of the narrative voice. Joseph Warren Beach pointed out that *The Mayor of Casterbridge* is 'like a moving-picture film': in 1922 this still meant what would later be called a 'silent movie'. Of Henchard, Beach writes: 'In a world of talk, he is almost inarticulate.'[19] As such, Henchard can be described from the outside, remorselessly and without fear of interruption, as it were, from the inside. Of course, Mrs Dalloway or Isobel Archer are often silent, but their thoughts, even if unspoken, intrude on the words of the narrative voice, are constantly being represented: theirs are articulated silences. By contrast, Henchard's silence is one in which even thinking goes unrepresented, so that we have little reason to suppose that Henchard is even capable of thought. That it should often have been noted (first by Beach) that Hardy appears to have anticipated the cinema is not so remarkable: the cinema, like oral storytelling, can lend no voice to free indirect discourse. The pictorialism of Hardy's novels is quite of a piece with their resolute representation of the outwardness of persons.

Not the least remarkable feature of free indirect discourse is that none of its early practitioners recognised the significance of what they were doing, nor gave it a label. *Style indirect libre* is the term devised in 1912 by a French linguist, Charles Bally, who had analysed the style of Flaubert's *Madame Bovary* (1857), on the assumption that Flaubert had deliberately set out to deploy this device. When others detected its presence in Jane Austen (Otto Jespersen was probably the first, in 1924), it could no longer be supposed that free indirect discourse was something consciously devised and deliberately exploited by an exceptionally self-conscious stylist. It appeared rather to be a linguistic feature, found only in writing, that developed autonomously, as if in response to the discursive possibilities opened up by the emerging practice of silent reading: by texts that exist, for the very first time, without the aim and purpose of finding realisation in voice.

One of the most suggestive comments in Hardy criticism over the past 15 years may be found in Judith Mitchel's essay on 'Hardy's Female Reader', noting 'Hardy's consistent avoidance of the technical device of free indirect speech, a favored technique among nineteenth-century novelists and a key distinction between film and the novel.'[20] That 'key distinction' is exactly right; however, it is inaccurate to speak of free indirect discourse as 'a favoured technique' given that, despite its prevalence, no novelist (not even Flaubert or Turgenev or James) appears to have been conscious of using it. Mitchell's phrasing raises the even more perplexing question: if no novelist acknowledged the use of free indirect discourse, or even its presence in his or her very own texts, how can we speak of Hardy deliberately avoiding its use?

Clearly the novelists of the generation of Hardy and James had a sense of something strange making itself present in what they still thought of as 'prose'.[21] And Hardy's strategy of avoidance, his determination, at any rate, to do things differently from James, was probably achieved not by a consciousness of the linguistic oddities in what Bakhtin called 'novelistic discourse'; whether as novelist or poet, Hardy displays an obsession with seeing, with describing, with remaining on the outside. Mitchell develops Judith Bryant Wittenberg's phrase, that Hardy's is a 'spectatorial narrator',[22] to assert that 'Hardy is undoubtedly one of the most scopophilic of novelists'. 'Scopophilia' (a word associated with Michel Foucault's theory of power and surveillance: an overseer is episcopal) suggests not only a 'lover of the view' but, less innocently, one who enjoys the sense of control and possession that viewing bestows. Hardy constructs a narrator who is first of all a viewer: the narrator is possessed of a gaze, he is one who stares, and prefers not to be disturbed in his staring. (With other novelists, the gender of the narrator should be thought to be undetermined. Hardy's narrators are almost unmistakably male, and this feature in itself works against the ambiguities conducive to free indirect discourse.)

While the dialogical is constituted by the discursive exchange between narrator and characters, Hardy's narrator is shamelessly monological: the one who watches is also the one who does the talking. In remaining loyal to the view, fixated by gazing, an obsessive scopophiliac, even in his novels, Hardy sticks to his poet's last, for he renounces the linguistic advantage afforded uniquely by the novel. This is an advantage in the sense in which Flaubert, Turgenev, Henry James and Virginia Woolf all

deployed *style indirect libre* (however unwittingly) by way of advancing
the claims of the novel to be treated as a literary genre not far below
poetry or the drama. By the use of free indirect discourse, the author, and
even the narrator, can be absolved of responsibility for the words that
appear under the author's name.[23] It is, however, a disadvantage if the
narrator wishes to remain in charge, wishes to claim full responsibility.
It should, therefore, be no surprise that Hardy took so personally the
abuse heaped on him by reviewers and readers of *Tess* and *Jude*: not
for him the stylish evasions of a Flaubert. Hardy evidently admired
the 'monological' authority vested in 'the epic, dramatic, or narrative
masterpieces of the past' and wished to preserve in his own novels the
personal and responsible voice found in those exemplars.

Judith Mitchell can claim, accurately, that '*Tess* is clearly one of the
most erotic novels of the Victorian period; Tess herself, however, by
virtue of such obsessive narratorial "looking", is a sexual object rather
than a sexual subject.'[24] This ought not to be presented as a paradox, for
the condition of the erotic is that mastery belongs to the one-way gaze
and the single voice. Despite its title, *The Portrait of a Lady* does not even
contest the title of 'most erotic novel'. The passivity of Tess, her lack of
resistance to the narrator's appropriations, and 'his' refusal to allow her
to engage with him discursively or to intercept him vocally, 'dialogically',
is not unrelated to the novel's astonishing title page in which title and
author are not distinct, but in which, rather, the author's name is merged
with the narrative theme: 'Tess / of the d'Urbervilles; / A Pure Woman, /
Faithfully presented / by / Thomas Hardy'.[25]

Simon Gatrell has ingeniously suggested that the 'Thomas Hardy' of the
title should be treated as a fictional creation of another Thomas Hardy,
the well-known novelist.[26] This is not a fanciful critical approach, but
rather a sound bibliographical deduction. Tess exists for the reader not
in the way that we know Emma Woodhouse or Emma Bovary, Jane Eyre
or Isobel Archer: hers is properly speaking a portrait, though no matter
how pure, she is no lady but only a woman. This portrait, unlike the
others, is the product of 'obsessive narratorial "looking"'.

One might assume that things would be different in *Jude the Obscure*,
yet, despite supposing that in his last novel 'Hardy did attempt to go
beyond the scopophilic objectification of his female characters', Mitchell
reckons that 'curiously, the reader seems to have no readier access to Sue's
consciousness than to that of Hardy's other female characters'. It is in
relation to Sue that Mitchell makes her suggestion concerning Hardy's
deliberate resistance to free indirect discourse: 'we are never given access

to [Sue's] consciousness, so that she remains an enigma rather than a subject. These elisions of female consciousness ... are at least partly a result of Hardy's consistent avoidance of the technical device of free indirect speech.'[27] Mitchell then points to the device which Hardy does use with obvious deliberation, the shifts in perspective and the general instability of the narrator's point of view and focus:

> such unobtrusive refocussing is a device that occurs with great regularity in Hardy's representation of women characters, reaching its culmination in *Tess* ... Hardy seems at once peculiarly intimate with and peculiarly dissociated from his female characters, creating an authorial distance from them that seems too close physically and too remote in other ways.

This division in the narrative method of Hardy's novels Mitchell further refines as that between 'their "narrative grammar", which empathises so deeply' and 'their "scopic economy", in which male consciousness is explored subjectively while female consciousness is quietly and systematically elided'.[28]

This is consistent with Gatrell's insight into the title page, and his discussion of the two narrators of *Tess*, the one detached, the other engaged. One might amplify this and say that the one narrator presents her, as an object, the other represents Tess, and speaks for her as her attorney, as if the 'Thomas Hardy' of the title page were to Tess as M. Sénard to Flaubert. Of the narratorial comments on Angel Clare, in chapter 36 of *Tess*: 'Some might risk the odd paradox that with more animalism he would have been the nobler man. We do not say it', Gatrell writes: 'The second sentence is Hardy's narrator at the height of evasiveness, and the plural pronoun, the characteristic note of the reviewer, is quite out of place.'[29] It is also, let us make clear, the characteristic note, and rhetorical device, of the counsel for the defence. We should note, carefully, that the phrasing is inconsistent and often jarring, and the narrator's voice, or voices, can be unstable to an extraordinary degree. Gatrell speaks of 'the remarkable flexibility of the narrative voice' and Lecercle has argued 'that the violence of style is Hardy's main object in *Tess*':[30] and yet there is still no blending with Tess's voice, no confusion of consciousnesses, no violation of Tess's 'purity' – as an object.

Qualifying the claim that Sue is every bit as objectified as Tess, no more than her a 'fictional subject', Christine Brooke-Rose has pointed out that we are given some glimpses of Sue's inwardness in 'Represented

Thought' (using Ann Banfield's terminology). Yet there are, as Brooke-Rose acknowledges, very few examples of this, perhaps just enough to give us the sense that Sue ought to be quite different in her presentation from Tess, but disappointing that hope.[31] Brooke-Rose's essay may be taken as symptomatic of the frustration of the theoretically sophisticated reader in the face of Hardy's novels.

Mitchell speaks of free indirect discourse as 'a key distinction between film and the novel', implying that in his avoidance of free indirect discourse, Hardy must be necessarily cinematic; Brooke-Rose points out that there is nothing very experimental or avant-garde about Hardy anticipating the cinema (as David Lodge and others have suggested): 'I doubt whether this treatment of perspective is all that new. Balzac was doing it in the first half of the century – indeed it could be argued that the cinema inherited all the clichés of the novel except the narrative voice.'[32]

The texture of Hardy's novels yields to precise linguistic analysis very little that would justify the pleasure that some of us take in their reading. Again, the contrast with Henry James is insistent: Ian Watt's essay may be held to exemplify the satisfactions of finding a critical instrument of adequate subtlety, and knowing its adequacy when the text itself bestows a confirming blessing on the critical approach: this circularity of satisfaction the texts of James, or Woolf, or Joyce, are able to supply in profusion. Hardy, by contrast, seems to withhold from his text the approving nod, the wink of recognition. We have tried and failed to establish free indirect discourse as the clue to the fictional text; nor can we pretend that the shifting of perspectives would provide the clue to Hardy's specificity. To replace discursive instability by optical uncertainty may be an attractive possibility, and I aim to pursue it a little further, but Brooke-Rose is right to warn us that it will not be and cannot be the whole story.

Ian Watt observed, in the opening of *The Ambassadors*, the frequency of *that*. The antithesis in the art of storytelling of the implied antecedent is the familiar formula 'Once upon a time ... '. This belongs to fairy-tales and the simplest forms of narrative. In the *Ars poetica* Horace had already noticed that the epic displays a degree of narrative sophistication in opening 'in medias res', in the middle of the events narrated: the epic poet does not begin the story of the Trojan Wars from the birth of Helen but 'carries his hearer right into the thick of it as though it were already known'.[33] Of course, the subject of myth, the theme of epic is, as a rule, familiar matter. By contrast, the shock of the opening demonstrative in the novel is that the matter is private: the reader is thus positioned initially as one overhearing, being privy to a discourse intended for another, or for no listener. Hardy, for all his desire to remain close to the traditional genres, does not imitate the epic in respect of traditional and familiar themes, perhaps because, as an Ancient Mariner, he demands that his material be new and unfamiliar.[34] And so Hardy can begin a novel as if everything needed to be explained, as from the birth of Helen:

> One evening of late summer, before the nineteenth century had reached one-third of its span, a young man and woman, the latter carrying a child, were approaching the large village of Weydon-Priors, in Upper Wessex, on foot. They were plainly but not ill clad, though the thick hoar of dust which had accumulated on their shoes and garments from an obviously long journey lent a disadvantageous shabbiness to their aspect just now.

The jarring shifts here concern not optical but temporal distance: at the beginning of the first sentence we are asked to take a long retrospective view back to the first third of the nineteenth century; and then, suddenly, at the end of the second sentence we are asked to think of this group of three persons as they are 'just now'.

We have already been subjected, subtly but predictably, to the optical machinery whereby a group of persons are seen on a road, in a frame that requires sufficient distance from the object to admit both the persons and the road and even the large town that they are approaching. This is the perspective familiar from landscape art: a rural prospect. Yet suddenly and without warning we are being shown dust that has accumulated on their shoes and clothing. This is the microscopic view soon to be familiar to the devotees of Sherlock Holmes, who made his first appearance in 1887 (*A Study in Scarlet*), the year after the publication of *The Mayor of Casterbridge*:

> 'You have come up from the south-west, I see.'
> 'Yes, from Horsham.'
> 'That clay and chalk mixture which I see upon your toe-caps is quite distinctive.'

> 'You must have started early, and yet you had a good drive in a dog-cart, along heavy roads, before you reached the station.'
> The lady gave a violent start ...

'There is no mystery, my dear madam,' said he, smiling. 'The left arm of your jacket is spattered with mud in no less than seven places. The marks are perfectly fresh. There is no vehicle save a dog-cart which throws up mud in that way.'[35]

While Conan Doyle and his narrator, Watson, draw our attention to the sharpness of Holmes's observations, Hardy, by contrast, tricks our reader's eyes into not seeing the brilliance of his narrator's perceptions. Instead we see the object itself, even the dust on the shoes.

This is as it were such a feat of prestidigitation that we hardly notice that a trick has been performed at all. Part of the effect, or peculiar lack of self-regarding effect, in the opening of *The Mayor* results from an alteration made between 1902 and 1912. From the earliest version up to the edition in the 'Wessex Novels' of 1895, and in printings until 1902, the opening sentence begins: 'One evening of late summer, before the present century had reached its thirtieth year, a young man ... '. By 1902 the present century had of course undergone a deictic shift, but it was not until the Wessex Edition of 1912 that the period was no longer indicated but denotated, as 'the nineteenth century'. The shock that the reader registers at the close of that paragraph, 'just now', is thus in part the result of an amendment. There is rather less disparity between 'just now' and 'the present century' (even in its first 30 years, thus 'at least fifty years ago') than between 'the nineteenth century' and 'just now'. The disparity is less of chronology than of rhetoric. From the text of the Wessex Edition onward we find a jarring discontinuity between temporal denotation and temporal indication.

The effect of 'just now' is not unlike that of *that*: it introduces the reader into the same time and space as the narrator, and removes the reader from the time and space of reading. The confusion is compounded when we read in the Preface, dated February 1895, written for the issue of *The Mayor of Casterbridge* in the Wessex Novels edition:

Readers of the following story who have not yet arrived at middle age are asked to bear in mind that, in the days recalled by the tale, the home Corn Trade, on which so much of the action turns, had an importance that can hardly be realized by those accustomed to the sixpenny loaf of the present date, and to the present indifference of the public to harvest weather.[36]

That Preface was slightly amended to stand as the Preface to the Wessex Edition in 1912, and in all subsequent editions it has born the subscript dates: 'February 1895; May 1912'. Very few readers in 1912 would have memories of the days recalled by the tale, and one must wonder why Hardy did not simply omit, in 1912, the now meaningless phrase, 'who have not yet arrived at middle age'. Meaningless according to the contractual obligations of the preface as a paratextual genre, this slippage is not unlike that of the title page of *Tess*. For to retain the deixis of a present, pointing to the 'now' of 1895, is in 1912 to render it, and the 'T. H.' who signs it, part of a fiction, a fictive indicative.

We should recall Donald Davidson's words: 'the characteristic Hardy novel is conceived as a *told* (or *sung*) story, or at least not as a literary story'. The use of deixis – the present century, just now – seems deliberately to mock the conventions of print, and even of writing. For the first condition of writing is that it will be read in a time and place different from that of its making. One cannot write 'today' without also inscribing the date. Hardy's novels do indeed, as Davidson says, seem to resent the fact that they are written; they resent, or mock, or, perhaps best, they play with the tensions that exist between the rhetoric of storytelling and the rhetoric of fiction.

Prose demands a stable point of reference, a clear announcement of the time and space from which indications, if any, will be made, and bearings taken. Writers of prose have understood their contractual obligations since classical times: to offer a representation of a single voice which, by a convention of mute notation, can be vocalised once again by a reader. Given the different spatial and temporal coordinates of writer and reader, prose cannot make use of deixis, the rhetorical conventions of pointing, much used in speech. 'Deixis usually means the function of certain grammatical and lexical features that relate utterances to the spatiotemporal coordinates of the act of utterance.'[37] Novelistic discourse (in Bakhtin's sense) differs from prose in two respects: voice undergoes the transformations of free indirect discourse; and deixis is allowed.

The opening of *The Mayor* would have reminded many more of Hardy's readers then, in 1886, or 1895, or even 1912, whatever age they might have attained, than those of today, of the opening of another novel:

> It was early on a fine summer's day, near the end of the eighteenth century, when a young man, of genteel appearance, journeying towards the north-east of Scotland, provided himself with a ticket in one of those public carriages which travel between Edinburgh and

the Queensferry, at which place, as the name implies, and as is well known to all my northern readers, there is a passage boat for crossing the Firth of Forth.[38]

Hardy never uses the phrase 'my readers' or even 'readers' except in prefatory or paratextual material; he would therefore, unlike Scott, be unable to divide his readers into those with local knowledge and those without. That in itself conditions Hardy's presentation of the local, as if it were generally accessible, and makes it very different from Scott's, or from Hardy's 'regionalist' followers. Hardy's audience, or his narrator's, is implied to be in the vicinity, perhaps within hearing, and certainly sharing the same (multiple) vantage points.

The man was of fine figure, swarthy, and stern in aspect; and he showed in profile a facial angle so slightly inclined as to be almost perpendicular. He wore a short jacket of brown corduroy, newer than the remainder of his suit, which was a fustian waistcoat with white horn buttons, breeches of the same, tanned leggings, and a straw hat overlaid with black glazed canvas. At his back he carried by a looped strap a rush basket from which protruded at one end the crutch of a hay-knife, a wimble for hay-bonds being also visible in the aperture. His measured springless walk was the walk of the skilled countryman as distinct from the desultory shamble of the general labourer; – while in the turn and plant of each foot there was, further, a dogged and cynical indifference, personal to himself, showing its presence even in the regularly interchanging fustian folds, now in the left leg, now in the right, as he paced along.

The first readers of Sherlock Holmes might have been reminded of this: the jacket that is newer than the rest of the suit, the walk that discloses occupation and status, the identification of that which can be ascribed neither to occupation nor standing but which is 'personal to himself'. All this has been deduced before the man has even opened his mouth. This narrator is challenged and provoked to brilliance by nothing so much as silence. (The philologically learned among his readers will also enjoy the concealed tautology of 'dogged and cynical'.) And the viewpoint is dizzying: we are shown the face in profile, we examine the suit closely, we stand back in order to watch the manner of walking, and from uncomfortably close up (and low down) we watch the alternating folds in the fustian of his breeches' legs. Unlike Sherlock Holmes, we may suspect, this narrator has seen all that he describes, all that he takes as clues. By contrast, Sherlock Holmes, or Watson, or Conan Doyle, fails to persuade us that there are actually seven marks of mud on the lady's left sleeve, because there is nothing significant attached to that number. With Hardy's narrator there is always a motivation for noticing such things. Observation is not neutral or indifferent but expresses the joy and power of the gaze, the power of the one who can know about others before they have spoken, before they know they are being watched. To read character from 'the turn and plant of each foot' is to make of the most quotidian action a detail of forensic significance.

The third paragraph seems indirectly to address the reader, as fellow-watcher or 'overlooker' (that is, the episcopal), and to make explicit the necessity of silence to the forensic gaze. Not by words but by fingerprints (or footprints, *vestigiae*) is guilt confessed, and conviction obtained.

> What was really peculiar, however, in this couple's progress, and would have attracted the attention of any casual observer otherwise disposed to overlook them, was the perfect silence they preserved. They walked side by side in such a way as to suggest afar off the low, easy, confidential chat of people full of reciprocity; but on closer view it could be discerned that the man was reading, or pretending to read, a ballad-sheet which he kept before his eyes with some difficulty by the hand that was passed through the basket-strap.

With the phrase 'reading, or pretending to read', the alert gazer may wonder whether we have not, all along, been merely pretending to read Hardy. For if the characters on the road are silent, they are, in this, figures of the reader. Indeed, the three figures become indifferently one when we are told of the woman: 'Virtually she walked the road alone, save for the child she bore.' As the woman is ambivalently bearing the child (that she had once borne), so the man is carrying 'with some difficulty' a ballad sheet: both carry burdens, as does a ballad. The man's burden is a text, as the woman's is: a child and a name that will be misinterpreted. But it is the silence of the pair that is so devastating to the reader. For it is as though Hardy had anticipated the criticism of Davidson, and presented us with a labourer carrying a ballad sheet, holding it with difficulty in front of his eyes, and yet making no noise. Well might one wonder if it is even possible to 'read' a ballad without giving it voice, and taking up its burden. We recall Walter Benjamin on the loneliness we feel in the company not of a storyteller, but of a novelist:

18. Auerbach, *Mimesis*, p. 532.
19. Joseph Warren Beach, *The Technique of Thomas Hardy* (Chicago, 1922), p. 154. Beach had already written monographs on Henry James and George Meredith: of all the critics writing on Hardy during his lifetime, Beach is by some measure the most sophisticated.
20. Judith Mitchell, 'Hardy's Female Reader', in Margaret F. Higonnet, ed., *The Sense of Sex: Feminist Perspectives on Hardy* (Illinois, 1993), pp. 172–87. The cited sentence is from p. 180.
21. For example, Henry James approaches recognition when he writes of the 'strange eloquence of suggestion and rhythm' that he is surprised to find in novels of slight artistic pretension. Cited in Charles Lock, 'The Sublime and the Giggly: on Iris Murdoch and John Cowper Powys', *Powys Journal*, XI (2001), p. 59.
22. Judith Bryant Wittenberg, 'Early Hardy Novels and the Fictional Eye', *Novel*, 16 (1983), p. 152.
23. This absolution of responsibility was put to the juridical test in the trial of Gustave Flaubert, whose defence lawyer, M. Sénard, came as close as anyone, before Charles Bally to an identification of *style indirect libre* in *Madame Bovary*; see Stina Teilmann, 'Flaubert's Crime: Trying Free Indirect Discourse', *Literary Research/Recherche Littéraire*, 17 (33) (2000), pp. 74–87.
24. Mitchell, 'Hardy's Female Reader', p. 178.
25. On the manuscript title-page the first seven words are all in upper case, of sizes diminishing over the three lines, the letters of 'TESS' being about twice the height of those of 'A PURE WOMAN'. In the remaining three lines there are only three letters in upper case, the initials F, T and H. The word 'presented' replaces 'depicted', which would have stressed the pictorial: 'presented' is cunningly neutral, both pictorial and discursive. For an image of the manuscript title page (which also holds the epigraph), see R. L. Purdy, *Thomas Hardy: A Bibliographical Study* (Oxford, 1954), facing p. 71.
26. Simon Gatrell, 'Introduction', in Thomas Hardy, *Tess of the d'Urbervilles*, eds Juliet Grindle and Simon Gatrell (Oxford, 1988), pp. xvii–xix.
27. Mitchell, 'Hardy's Female Reader', pp. 179, 180. To this, one might object that the antithesis of 'subject' is not 'enigma' but 'object'. That Sue is an enigma – as of course she is – must follow from her being presented as an object to whose inner discourse we are granted only a very restricted access.
28. Mitchell, 'Hardy's Female Reader', pp. 182–4.
29. Simon Gatrell, *Hardy the Creator: A Textual Biography* (Oxford, 1988), p. 106.
30. Gatrell, *Hardy the Creator*, p. 106; Jean-Jacques Lecercle, 'The Violence of Style in *Tess of the d'Urbervilles*', in Lance St John Butler, *Alternative Hardy* (London, 1989), p. 2.
31. Christine Brooke-Rose, 'Ill Wit and Sick Tragedy: *Jude the Obscure*', in Butler, *Alternative Hardy*, pp. 26–48.
32. Brooke-Rose, 'Ill Wit and Sick Tragedy', p. 32.
33. Horace, 'The Art of Poetry', trans. by D. A. Russell, in D. A. Russell and M. Winterbottom, eds, *Classical Literary Criticism* (Oxford: World's Classics, 1989), p. 101.

34. The one exception is of course not a novel but the composite of traditional genres entitled *The Dynasts*. Its subject matter, the Napoleonic Wars, would be as familiar as any sequence of events in British history.

35. Arthur Conan Doyle, *The Adventures of Sherlock Holmes* (London, 1893), citing 'The Adventure of the Five Orange Pips', p. 107, and 'The Adventure of the Speckled Band', p. 183.

36. In Harold Orel, ed., *Thomas Hardy's Personal Writings* (London, 1967), p. 18.

37. Jeffrey Kittay and Wlad Godzich, *The Emergence of Prose: An Essay in Prosaics* (Minneapolis, 1987), p. 19.

38. Walter Scott, *The Antiquary* (1816): many of Scott's novels approximate to the time-honoured formula. The only novel (to my present recollection) that actually begins 'Once upon a time' is far from innocent in so doing: 'Once upon a time and a very good time it was there was a moocow coming down along the road … ' (James Joyce, *A Portrait of the Artist as a Young Man*).

39. Hardy's concern with silent reading and other forms of 'mute perception' (such as dumb-shows) is further elaborated in *The Dynasts*; see Charles Lock, 'Hardy Promises: *The Dynasts* and the Epic of Imperialism', in C. Pettit, ed., *Reading Thomas Hardy* (London, 1998), pp. 83–116.

2
hardy and his readers
richard nemesvari

Thomas Hardy's relationship with his audience has always been intense and complex. The controversial subjects that he explored, united with his often demanding experiments in form provoked his Victorian readers and challenged critics throughout the twentieth century and beyond. In particular Hardy's fraught association with the realist project initiated by George Eliot created a series of tensions within his texts which invited 'readerly' attempts to reconcile their apparent conflicts. Hardy tantalises his audience by appearing to fulfil culturally constructed literary expectations while at the same time frustrating them; thus Jakob Lothe's assertion that the 'variants on genre observable in Hardy's novels ... need to be considered in the context of his understanding of literature ... as a blend of genres' pinpoints the issue crucial to understanding reader response to his prose fiction.[1] The unity of approach/reaction endorsed by the standards of generic realism is simply not available in a Hardy text, and the anxiety this produces in some readers can be as severe as that created by his exploration of class, gender and sexual conflict. Something very similar happens with Hardy's poetry, since it also refuses to conform to established ideas of consistent metre and treatment of subject, thus preventing any attempt at what Bakhtin would call a monologic response. Instead, Hardy's writing insists upon, and indeed forces, a dialogic inter-action that engages his audience as active textual constructors.

A theoretical framework that helps to understand how this process works can be found in modern reception theory. Hans Robert Jauss's concept of a 'horizon of expectation' is especially useful in elaborating the sometimes ambivalent link between Hardy and his readers.[2] Jauss insists that literary meaning can only be determined through the relationship of author, cultural context and the aesthetic reactions which each encourages in a specified audience. Thus 'literature and art only obtain a history that has the character of a process when the succession of works is mediated not only through the producing subject but also through the consuming subject – through the interaction of author and public.'[3] The elements of this process are neither random nor based solely on individual taste. Jauss argues that the

> psychic process in the reception of a text is, in the primary horizon of aesthetic experience, by no means only an arbitrary series of merely subjective impressions, but rather the carrying out of specific instructions in a process of directed perception, which can be comprehended according to its constitutive motivations and triggering signals.[4]

The horizon of expectation, then, is the set of 'directed' perceptions and aesthetic signals that are the given backgrounds for artistic production, and a text or body of texts can only be interpreted by being 'silhouetted' against them. Far from being static, however, Jauss's horizon of expectation generates a constant state of dynamic adjustment not only as readers and authors negotiate whether a work accepts ('blends in' with) or subverts ('stands out' against) the expectations, but as the horizon itself shifts under the influence of the works it attempts to define. This dynamism is crucial to the complex responses Hardy's writing provoked.

For Hardy, as for most Victorian authors, the negotiation between writer and reader was tied to being reviewed in the journals and magazines which shaped Victorian opinion. Such reviews were crucial in establishing the parameters of reader response available to both the 'producing' and 'consuming' subjects. Hardy was notoriously sensitive to reviewer opinion, so that his sense of what was expected of him was shaped by its influence throughout his career. And what the majority of reviewers seemed to want was more idyllic tales of Wessex. Increasingly, as his career advanced, whenever Hardy ventured outside of the region that was 'natural' to him, or when his perspective on that region became too grim, reviewers reacted with disappointment or resentment. This was clearly expressed in the often hinted (and occasionally directly stated) desire that Hardy rewrite some version of *Far from the Madding Crowd* over and over again. As the element of his writing most easily associated with realism, reviewers insisted that Wessex was both his unique and his most successful contribution to literature. Few authors would have been able to completely resist such concerted 'encouragement' to develop in a certain direction, although possibly equally few authors could avoid resenting the thinly concealed coercion involved.

Thus Hardy, in his essays, prefaces, and conversations, can be seen both internalising and resisting such opinion, attempting in his turn to project a set of expectations, and to encourage certain ways of reading his texts. These sometimes aggressive acts of 'self-shaping', along with the pointed textual revisions in subsequent editions of his novels, mean that Hardy became an active participant in the cultural reception of his work. Far from the simple victim of reviewers determined to misrepresent his achievement, a persona which Hardy found especially attractive to cultivate given the furore surrounding the publication of *Tess of the d'Urbervilles* and *Jude the Obscure*, he instead played a significant role in defining the horizon of expectation of his audience. By retroactively defining himself as a writer focused primarily on 'character and environment' Hardy appears to accept the dominant discourse of his time, which Jauss explicitly identifies in working out his theories.

> The functional connection between literature and society is for the most part demonstrated in traditional literary sociology within the narrow boundaries of method that has only superficially replaced the classical principle of *imitatio naturae* with the determination that literature is the representation of a pregiven reality, which therefore must elevate a concept of style conditioned by a particular period – the 'realism' of the nineteenth century – to the status of the literary category par excellence.[5]

Yet the aspects of Hardy's texts which refuse to conform to this 'literary category par excellence', his use of coincidence, the grotesque, sensationalism, melodrama and mannered vocabulary, are consistent from first to last, and demonstrate his resistance to this mode of fiction. Hardy hoped to appropriate realism's status and yet avoid its limitations. The difficulties inherent in such an effort generate the tensions at the core of Hardy's writing.

This combination of reviewer response and authorial reaction served to create the horizon of expectation against which Hardy's works were measured up until his death. Indeed, Hardy did his best to exert his influence beyond that usually terminal event, with the publication over Florence Hardy's name of *The Early Life of Thomas Hardy, 1840–1891* (1928) and *The Later Years of Thomas Hardy, 1892–1928* (1930). Ostensibly written by his second wife, this was largely Hardy's creation, and served as his last effort to control his public image. As the twentieth century proceeded, reader response, shaped by these earlier constructions of Hardy, divided into two main branches. The first of these can be traced back to those same constructions, and an increasing emphasis on them saw the cultural creation of the author as the chronicler of a lost age. Hardy's eventual position as the grand old man of English literature generated a powerful sense of nostalgia for the agrarian, pre-industrial world of Wessex that was increasingly seen as the focus of his writings; and, as that world retreated even further into the past, its attraction increased. The result was an emphasis upon topographical and biographical approaches to his writing that reinforced Hardy's reputation as the quintessential writer of an 'Englishness' lost amidst the uncertainties of modern experience. The ensuing development of the 'Hardy industry' is at least partially generated by the desire to relive that lost past, and helps explain Hardy's continuing appeal through what Charles Lock calls 'the astonishing demand for popular editions' of his works.[6] This development moves beyond the texts themselves into the realm of an author's ideological construction by his audience, and while there is no doubt that this has contributed to preserving Hardy as a writer who continues to be read, it also tends to homogenise and oversimplify crucial elements of his canon. This reduction of complexity is reproduced in a parallel critical attitude, which would have a significant impact on readings of Hardy as the century progressed.

This stance appears very clearly in Virginia Woolf's essay 'The Novels of Thomas Hardy', written in January 1928 shortly after Hardy's death, and collected in *The Common Reader: Second Series*. Woolf, who knew Hardy through his friendship with her father Leslie Stephen, states that there are two kinds of writers: the conscious and the unconscious. In the 'conscious' category she places writers such as Flaubert and James, and suggests that they are able 'not merely to make the best use of the spoil their gifts bring in, but control their genius in the act of creation; they are aware of all the possibilities of every situation, and are never taken by surprise'. Hardy, in contrast, is placed in the 'unconscious' category, along with authors like Dickens and Scott, authors who 'seem suddenly and without their own consent to be lifted up and swept onwards. The wave sinks and they cannot say what has happened or why.' This means that with Hardy it is 'as if [he] were not quite aware of what he did, as if his consciousness held more than he could produce, and he left it for his readers to make out his full meaning'.[7] This is a characteristically astute observation, since it recognises the way Hardy invites reader participation in his texts. It also, unfortunately, suggests that he is essentially 'inartistic' in his writing: that he is not in control of his creativity. The longevity of this attitude is demonstrated in an entry by John Bayley for the *Oxford Reader's Companion to Hardy*, in which he asserts that '[e]verything great in the art of his novels depends on a kind of freshness .... Hardy himself remained in many ways a naïve and even childlike man, however much that simplicity was tempered with native cunning and shrewdness.'[8] Bayley is a perceptive reader, but the danger of typecasting Hardy as a 'naïve' yet somehow 'shrewd' author is its implication that if the writer strives to achieve an intended effect he is somehow moving away from his natural idiom. Although Edward Neill overstates when he describes such constructions as the 'philistine patronage which disfigures Hardy', he is right to note that they do not grant him sufficient credit as an artist consciously engaged with the literary and social issues of his time.[9]

These two approaches, then, unite to create a set of expectations that potentially neutralise or efface some of the more demanding aspects of Hardy's writing. This tendency, however, has been challenged by methodologies which foreground textual and critical ideology. In particular issues of gender and class have found expression through feminist and Marxist interpretations, while post-structuralist metacriticism has called attention both to his resistance to realism and to the ways in which interpretive strategies create the readings they set out to discover. Such perspectives serve to rebut ideas about Hardy's 'unconscious' artistry by demonstrating its direct, successful involvement with his cultural context. Readers of Hardy are increasingly self-reflexive about their subject: commentary can no longer assume an unproblematic relationship with his texts, but must instead recognise the ongoing exchange with previous audiences and modes of interpretation. This intertextual manner of reading locates Hardy in a web of significances, and complicates the determination of his 'meaning' in ways that recognise and require a constant critical dialogue. Once begun it is unlikely that such a process can be stopped, so it will continue to shape Hardy studies for the foreseeable future. Determining the horizon of expectation against which Hardy is understood, therefore, requires a diachronic analysis of the interlocking stages through which it developed and continues to develop. In this way it is possible to perceive more fully the complicated process which created the 'Thomas Hardy' whose texts continue to fascinate contemporary readers.

speculating in smut: hardy and the reviewers

As Nicola Thompson points out in her study *Reviewing Sex: Gender and the Reception of Victorian Novels*, in the 1850s '[t]he literary review and literary article became important mediators between literature and the reading public'.[10] By the time Hardy began publishing in the 1870s, this system of sanctioned public evaluation was firmly in place, and needed to be reckoned with by any aspiring writer. Hardy's first attempt at fiction, *The Poor Man and the Lady*, had been turned down by both the Macmillan and the Chapman publishing houses, and he aggressively followed the advice of Chapman's reader, George Meredith, that for his next effort he 'attempt a novel with a purely artistic purpose, giving it a more complicated "plot"' (*Life*, p. 64).

The result was a text modelled on the works of Wilkie Collins and Mary Braddon, two writers whose facility for 'plotting' was matched by their impressive sales figures. That the anonymous author of *Desperate Remedies* made his debut with a piece of sensation fiction was not, however, the best way to get on the good side of the reviewers, although it was an understandable attempt to work in a still-popular genre. The widely publicised sensationalism debate of the 1860s, which had in many ways supported the role of literary reviewers as the arbiters of proper taste, had relegated sensation novels to the status of second-rate art, and just as decisively established realism as the form of serious fiction. Thus Hardy's decision, forced or not, to begin his career as a professional author with a sensation novel helped to establish the parameters of his relationship with his readers in a way which would continue in different guises to its end.

Desperate Remedies received little reviewer attention, but such notices as it did get provide some interesting foreshadowings. An anonymous piece in the *Athenaeum* asserts that the novel, 'though in some respects an unpleasant story, is undoubtedly a very powerful one', and that 'the chief blemish of the book will be found in the occasional coarseness to which we have alluded, and which we can hardly further particularize'.[11] The *Spectator* was considerably harsher.

This is an absolutely anonymous story; no falling back on previous works which might give a clue to the authorship, and no assumption of a *nom de plume* which might, at some future time, disgrace the family name, and still more, the Christian name of a repentant and remorseful novelist – and very right too. By all means let him bury the secret in the profoundest depths of his own heart, out of reach, if possible of his own consciousness ... Here are no fine characters, no original ones to extend one's knowledge of human nature, no display of passion except of the brute kind, no pictures of Christian virtue.[12]

Although Hardy could hardly be pleased with such comments, these were stock reactions to sensation fiction in the post-1860s. The grudging acknowledgement of a story's force is almost invariably followed by a qualifying accusation of 'coarseness' which is meant to suggest that its appeal is of the lowest order, while the assertion that the author should be ashamed of him/herself for producing a text that explores vice instead of virtue was regularly levelled at writers such as Collins and Charles Reade, and at Braddon practically every time she put pen to paper. Leaving aside the generic nature of these observations, they do establish ideas that will recur. Hardy's ability to write novels which grip the imagination, 'despite' their supposedly inappropriate language and coarse presentation of improper subject material, is a constant theme up to and including *Jude*, while the moral failings of his fiction become the increasing focus of hostile reviews.

However, these reviews also touch on positive elements of the text. The *Athenaeum*, commenting on Hardy's use of chronological information in his chapter headings, declares that this 'gives an air of reality which is far more satisfactory than the popular mottoes from some book of quotation' that served as conventional novelistic epigraphs.[13] The admission of an 'air of reality' is unusual when discussing sensation fiction, as is the *Spectator*'s observation that the author has a

> very happy facility in catching and fixing phases of peasant life, in producing for us not the manners and language only, but the tone of thought – if it can be dignified by the name of thought – and the simple humour of consequential village worthies and gaping village rustics.[14]

In addition, '[t]his nameless author has ... one other talent of a remarkable kind – sensitiveness to scenic and atmospheric effects, and to their influence on the mind, and the power of rousing similar sensitiveness in his readers'.[15] Such comments recognise Hardy's ability to combine sensationalism and realism, while at the same time pointing the expression of that realism towards representations of 'peasant life' and 'atmospheric effects'. The writers are ambivalent about the success of such blendings, but both are forced to concede that the genre expectations with which they are familiar are inadequate in dealing with this particular 'nameless author'. Such a response was hardly conducive to sales, however, and the novel was quickly remaindered. There was, nonetheless, a further review of Hardy's first published novel in a well-recognised journal, and to that reviewer the author was not nameless at all.

The unsigned piece in the *Saturday Review* of 30 September 1871 was written by Hardy's friend Horace Moule, and according to Michael Millgate he quite intentionally set out to 'salvage the situation with a laudatory notice'.[16] One way of doing this, while acknowledging the inescapable fact of the novel's sensationalism, was to assert that this was not its main impetus. Moule insists that

> there are situations well fitted to enchain the fancy of the sincerest lover of melodrama; but not one of these is a *purpureus pannus* stitched into a circumjacent groundwork of dullness; nor, when all are taken together, can it be said that of these is the essence of the book. The essence of the book is precisely what it ought to be – namely the evolution of character.

That the 'essence' of a novel 'ought' to be the development of character was by this cultural moment the consensus of serious readers; Moule attempts to align *Desperate Remedies* with an aesthetic he hopes will increase its status in spite of the lack of genre respectability. But he goes one step further. When briefly discussing the character Richard Crickett, the parish clerk in the novel, Moule claims that 'he is drawn something after the idea of Mr. Macey in *Silas Marner*; and, though he is far from equalling that admirable sketch, yet neither is he a copy, nor does he want life and movement of his own'. Later he makes this link even more explicit by noting that '[l]ike George Eliot the author delights in running off to *sentientiæ*, in generalizing abstractions out of the special point in hand'.[17] While neither of these observations is completely positive, they do suggest that this unknown, first-time novelist deserves to have George Eliot mentioned in a review of his work – a fairly bold vote of confidence in itself. Eliot's reputation as the dominant novelist of the mid-Victorian period, and as the pre-eminent advocate of realism in English fiction, was already well established. Aside from providing Hardy with a (somewhat muted) compliment, Moule's invocation of Eliot also urged Hardy's early audience to situate him in the mainstream of novelistic development, not in the side channel of the sensational. Although his review had no noticeable effect on the novel's sales, Moule did his best to direct reader response in the way most likely to advance his friend's career.

Desperate Remedies has sometimes been perceived as an anomalous beginning to Hardy's career, not least because he himself later presented it that way. In these reviewer responses, however, can be seen a series of reactions which establish the outlines of future commentaries, and which suggest the book is more representative than its subsequently famous author wished to acknowledge. The blend of sensationalism and realism, the skill at portraying rural characters and their environment, the presentation of improperly risqué material, and the evocation of George Eliot, are all elements that will be repeated in evaluations of his later fiction.

Hardy's next two novels, *Under the Greenwood Tree* and *A Pair of Blue Eyes*, were both reviewed with considerably more kindness. The *Athenaeum*, giving itself an undeserved pat on the back, implies that the still-anonymous author has done both himself and his audience a favour by following its advice.

> [W]e are glad to meet again with the author of *Desperate Remedies*, and to find that in his new novel he has worked principally that vein of his genius which yields the best produce ... Our readers may possibly remember, that while praising *Desperate Remedies* for many marks of ability, we especially commended it for its graphic pictures of rustic life somewhere in the West Country. Here the author is clearly on his own ground, and to this he has confined himself in the book before us.[18]

Richard L. Purdy, however, notes that parts of *Under the Greenwood Tree* 'must date from the autumn of 1867, since it incorporates material from ... The Poor Man and the Lady',[19] and Millgate asserts that 'there is no evidence that the reviews were in any sense influential upon its conception and composition'.[20] Nonetheless, the reinforcement of a certain fictional focus is clear. Almost as significant is the same review's identification of what it sees as one of the novel's flaws, 'the tendency of the author to forget his part ... and to make his characters now and then drop their personality, and speak too much like educated people'.[21] Moule, again reviewing his friend in the *Saturday Review*, echoes this by identifying

> one definite fault in the dialogues ... an occasional tendency of the country folk, not so much to think with something of subtle distinction (for cottagers can do that much more completely than the well-dressed world are apt to suppose), but to express themselves in the language of the author's manner of thought, rather than their own.[22]

This becomes close to a standard refrain about Hardy's rustic characters, and it has interesting implications. Although Moule attempts to mitigate some of the snobbery explicit in such observations, the contradiction is clear. The author is said to be 'on his own ground' when describing the world of Dorset, yet the reviewer sees fit to dispute the presentation of dialogue which he somehow knows to be incorrect. In other words, even when Hardy is being realistic in ways endorsed by the literary magazines, he is not realist 'enough' to meet their expectations. Antagonistic critics, as a way of denigrating later novels, refined this charge to suggest that it represents the foundational unreality of *all* his characters, and therefore the failure of his texts in general. The reappearance of this charge throughout Hardy's career demonstrates reviewer uneasiness with the hybrid nature of his style, which blends close observation of rural realities with a storyteller's licence to embellish the individuals who live and embody them.

A Pair of Blue Eyes, the first novel to carry Hardy's name, provided reviewers with the opportunity to add one more element to the growing list of characteristics for this now specifically identified author. Thus the anonymous writer for the *Saturday Review* announces that '[t]he distinctive feature of this novel is that out of simple material there has been evolved a result of really tragic power', and that 'Mr. Hardy has in the book before us developed, with something of the ruthlessness of George Eliot, what may be called the tragedy of circumstance.'[23] That Eliot is invoked again illustrates how strong this association was in the reviews of his early work, although just before that statement the same reviewer declares that 'no two writers could be more unlike in their general methods', showing a characteristic unwillingness to give this newcomer too much credit. In contrast to the fates of Michael Henchard, Tess Durbyfield and Jude Fawley, the death of Elfride Swancourt may seem more pathetic than tragic, but this is only apparent in hindsight. The introduction of Hardy's eventually notorious darkness of vision, his so-called pessimism and his sense of the tragedy of human consciousness, became another focal point for future reader response.

The process occurring in these early reviews is significant. Not only is Hardy being fitted into the prevailing horizon of expectation, in ways that suggest the fit is none too comfortable, but there is also a horizon of expectation being developed for his own fiction. The patterns of response being generated are foundational, and although variations and evolutions on them will occur, they are never abandoned. Thus, for example, *Far from the Madding Crowd*, Hardy's first major success, leads to a series of reprises on these themes. The *Westminster Review* states that the novel 'stands to all contemporary novels precisely as *Adam Bede* did to all other novels sixteen years ago', but then qualifies this with the criticism that 'the fault of *Far from the Madding Crowd* is undoubtedly its sensationalism ... if we analyse the story we shall find that it is nothing else but sensationalism'.[24] The *Athenaeum* reviewer declares himself 'unable to say whether the author is an ill-regulated genius or a charlatan with some touches of cleverness', and states that 'some of the scenes, notably that where Sergeant Troy goes through the sword exercise before Bathsheba, are worthy, in their extravagance, of Mr. Reade, and of him only'.[25] The *Spectator* asserts that 'a more incredible picture than that of the group of farm labourers as a whole which Mr. Hardy has given us can hardly be conceived',[26] while the *Observer* decries 'the fundamental absurdity and impossibility of much of the story' even while it encourages 'everybody who cares for a novel to read this one'.[27] Henry James, perceiving the incompatibility of Hardy's method with his own, and no doubt irked by the novel's popularity, wrote a characteristically condescending review for the *Nation*, concluding with the Olympian dismissal that 'the only things we believe in are the sheep and the dogs'.[28]

The pattern is thus firmly established. Of *The Return of the Native* we are told that Hardy's 'Wessex peasantry, though full of picturesque and humorous elements, are never so presented that the reader is able to accept them as true pictures of rustic life',[29] that it 'is all very mournful, and very cruel, and very French',[30] and that the 'harmony of ill-tutored minds so highly pitched could hardly fail in a sensational novel to end in discord and tragedy'.[31] Comments such as these help explain the almost palpable relief with which a novel like *The Trumpet-Major* was received, with the *Spectator* declaring that it is 'both readable and good', that it is 'calculated to show the author in his happiest light', and that the 'story from beginning to end is conceived and put together with capital ingenuity'.[32] Later critics have sometimes wondered over the universally positive reviews directed towards this 'minor' novel, but the attempt to encourage certain perceived proclivities in Hardy, while discouraging others, helps explain the response. This goes for naught, however, within what is usually considered the major phase of his prose fiction, which produced *The Mayor of Casterbridge*, *The Woodlanders*, *Tess of the d'Urbervilles* and *Jude the Obscure* within a ten-year span. The first of these is described as 'not equal to the author's great and most picturesque romance of rural life, *Far From the Madding Crowd*', because it presents a 'story, which is very slight and singularly devoid of interest [and] at the

same time, too improbable'.[33] As well, it presents 'hints of ... fashionable
pessimism, a philosophy which seems to us to have little appropriateness
to the homely scenery and characters ... these very pagan reflections
are as much out of place as they are intrinsically false'.[34] Similarly, *The
Woodlanders* is described as 'a very powerful book, and as disagreeable as it
is powerful', because it is 'written with an indifference to the moral effect
it conveys ... which, in our opinion, lowers the art of [Hardy's] works
quite as much as it lowers the moral tone'.[35] The growing conflation of
Hardy's distinctive fictional style, its compelling effect on his audience
and his 'questionable' morality, is obvious throughout these responses
and is preparing the way for the firestorm which broke out around his
last two novels. The result of this debate was a bifurcation in reaction,
as those who supported Hardy's innovations were called on to defend
him against those who saw his texts not just as failed fiction, but as
pernicious fiction.

The extremity of response to *Tess of the d'Urbervilles* and *Jude the Obscure*
is well documented, and does not need to be rehearsed here. All the
commentary on Hardy's earlier work is repeated at twice the volume,
as it were, so that, for example, D. F. Hanigan says of *Tess* that 'from
beginning to end it bears the hall-mark of Truth on every page ... It is
a more impressive narrative of crushing facts than George Eliot's *Adam
Bede*. It is more deep and poignant than anything that either Zola or Guy
de Maupassant has written. It is a work worthy of Balzac himself.'[36] In
the opposing camp is the reviewer for the *Athenaeum*, who says of *Jude*
that in it 'we have Mr. Hardy running mad in right royal fashion',[37]
while *The Bookman* declares 'in our judgement frankly and deliberately
expressed, in *Jude the Obscure* Mr. Hardy is merely speculating in smut'.[38]
Hannigan's observation, however, reveals a shift in approach which is
shared by both sides of the debate. It is an echo of earlier statements about
the 'Frenchness' of Hardy's method and subject matter, and shows an
ironic development in that he is now lauded for (or accused of) following
a different kind of 'realism': that aggressively advocated by Flaubert
and Zola.[39] It would make things clearer if Victorian reviewers did not
use the words 'realism' and 'naturalism' interchangeably at this time,
since in fact Eliot's intensely moral narrative commitment in her realist
novels could not be further from Flaubert's naturalistic detachment.
Nonetheless, the purpose of analysing Hardy in these terms is clear. He
is being read through a horizon of expectation that has shifted in the
25 years since he began writing novels, only now he is seen as a leading

exponent of a particular approach instead of a follower. Thus references to Eliot, although never quite disappearing, are reduced, while writers such as Margaret Oliphant, in her attack on *Jude* proudly declare their provincialism as a comment on the corruption of foreign fictional values: 'The present writer does not pretend to a knowledge of the works of Zola, which perhaps she ought to have before presuming to say that nothing so coarsely indecent as the whole history of Jude in his relations with his wife Arabella has ever been put in English print.'[40] Those who saw French naturalism as perverse and dangerous now had a way of uniting their opposition to Hardy's content *and* style, since the supposed focus on sensationally sordid topics is reinforced by the supposedly amoral method of presentation. Those, on the other hand, who saw English fiction as in desperate need of reform, as needing to escape the deadening control of Mrs Grundy and the circulating libraries, constructed Hardy as not only in the vanguard of contemporary fiction, but as potentially superior to his Continental peers. That Hardy no more desired to be Flaubert or Zola than he wished to be George Eliot was beside the point.

An exploration of Hardy's experience with reviewers reveals the ways in which an author's 'meaning' is shaped by cultural expectations. A writer can only be understood in terms of the artistic context through which he or she is perceived, and the attempts to fit that writer into that context influence all subsequent responses. For Hardy this meant being placed in a relationship with realism, and later naturalism, that somehow had to accommodate the sensational and the tragic, along with a powerfully fictionalised Wessex setting which was both mimetic and yet never quite mimetic enough. These struggles to define him demonstrate that his writings were strong enough not so much to escape the dominant horizon of expectation as to force an evolution in its structures. Hardy plays a significant role in changing the parameters of Victorian fiction, although he can never fully evade the ways in which official critical response constructed his work. He nonetheless refused to accept what he felt were its misrepresentations, and made a conscious effort to resist them. This was focused not just on his novels but also on his poems, which constituted Hardy's second career as an author. Since such efforts at artistic self-construction were only really possible after he had achieved financial security and fame, however, they will be dealt with in a separate section, following the discussion of Hardy's efforts to shape his legacy as a novelist.

a good hand at a serial: hardy and his novels

In 1920 Robert Graves visited Hardy at his home, Max Gate, and reported that he regarded professional critics 'as parasites no less noxious than autograph-hunters, and wished the world rid of them. He also wished that he had not listened to them when he was a young man.'[41] Since there was little Hardy could do to rid the world of these parasites, and equally little he could do to erase their influence on his younger self, the most he could hope for was to counter their impact by retroactively shaping both his work and the image of himself it presented. This he set out to do with a force of commitment which would not have been misplaced in a Michael Henchard, and which generated, perhaps, the same kind of mixed results. Hardy felt Victorian reviewers had victimised him, and did not feel much better treated by their twentieth-century successors. Since he was not willing to let them have the uncontested last word on his literary reputation, he would put in some words of his own.

Writing to Leslie Stephen in 1874, while working on *Far from the Madding Crowd*, Hardy declared that

[t]he truth is that I am willing, and indeed anxious, to give up any points which may be desirable in a story when read as a whole, for the sake of others which shall please those who read it in numbers. Perhaps I may have higher aims some day ... but for the present circumstances lead me to wish merely to be considered a good hand at a serial.[42]

Whether Hardy's ambitions were so limited even at this early point is open to question, but what is certain is that as his career advanced he became less willing to 'give up' points which he felt essential to the understanding of his fiction. The obvious way to defend his writing was in the form of essays which supported it, and between 1888 and 1891 he was given three opportunities to do this. The resulting pieces, 'The Profitable Reading of Fiction', 'Candour in English Fiction', and 'The Science of Fiction', were each invited contributions, and within their predetermined topics gave Hardy the chance to outline his own position. Charles Lock rightly notes 'how seldom Hardy's critics defer to the critical writings of their author, in comparison with, say, the critics of James, or Conrad, or Lawrence'.[43] Yet it is clear that Hardy, if not explaining his 'theory' of literature in the way that James might, is attempting to guide reader response to his own characteristic style. Thus, in 'The Profitable Reading of Fiction', when discussing reading for pleasure, he argues that 'the narrative must be of a somewhat absorbing kind, if not absolutely fascinating', as well as that the reader should be willing to accept whatever conventions are being employed: 'However profusely [the author] may pour out his coincidences, his marvellous juxtapositions, his catastrophes … let him never be doubted for a moment.'[44] Although there may be some special pleading in such comments, they are consistent with Hardy's reiterated assertions that a story must be entertaining to be effective, and that providing entertainment is a crucial part of the agreement entered into by the author with his or her audience. It was the critics' apparent distaste for such enjoyment that he found increasingly difficult to take, and which he counters by encouraging in the reader

> the exercise of a generous imaginativeness, which shall find in a tale not only all that was put there by the author, put he it never so awkwardly, but which shall find there what was never inserted by him, never foreseen, never contemplated. Sometimes these additions which are woven around a work of fiction by the intensitive power of the reader's own imagination are the finest parts of the scenery.[45]

This remarkable invitation for readerly participation in the text is both a plea for an honest engagement with his novels and, given Hardy's increasingly dedicated attempts to shape the reception of his fiction, a disingenuous invitation to respond in ways which he hopes to guide, if not control. Nonetheless, it suggests a significant recognition of textual fluidity that encourages audience involvement in deriving textual meaning.

But Hardy is also using the passage to establish its inevitably negative opposite. Towards the end of the essay he presents a different picture:

> It is unfortunately quite possible to read the most elevating works of imagination in our own or any language, and, by fixing the regard on the wrong sides of the subject, to gather not a grain of wisdom from them, nay, sometimes positive harm. What author has not had his experience of such reader? – the mentally warped ones of both sexes, who will, where practicable, so twist plain and obvious meanings as to see in an honest picture of human nature an attack on religion, morals, or institutions. Truly has it been observed that 'the eye sees that which it brings with it the means of seeing'.[46]

For Hardy, then, there are two types of readers. The first is open-minded, sympathetic, and willing to assume an authorial good faith without which there is no point in writing at all. This kind of reader enters into a collaborative exchange with the creative act, which makes reading fiction 'profitable'. The second type is close-minded and unreflectingly antagonistic to the author. Having decided to assume the worst, such readers impose their perspectives on the text, and thus derive nothing profitable at all. It is noteworthy that Hardy does not specifically mention content here, but instead focuses on a relational link between producing and consuming subject that requires a mediated commitment from both sides to be successful. Content is, however, very much the concern of his next essay.

Hardy is not the first author to construct an ideal reader, but given his often controversial subject matter he perhaps needs that reader more than most. Still, 'Candour in English Fiction' is a fairly restrained statement. Its claim that 'taste is arriving anew at the point of high tragedy'[47] serves both to suggest that Hardy's specific proclivities are part of a cultural movement, and to prepare for his claims about the requirements for successful tragic effects. One of these is 'original treatment: treatment which seeks to show Nature's unconsciousness not of essential laws, but of those laws framed merely as social expedients by humanity, without a basis in the heart of things.'[48] The suggestion that modern tragedy requires social criticism as a way of explaining the protagonist's destruction combines genre with content in a way which allows the author to avoid accusations of revelling in the negative for its own sake. Positioning himself as part of the *Zeitgeist*, Hardy can use this as a way of criticising obstacles that block its expression. He therefore attacks Victorian modes of publication, specifically serialisation in magazines and such institutions as Mudie's Circulating Library, because their dominance of distribution stifles experimentation and rewards conformity: 'the magazine in particular and the circulating library in general do not foster the growth of the novel which reflects and reveals life. They directly tend to exterminate it by monopolising all literary space.'[49] As well, since the 'crash of broken commandments is as necessary an accompaniment to the catastrophe of a tragedy as the noise of drum and cymbals to a triumphal march',[50] their timidity about offending their putative audience of 'the young person' (and the parents of the young person) means that the English novel is severely compromised. It is thus 'in the self-consciousness engendered by interference with spontaneity ... that the real secret lies of the charlatanry pervading so much of English fiction'.[51]

Hardy was writing this essay at around the same time he was struggling with editors' reactions to *Tess*, and it expresses some of the frustration of that process, though he had yet to endure the negative reviews that the novel received. Nonetheless, in 'Candour in English Fiction' we can see the beginnings of a pose that Hardy would later adopt with some enthusiasm: that of the persecuted artist. Such a role was not completely fabricated, as the *ad hominem* attacks on both *Tess* and *Jude* demonstrate, but it tended to ignore the equally partisan support for each novel. Mainly, however, this persona helped to create a more sympathetic response to both the author and his works. This is not to say that Hardy was being hypocritical, but rather that his sensitivity to negative criticism produced a beleaguered response which could also be employed as a rhetorical position. In any case, Hardy was quite right in identifying the systemic publishing barriers inhibiting Victorian novelists, and equally perceptive in noting that English fiction was evolving in directions which could no longer be constrained by older ideologies of proper and improper subject material. His third essay confronted one of the major influences in that evolution, and in doing so provided him the opportunity to make his most explicit 'theoretical' statements about his own novels.

The title 'The Science of Fiction' immediately identifies the controversy it is meant to address. Explicitly invoking the Continental naturalists' claim to be creating fiction along 'scientific' lines, by which they meant a supposedly rigorous objectivity which restricted itself to empirical description of reality, the journal sponsoring the symposium naturally turned to Hardy. Reviewers had been associating him with 'French' attitudes and approaches since *The Return of the Native*, and so he might be expected to have a position on the issues raised. His response may have been taken as surprising by some, however. After beginning with the apparently conciliatory statement that '[s]ince Art is science with an addition, since some science underlies all Art, there is seemingly no paradox in the use of such a phrase as "the Science of Fiction"',[52] Hardy becomes considerably more aggressive:

> The most devoted apostle of realism, the sheerest naturalist, cannot escape, any more than the withered old gossip over her fire, the exercise of Art in his labour or pleasure of telling a tale. Not until he becomes an automatic reproducer of all impressions whatsoever can he be called purely scientific, or even a manufacturer on scientific principles. If in the exercise of his reason he select or omit, with an eye to being more

truthful than truth (the just aim of Art), he transforms himself into a technicist at a move.[53]

The rejection of attempted scientific objectivity and the embrace of artistic subjectivity is clear, and demonstrates Hardy's essential problem with the realist/naturalist project. Its bluntness suggests a growing impatience with attempts to assign him to a movement with which he has some sympathy, but which is finally not reconcilable with his own method. Indeed, in a passage in the *Life* dated 5 August 1890, he is more insistent yet: 'Art is a disproportioning – (i.e., distorting, throwing out of proportion) – of realities, to show more clearly the features that matter in those realities, which, if merely copied or reported inventorially, might possibly be observed, but would more probably be overlooked. Hence "realism' is not Art' (*Life*, p. 239). Here Hardy is not just addressing the Continental naturalists, but also the required verisimilitude of Eliot herself. His acceptance of disproportion and distortion rejects the need for strict mimesis as well as attempts at objectivist reproduction, clearing the way for his own eclectic blend of styles and genres.

Further, Hardy observes that even those who claim to follow such methods have a difficult time actually doing so. Invoking the author with whom he was most often aligned, Hardy observes

> that [naturalism] should ever have been maintained by such a romancer as M. Zola, in his work on the *Roman Expérimental*, seems to reveal an obtuseness to the disproof conveyed in his own novels which, in a French writer, is singular indeed … But to maintain in theory what he abandons in practice, to subscribe to rules and work by instinct, is a proceeding not confined to the author of *Germinal* and *La Faute de l' Abbé Mouret*.[54]

Ironically, then, reviewers who link Hardy with Zola may be correct, because in practice *neither* of them is a naturalist. But Hardy astutely recognises how such a categorisation may serve a broader purpose: 'Realism is an unfortunate, an ambiguous word, which has been taken up by literary society like a view-halloo, and has been assumed in some places to mean copyism, and in others pruriency, and has led to two classes of delineators being included in one condemnation.'[55] The loose identification of a writer as a 'realist' provides the opportunity already mentioned for a combined attack on his or her fictional method and choice of material, a critical ploy which had been employed against Zola early on, and which would achieve its most violent expression against Hardy with the appearance of *Jude*. That Hardy can see this coming five years before the volume publication of that novel suggests that his expressed surprise at the extremities it produced was somewhat overstated.

By presenting himself as anti-realist, in both the English and French senses of the word, Hardy suggests that his fiction be evaluated outside of constraints that obviously do not suit his writing. And if his three essays are examined as a unit, although they do not possess anything like a rigorous coherence, they do provide the broad outlines of how he wishes to be read. The emphasis on an author's right to engage the audience on his or her own terms in order to provide an involving story, and the need for that audience's response to fulfil those terms, becomes a justification for the novelist's exploration of both the cultural moment and the unique perspective that is at the heart of creativity. This may come into conflict with established modes of reading, in which case those modes should be questioned and modified. The realist horizon of expectation under which Hardy is working, however, was too established to be resisted through even the baldest of statements. Hardy's public assertions did next to nothing to shift the terms in which his novels were read. Ironically it was through an all-but-invisible series of decisions that he would most dramatically influence reader response to the fiction, and in a typically Hardyan twist, those decisions would essentially subvert the statements he had gone to such trouble to provide.

After the publication of *Tess*, Hardy's status as the premier English novelist of the last third of the century was unassailable, and the possibility of collecting his works and printing them under a unified format became attractive from both a literary and an economic point of view. The resulting 'Wessex Novels' edition (1895–96), published by the firm of Osgood, McIlvaine, had a profound effect on the reception of his texts. The name itself is revealing, in that it demonstrates the increasing emphasis on Hardy's imaginative re-creation of south-west England. As Simon Gatrell has pointed out, however, 'the complex social and environmental organization that readers and critics think of as Hardy's Wessex did not exist in the novelist's imagination when he first began to write'.[56] Far from possessing any overarching plan to 'create' Wessex, Hardy only gradually came to understand its potential as an imaginary landscape, and his shaping of it was profoundly retroactive. The Osgood, McIlvaine edition gave him his first chance at a systematic reworking of his existing canon to make its setting consistent, and to reinforce its centrality in his writing. He thus embarked on a series of textual revisions to bring into line those novels whose original composition had taken place before the concept of Wessex was firm. And revising the texts was not his only strategy. Millgate notes:

> [t]he first volume ... had a portrait of Hardy as its frontispiece, but the frontispieces to the other volumes all showed relevant Wessex scenes – chosen by Hardy himself in active collaboration with the illustrator – and these combined with the map and the occasional footnotes on topographical and dialectal matters to demonstrate and indeed firmly register Hardy's claim to be both the originator of Wessex and its only legitimate exploiter.[57]

Having staked his claim Hardy was committed, and it is striking that, given the opportunity to re-evaluate his novels, he did not 'make any fundamental alterations of structure, story, characterization, or theme'[58] in the individual texts. It was the consolidation of Wessex that was most important, and he pursued it diligently.

Tracing the actual changes Hardy made is unnecessary here, and has been done comprehensively elsewhere.[59] It is worth mentioning, however, that it was in *Far from the Madding Crowd* that the word 'Wessex' first appeared, and that *The Mayor of Casterbridge* was the novel in which this focus achieved a coherence that would develop through subsequent novels. In other words, Hardy's first fully successful piece of fiction initiates this movement, and it picks up an increasing momentum beginning with the text that marks the 'major' phase of his career as a novelist. Yet while the 'Wessex Novels' were crucial in giving Hardy the chance retrospectively to solidify this development, it was the agreement with his later publisher, Macmillan, to produce another collected edition that ensured its influence. The 'Wessex Edition' (1912–14) included not just the novels but also the volumes of poetry that Hardy had produced in the interim, beginning with the first, *Wessex Poems* (1898). Again, the title of the edition and of the volume of poems indicates just how important Wessex had become; by this point it 'was the aspect of his writing that distinguished him most prominently, in the eyes of general readers and critics alike, from the mass of publishing [authors]'.[60] Once more the texts were revised to make Wessex place names more consistent from novel to novel, distances and directions between locations were made more accurate in their relationship to Dorset and its surrounding counties, with the overall result that it became easier to identify the 'originals' of buildings, landmarks and villages within the narratives.

The Macmillan collection also provided an expanded map, first drawn by Hardy himself, photographic frontispieces of actual places and settings, based on Hardy's specific instructions, and a companion guidebook in a matching binding, *Thomas Hardy's Wessex*, illustrated by Hermann Lea and, again, directly approved by Hardy. By this stage Hardy's acceptance of Wessex as his fictional 'brand mark' was complete, and since he was quite specific that the Wessex Edition was to be taken as definitive, it became the basis for the literally thousands of reprints of his works which were read throughout the twentieth century.

The impact of this transformation on his audience cannot be overstated. Hardy's decision to accept the mantle of the historian of Wessex has obvious corollaries, not least in his relationship to the realism he seemed so determined to resist in his essays. By directly linking his fiction to 'actual' sites and places, although always careful to remind his audience that he reserves the right to modify them, Hardy encourages the belief that his books are direct records of a world which exists (or existed) 'outside' of them. That this was often the case, that he explicitly employed settings, locations, and occasionally characters, he knew from childhood or adulthood, does not alter the complex tensions established by the 'Wessexisation' of his canon. Within individual texts it can have a significant effect. A novel such as *The Trumpet-Major*, which in its first edition has historical figures such as George III and Thomas Masterman Hardy strolling through actual places such as Weymouth and Dorchester, is a very different thing when those same historical figures pass through fictional Budmouth and Casterbridge. More widely, the creation of a unified Wessex shows Hardy accepting reviewer commentary suggesting that representations of rustic characters and situations are his strength. Novels such as *Desperate Remedies* and *The Hand of Ethelberta*, which can only be awkwardly integrated into the rural Wessex template, are thus implicitly marginalised, and indeed that marginalisation becomes more than implicit, as we shall shortly see. Hardy's alterations encourage his readers to respond to his fiction in ways which include nostalgically experiencing a society which has passed, connecting that society to an apparently identifiable physical terrain which persists, and granting the writer presenting the picture a unique authority to explore its complexities. The continuing desire of readers to 'walk through' the books, via tours of Dorset and its environs, demonstrates the powerful reality which they provoke, along with Hardy's canny recognition of the saleability of such representations. For an author who so specifically rejected mere 'copyism' to rest his popularity on detailed topographical description may seem odd, but of course Hardy's earlier comment on Zola about the discrepancy between theory and practice can cut both ways. The Macmillan collection is crucial in that its revisions establish once and for all the symbolic setting of Hardy's fiction, even while those revisions encouraged that it be read within a realist context. But it is almost equally important because it gave him the opportunity for yet another 'official' statement on his texts.

Penny Boumelha observes that throughout Hardy's career 'there remains a consistent attempt to accommodate that which is unusual or innovatory to normative popular taste',[61] and his General Preface to the Wessex Edition provides a good example of this. Millgate describes it as his 'most substantial piece of critical writing, at once a description of his methods and a justification of his literary ambitions',[62] so it must be taken into account as a specific effort to direct reader response. Most importantly, Hardy uses the General Preface to divide his fiction into three categories that are 'ostensibly descriptive but effectively judgemental'.[63] Thus the 'Novels of Character and Environment' are those 'which approach most nearly to uninfluenced works; also one or two which, whatever their quality in some few of their episodes, may claim a verisimilitude in general treatment and detail'.[64] It is no coincidence that the texts grouped under this heading are the six novels now generally accepted as 'major', along with *Under the Greenwood Tree*, nor that in describing them Hardy uses the word 'verisimilitude', a term which is crucial in realist theory. He has selected the novels that focus most prominently on Wessex, aligned them with realism, defined them as the most 'uninfluenced' (that is, the most uniquely characteristic) of his works, and then granted them first-rank status. Hardy supports this later in the Preface by asserting 'that the description of these backgrounds [has] been done from the real – that is to say, has something real for its basis, however illusively treated'.[65] This helps explain the inclusion of so slight a work as *Under the Greenwood Tree*, which, because it is based heavily on Hardy's family experience, can be slotted into the Wessex paradigm with relative ease. The result is a retrospective acceptance of the realist horizon of expectation that acts to ensure Hardy's canonical and critical acceptance by reinforcing his place as a chronicler of truthful human experience based in an 'actual' location. Even as such a categorisation reinforces the revisions made for the Osgood, McIlvaine and Macmillan editions, however, it also manages to act as cover for those elements of the novels which do *not* fit the conventional realm of realist portrayal and which have remained unmodified. It is an exaggeration to describe what

Hardy is doing here as camouflage, since on one level he wants what he now perceives as his 'serious' books to be given the kind of consideration meted out to realist texts. Yet even as he positions them for acceptance, his refusal to rewrite them indicates a resistance to accepted literary standards which is consistent with his statements in his earlier essays.

Nonetheless, if the 'Novels of Character and Environment' are to be given their due, Hardy needs to distinguish them from his other fiction, and he achieves this neatly. The title of his second category, 'Romances and Fantasies', is calculated to suggest a lowering of expectations. Some of the earliest debates involving the novel as a genre centred on the conflict between romance narratives and realist narratives, with novels such as Jane Austen's *Northanger Abbey* actually incorporating that conflict into their plots. By the 1870s, when Hardy began publishing, there was no doubt which type carried the greater cultural capital certainly, by 1912, to designate a book a romance or a fantasy was to put it thoroughly in its place. Providing such a 'sufficiently descriptive definition' to *A Pair of Blue Eyes*, *The Trumpet-Major*, *Two on a Tower* and *The Well-Beloved* all but guarantees they cannot challenge the 'true' Wessex novels for a committed reader's attention.[66] And the final category takes this process even further. The 'Novels of Ingenuity' are said to

> show a not infrequent disregard of the probable in the chain of events, and depend for their interest mainly on the incidents themselves. They might also be characterized as 'Experiments,' and were written for the nonce simply; though despite the artificiality of their fable some of their scenes are not without fidelity to life.[67]

The faint praise of the last sentence can hardly undo the damage that has been done to *Desperate Remedies*, *The Hand of Ethelberta* and *A Laodicean*, since they have been effectively dismissed as improbable, incidental, and ephemeral 'experiments'. And a reading of the novels demonstrates the need for this, since all three are in essence sensational. The last thing Hardy wants at this point is to be associated with sensation fiction, and thus he puts as much space as possible between these books and what he has now identified as his realist texts. Identifying them as the 'third class' of his fiction, with the hierarchical implications that term connotes, sends a signal to the readers of the Wessex Edition that they are not representative of his work, and need not be held against him.[68]

It is, therefore, accurate to describe the General Preface as a 'conscious gesture of canon-formation'.[69] In it Hardy attempts to influence his audience's reception of his novels in order to support revisions to the texts which the vast majority of readers will never know he made. Thus he achieves a significant compromise with his audience's realist expectations, but in doing so retains important elements that refute those expectations in ways which are distinctively his own. As far as canons go, however, there is a further issue, for the General Preface is also his first opportunity to talk extensively about his growing body of published poetry. That he would attempt to also shape audience reaction to his verse should be, by this point, unsurprising.

a more concentrated form of art: hardy and his poetry

The Macmillan Wessex Edition originally included, along with the novels, *Wessex Poems, Poems of the Past and the Present*, all three volumes of *The Dynasts* and *Time's Laughingstocks*: three collections of poetry, and Hardy's ambitious verse-drama about the Napoleonic Wars. Unfortunately, he had reason to find the critical response to his verse roughly as satisfying as that to his fiction. The *Saturday Review*, an erstwhile defender of Hardy in his first career, turns on *Wessex Poems* with a vengeance.

> Mr. Hardy enjoys a great reputation for his very clear, and sometimes powerful, presentation of the limited life of country folk … . But as we read this curious and wearisome volume, these many slovenly, slipshod, uncouth verses, stilted in sentiment, poorly conceived and worse wrought, our respect lessens to vanishing-point, and we lay it down with the feeling strong upon us that Mr. Hardy has, by his own deliberate act, discredited that judgment and presentation of life on which his reputation rested. It is impossible to understand why the bulk of this volume was published at all – why he did not himself burn the verse, lest it should fall into the hands of the indiscreet literary executor, and mar his fame when he was dead.[70]

The *Spectator*, writing about *Poems of the Past and the Present*, is more specific, but not much more laudatory.

> Poetry is not [Hardy's] proper medium. He is not at home, he does not move easily, in it … . Mr. Hardy is a master of fiction, but not a master of music. Not that he has no music, for he has at time a haunting rhythm and a wild, eerie, melancholy *timbre* and ring all of his own. But either he is not certain of his effects, or else he deliberately

chooses to be harsh and rough, uncouth and uncanny ... 'Did you ask, dulcet rhymes from me?' he would very likely say, ironically, with Walt Whitman. The reader certainly gets neither dulcet rhymes nor dulcet themes from Mr. Hardy. For in his poetry as in his prose; nay, in his poetry even more than in his prose, Mr. Hardy seems to prefer the unpleasant to the pleasant, the ugly to the fair. He is very much of what is called a realist. That is to say, he prefers the seamy to the smooth side of life, and appears to think that it is necessarily the more real, or, at any rate, the more important.[71]

One can only imagine Hardy's chagrin as the deprecating accusation of being a 'realist' pursues him across the divide between fiction and poetry, apparently never to be outrun. These two passages are worth reproducing because they summarise the negative critiques of his poetry. Hardy's refusal to provide the flowing metre and careful poetic polish which characterised so much nineteenth-century verse, along with his often darkly ironic or tragic subject matter, becomes as offensive to some reviewers as the parallel characteristics in his novels. Thus even so sympathetic a visitor to Max Gate as Siegfried Sassoon was moved to suggest that '[t]he Victorians laid too much stress on melody. And many of the poets of to-day in their reaction place too little stress upon it ... [which] I personally feel to be the weakness of Hardy's poetry.'[72] But, as Sassoon's comment reveals, Hardy's method was very much 'of today' in its early twentieth-century cadences and he found more than a few defenders. Lytton Strachey appears ready to level the usual attack when he declares that Hardy's verse is 'full of ugly and cumbrous expressions, clumsy metres, and flat prosaic turns of speech',[73] but he then reverses direction neatly:

what gives Mr. Hardy's poems their unique flavour is precisely their utter lack of romanticism, their common, undecorated presentment of things. They are, in fact, modern as no other poems are ... . He is incorrect; but then how unreal and artificial a thing is correctness! He fumbles; but it is that very fumbling that brings him so near to ourselves.[74]

Strachey quite rightly identifies the quality that places Hardy in the company of other early modernists such as Gerard Manley Hopkins and Emily Dickinson, but of course Hardy's prominence at the time was vastly greater. He therefore felt called upon to protect his poetry, especially as he saw it as a more vulnerable form of writing.

His first line of defence was to address directly the increasingly vexed subject of his pessimistic 'philosophy', a designation that was eventually to replace the 'realist' label that was losing its impact as the new century advanced. In the 1912 General Preface Hardy insists that 'views on the Whence and the Wherefore of things have never been advanced by this pen as a consistent philosophy. Nor is it likely, indeed, that imaginative writings extending over more than forty years would exhibit a coherent scientific theory of the universe even if it had been attempted.'[75] This statement, which he would make with variations for much of the rest of his life, has several components. First of all, Hardy carefully defines 'philosophy' as a 'consistent' and 'coherent' explanation of the universe. He can then rightly declare that this has never been his goal, because by focusing on consistency and coherence he neatly sidesteps the issue of an overall *attitude*, which may be quite obviously present, but which is not rigorously systematic. Hardy is well aware that by controlling the definition he controls the argument, and he exploits his critics' own weak assumption that fiction can somehow 'be' philosophy. This in turn allows him to say later that 'the sentiments in the following pages have been stated truly to be mere impressions of the moment, and not convictions or arguments'.[76] Reviewers and readers who attack him for his philosophy, therefore, are attacking something that is not there. In this can be seen an echo from 'The Profitable Reading of Fiction', which also derides anyone who insists on 'fixing [their] regard on the wrong sides of the subject'. So once again Hardy is constructing sympathetic and antagonistic audiences, and inviting the individual reader to choose where he or she belongs. An elaboration on this is provided later:

Differing natures find their tongue in the presence of differing spectacles. Some natures become vocal at tragedy, some are made vocal by comedy, and it seems to me that to whichever of these aspects of life a writer's instinct for expression the more readily responds, to that he should be allowed to respond. That before a contrasting side of things he remains undemonstrative need not be assumed to mean that he remains unperceiving.[77]

Again, Hardy argues for an acceptance of authorial perspective that, if granted, generates the possibility of productive exchange between writer and audience. The General Preface explicitly attempts to 'tutor' the audience to avoid what he sees as critically imposed distractions. Of course this argument applies to both the poetry and the fiction, as is suitable to a General Preface of an edition with volumes of each. A more specific argument for the poetry alone came later.

Hardy's 'Apology' to *Late Lyrics and Earlier* 'reflected his long-standing resentment against those who insisted upon the ungainliness of his verse and the bleakness of his philosophy',[78] and he had some doubts about publishing it. Nonetheless, he did so, and along with another repudiation of the idea of pessimism in his poems, it contains an attack not only on those who misread his verse, but also on those who are *incapable* of reading it. Noting that the book collects poems written 'years apart', and that this creates 'juxtaposition[s] of unrelated, even discordant, effusions', he goes on to observe that '[a]n odd result of this has been that dramatic anecdotes of a satirical and humorous intention following verse in grave voice, have been read as misfires because they raise the smile that they were intended to raise, the journalist, deaf to the sudden change of key, being unconscious that he is laughing with the author and not at him'.[79] This image of the deaf journalist, one who does not possess the poetic 'ear' to follow his challenging poetry, or to recognise humour when he 'hears' it, was to become a staple weapon in Hardy's battle against inadequate reviewers. Thus the *Life* contains observations such as this:

> In the reception ... of Hardy's poems there was, he said, as regards form, the inevitable ascription to ignorance of what was really choice after full knowledge. That the author loved the art of concealing art was undiscerned. For instance, as to rhythm. Years earlier he had decided that too regular a beat was bad art ... He shaped his poetry accordingly, introducing metrical pauses, and reversed beats; and found for his trouble that some particular line of a poem exemplifying this principle was greeted ... with a jocular remark that such a line 'did not make for immortality', the writer being probably a journalist who had never heard of pauses or beats of any kind ... One case of the kind ... disclosed that the reviewer had tried to scan the author's sapphics as heroics, having probably never heard of the other measure. (*Life*, pp. 323–34)

This is Hardy on the full offensive, insisting that while readerly misapprehension may be one thing, readerly ignorance is something else. Such an aggressive approach was reserved for professional critics, but it could hardly fail to influence any general reader who encountered it.

Having constructed himself as the unappreciated poet, Hardy attempts to assure as well disposed a reading for his verse as possible, while providing instructions as to how that sympathetic reading should proceed. His audience must be prepared for unusual, but not unstructured, metrical forms; it should likewise be prepared for mixed genres, including satire and comedy, along with darker modes; and it should not make the grave mistake of thinking this poetry is somehow philosophy. The defensiveness in such a posture is clear, and the reasons for it lead to Hardy's final attempt to direct reader response.

The 'Apology' closes not by discussing the specifics of Hardy's poetry, but by making general comments on 'the precarious prospects of English verse at the present day'.[80] The fear that poetry was losing its appeal could not help but suggest the danger that his contributions would be lost in the widespread 'barbarising of taste' which he saw sweeping the English-speaking world.[81] Hardy's way of dealing with this was to insist, as he grew older, that he held his poetry in much higher esteem than his novels. Ellen Glasgow, who visited Hardy in 1914, noted that he 'talked to me, freely and frankly, about his books. His poetry would outlive his novels, he believed, and he gave the impression of caring little for the Wessex Tales, which had brought him fame.'[82] Similarly, when William M. Parker was invited to Max Gate in 1920, Hardy told him that his 'interest had almost entirely deserted fiction and centred on poetry ... Poetry was a more concentrated form of art. You could gain more from reading one or two lines of poetry than from several pages of fiction.'[83] A full circle has been travelled. Near the beginning of his career Hardy had claimed limited aspirations for his novels, and near the end of it he was maintaining that such low aspirations were all that could be expected of the genre anyway. But of course the later denigration is as untrustworthy as the earlier declaration. Millgate is surely correct when he describes Hardy's stance as 'essentially a public strategy designed to downplay the prose, which could well take care of itself, in order to emphasize the importance of the verse, which had by no means gained such wide acceptance'.[84] Hardy's efforts to guide his readers find their final expression in an attempt to direct them away from one form of his writing to another, in order to assure his poetic legacy as firmly as he had assured his legacy as the historian of Wessex. That in the end he could not fully control cultural perceptions during his lifetime, or the literary and cultural constructions of himself after his death, makes Hardy human. That he managed to have as much influence on those perceptions and constructions as he did makes him highly unusual.

outside the great tradition: hardy and the critics

Even before Hardy died he was being subjected (and that word describes how he perceived the process) to retrospective, often biographical, critical overviews of his work. Indeed, the creation of the *Life* was spurred by what he perceived as the effrontery of works such as Frank Hedgcock's *Thomas Hardy: Penseur et Artiste*, published in 1911. Ultimately, however, his self-created biography was unable to prevent this type of study, so that history, setting, and authorial background continued to play major roles in the reading of his work. Hardy had created a conflicting situation for himself. His insistence on the centrality of Wessex generated the idea that personal experience lay at the heart of his literature, even as his intense desire for privacy deprecated attempts to unearth that same personal information, leading to the pre-emptive strike of the *Life*. His eventual inability to fend off the biographers does not represent an absolute defeat, however, for those same biographers, 'forced into dependence upon [the *Life*'s] unique record of many aspects of Hardy's life, have found themselves trapped within the limiting patterns established by its silences, special emphases, inaccuracies, and textual distortions'.[85] In this particular contest, therefore, Hardy may be said to have achieved at least a draw.

The early emphasis on the biographical and topographical established a reader response which is still very powerful, and which contributed significantly to Hardy's popularity. For one thing, it provided a method for unifying his often heterogeneous texts. Focusing on the 'Novels of Character and Environment' through the lens of Wessex, as Hardy had encouraged his audience to do, provided a useful, if limiting, way of coming to terms with both the fiction and the poetry. In turn, Hardy's evocation of a vanished time and place caused him to be thought of as the chronicler of a national character under threat, a position especially easy to establish given his fascination with Napoleon and the Peninsular War. Anecdotes of British soldiers in both world wars carrying copies of Hardy's texts in their packs illustrate how his effort at cultural preservation could inspire further efforts to defend that culture in the face of military and political enemies. A great deal of Hardy's continuing non-academic popularity can be traced back to the kinds of reactions encouraged by reading him in this way, through a nostalgia which acts as a powerful ideological background to his plots. Although some may dismiss the resulting 'literary tourism' as a cheapening of his art, it has kept his writing alive in a way that many authors might envy. Within academe, however, developments occurring at the same time had a less positive affect.

The rise in the 1930s of the formalist method known as 'New Criticism' had an impact on critical approaches to Hardy that lasted well past the middle of the twentieth century. Lock observes that 'New Criticism was utterly opposed to the complex of nostalgia, social history and topography connoted by "Wessex"',[86] and since by now these elements were firmly constituted as essential to Hardy's canon, they became, in some circles, a liability rather than an asset. Although the originators of New Criticism were American, in England it was embodied in the influential figure of F. R. Leavis, and his attitude towards Hardy was unremittingly negative. Leavis's *New Bearings in English Poetry* first appeared in 1932, the same year Woolf collected her essay on Hardy in *The Common Reader: Second Series*, and in it he asserts that Hardy's reputation as a great poet 'rests upon a dozen poems'.[87] Since Hardy's poetic output consisted of over 900 poems, to say that Leavis is dismissive of his verse is a serious understatement. And he continued his attack in the special issue of *The Southern Review* published in 1940, the centenary of Hardy's birth. This important collection of 14 essays devoted eight to Hardy's poetry, and provided an extended New Critical evaluation of his work. Leavis's attitude is summarised in his response to Hardy's poem 'A Commonplace Day':

> The effect is boldly idiosyncratic, but one's feeling that there has been something excessive, an unjustifiable violence, gets confirmation when, in the second stanza, 'the twilight's stride extends'. This produces a slow-motion effect that contrasts, in grotesque caricature, with the speed-up of 'scuttles' [in the first stanza] ... the generally-reflective rest of the poem is poor stuff, though the final two lines might have been the close of something better.[88]

The formalist emphasis on the lack of 'organic unity' is clear here, and Leavis's language reveals what he finds unacceptable. Hardy's idiosyncrasies are 'excessive' and lead to an 'unjustifiable violence' which creates 'grotesque' effects. The failure of the poem lies in its failure to create a unified effect, and this can only be attributed to its author's lack of skill. Ironically, Leavis is reproducing, from a different angle, the position of many Victorian reviewers. Their accusation that Hardy lacked proper metrical structure is echoed by his that Hardy lacks proper poetic form, and in both cases the results are judged irredeemable. Although other New Critics, such as I. A. Richards, were less belligerent in their appraisal, the overall impact was the same. Enjoyment of Hardy's poetry became something a reader should feel apologetic about, since it was mostly 'poor stuff'. The wide influence of New Criticism, especially through its pedagogic adoption in North America, resulted in a marginalisation of Hardy's poetry which has never been fully reversed. That his novels did not suffer a similar fate was not, as far as Leavis was concerned, from lack of trying, for having established Hardy's poetry as second-rate he next turned to the fiction.

Originally New Criticism focused solely on poetry, but its formalist emphasis was joined to an ideology centred on creating hierarchies of literary worth, and this allowed, and indeed required, an expansion beyond verse. Canon formulation is crucial to Leavis's *The Great Tradition: George Eliot, Henry James, Joseph Conrad* (1948), and there is no room for Hardy in either the 'greatness' or the 'tradition' being generated. Two authors not mentioned in the title, Jane Austen and D. H. Lawrence, also play an important role in the book's evaluations, and are crucial in understanding this exclusion. With Austen acting as the 'bridge' from the eighteenth-century novel, the line that Leavis constructs not only possesses the unity of effect that he maintains identifies great art, but is also based on the realist paradigm which, as already noted, fits Hardy very poorly, despite efforts to force him in that direction. Indeed, the New Critical repudiation of the sociological underpinnings of Wessex for the sake of 'the text in itself' effectively removes the fiction's one author-generated connection to such a lineage. What is left is the disjunctive mixing of genres and narrative effects that is the prose corollary to the poetry's abrupt rhythms and intentionally eclectic structures, which therefore receives the same rejection. Woolf's association of Hardy with writers who are 'not quite aware' of what they are doing is clearly accepted by Leavis, and thus detaches him from the company of the self-conscious novelists being celebrated.

Further, Leavis's championing of Lawrence makes it necessary for him to excise an author whose prominence obscures the writer he is supporting. Once again irony abounds, since it is clear that Lawrence's fiction owes a significant debt to Hardy. Neill is thus right to observe that Leavis 'had put Hardy in a *salon des refusés* precisely because, as Lawrence's primal artistic ancestor ... he came to function as a kind of anti-Lawrentian to be purged away'.[89] Lawrence's own *Study of Thomas Hardy* is characteristically much more about himself than about Hardy, but it also recognises, with some anxiety, the ways in which the older author had prepared the way for the younger's novels. Leavis is therefore less successful in 'containing' Hardy's fiction because of an inherent contradiction in his own criteria. If Lawrence belongs in the tradition being constructed, the denial of Hardy (let alone the inclusion of James) creates an incoherence of analysis that is a serious weakness. Thus when New Critical influence began to wane in the 1960s and 1970s, it was largely the novels which benefitted, as Hardy's reputation began to catch up with his always secure popularity.

Appropriately, one significant approach that began the shift away from this kind of formalist dismissal was a differently focused sociological criticism. Authors such as Raymond Williams began to argue that Hardy's texts did not just represent the passing of a nostalgically idyllic past, but were quite clear about the materialist conditions causing its destruction. The social recontextualisations required for such readings served as an antidote to the decontextualisations of the New Criticism, and therefore reintroduced Wessex into evaluations of Hardy. Questions of status and social mobility, which pervade Hardy's fiction from start to finish, and encompass both 'major' and 'minor' novels, are crucial in understanding his constructions of character, plot, and indeed setting, since locations such as Egdon Heath in *The Return of the Native* or the Isle of Slingers in *The Well-Beloved* become crucibles for exploring conflicting class expectations. Hardy's designation as a 'regional novelist' does not marginalise his rural Wessex characters as quaint rustics outside the mainstream of nineteenth-century life, but rather insists on their representative value to illustrate core issues of the period. Explicitly Marxist interpretations of Hardy, such as Terry Eagleton's Introduction to the Macmillan New Wessex Edition of *Jude the Obscure* (1974), or George Wotton's *Thomas Hardy: Towards a Materialist Criticism* (1985), re-establish the radical author of *The Poor Man and the Lady* who, as Alexander Macmillan noted when rejecting the novel, 'mean[t] mischief'.[90]

Politicised readings demonstrate something else about Hardy: his politics are no more coherent or consistent than is his 'philosophy'. Since he had already warned his readers about the one, we should not be surprised about the other. While there can be no question that Hardy challenges many Victorian social assumptions, there are elements in his books which also reinforce aspects of them, most notably his simultaneous subversion and exploitation of the 'Hodge' stereotype of rural labourers. The difference is that later critics do not see such 'incoherencies' as necessarily failures, but rather as unavoidable aspects of textuality, and perhaps even as enhancements of the books' ideological perspective. The refusal to create an artificial unity of effect, either structural or thematic, acts itself as a covert critique of bourgeois biases, a position explored in John Goode's *Thomas Hardy: The Offensive Truth* (1988) and Roger Ebbatson's *Hardy: The Margin of the Unexpressed* (1993). Both of these build on Wotton, and contain a significant amount of Marxist material, but they also each blend it with post-structuralist approaches that recognise the significance of textual disjunction. Their exploration of Hardy's discontinuities is important, first because it provides an escape from the realist/formalist horizon of expectation that had constrained readers for so long, and second because their eclectic methodology shows how Hardy is best approached by contemporary theoretical models. The relative scarcity of 'pure' efforts to read him through, say, deconstruction or New Historicism, suggests that the heteroglossia of his writing demands a combinational interpretive strategy in order to be successful. Since this is the direction in which post-structuralism is heading in any case, Hardy is uniquely positioned to benefit from such readings. And this is most obvious in the way gender criticism has flourished around him.

The centrality of women characters in Hardy was commented on almost as soon as his name was officially attached to his novels. His sympathetic presentation of female experience was often crucial to his social criticism, but that meant it often also partook of the ambiguity of that critique. Contemporary feminist analyses of Hardy have been crucial not only in exploring his often radical questioning of gender constructions, but also in demonstrating the inescapability of gender conditioning in even the most well-intentioned male author. The question of whether Hardy is or is not a feminist author, whether he does or does not produce feminist texts, is thwarted by the oversimplified either/or binary of the issue's formulation. Thus although an early article such as Mary Jacobus's 'Sue the Obscure', which appeared in *Essays in Criticism* in 1975, set off an intense debate about Hardy's attitude towards Sue Bridehead, a final 'resolution' to the argument about whether she is a destructively weak neurotic or a tragically defeated subversive is unachievable. Linda Shires drives this idea home when she asserts that 'Hardy relies on multiplicity and incongruity ... He wants his reader to become conditioned into thinking simultaneously in terms that are multiple and even contradictory.'[91] Since gender is attached to so many other cultural determinants, only varied perspectives can come to terms with it, and purely oppositional divisions are inadequate. This is also demonstrated in Boumelha's *Thomas Hardy and Women: Sexual Ideology and Narrative Form* (1982) and Rosemarie Morgan's *Women and Sexuality in the Novels of Thomas Hardy* (1988). Both place Hardy in literary and social contexts that prevent easy reader responses to his presentation of women, and preclude single dimension critical scrutiny. Margaret Higonnet's 1993 collection *The Sense of Sex: Feminist Perspectives on Hardy* also illustrates this through the diversity of its selected essays.

Recent studies along the same lines, therefore, engage almost as much with previous critics as they do with Hardy's texts. Jane Thomas's *Thomas Hardy, Femininity and Dissent: Reassessing the 'Minor' Novels* (1999) is, as its title suggests, a 'reassessment' that combines gender analysis with Foucauldian criticism to challenge the accepted status of certain texts. In this she is also entering into a dialogue with Hardy and his categorisations for the 1912 Wessex Edition. Similarly, Shanta Dutta's *Ambivalence in Hardy: A Study of his Attitude to Women* (2000) argues that while Hardy's ambivalence towards women is real, it has been exacerbated by a critical ambivalence imposed from without that has constructed for him an inappropriate persona. Coming to terms with one's critical predecessors is hardly a startlingly new activity, but the centrality and self-consciousness of this process suggests that something larger is going on. An author like Hardy, who provoked discomfort in his readers from the start, who attempted directly and indirectly to shape his audience, and who has been the subject of repeated 'constructions' based on these early influences, has accreted layers of meaning which need to be recognised and acknowledged. The most important example of such metacriticism is Peter Widdowson's *Hardy in History: A Study in Literary Sociology* (1989). The title of his first chapter, 'The critical constitution of "Thomas Hardy"', announces the overall direction of his argument, which combines general analysis of Hardy's cultural and critically generated significance with specific readings of the *Life* and *The Hand of Ethelberta*. Subsequent surveys, such as Lock's *Thomas Hardy* (1992) in the Criticism in Focus series and Neill's *Trial by Ordeal: Thomas Hardy and the Critics* (1999), provide important additional information, although they do not match Widdowson's ability to theorise the subject they address.

One of Hardy's great strengths is his ability to create an intensely committed community of readers through his fiction and poetry. This is, of course, completely appropriate, given the emphasis on community that permeates his writing. For good or ill, his works tell us, individuals must negotiate their relationship to the group, for only in that way can either be understood. It is equally appropriate, therefore, that Hardy's own canon of writing be approached in this way. The first-time reader of a Hardy novel or poem is entering a world which has been profoundly mediated by the author and his previous audiences, and the further a reader enters that world the more necessary it is to comprehend that mediation. Any author who has attracted the sheer mass of critical attention directed at Hardy becomes, at least in part, a construction of its focuses, but Hardy's own artistry encourages and requires interpretive participation in a way that makes him unique among his Victorian peers. His refusal to fit easily within the horizon of expectation of his time, and his constant shifting within the horizons of expectation he developed for himself, means that no absolutely secure vantage point can be established from which to view his literature. Hardy's relationship with his readers, then, is a process in which knowledge of the past is integral to knowledge of the present, as contemporary critics are recognising in their efforts to theorise how earlier conceptualisations of 'Thomas Hardy' influence responses to the texts. That the community of readers established extends back in time would have been appreciated by an author who believed deeply that history was never left behind, but instead was an inescapable part of the now.

notes

1. Jakob Lothe, 'Variants on Genre: *The Return of the Native, The Mayor of Casterbridge, The Hand of Ethelberta*', in Dale Kramer. ed., *The Cambridge Companion to Thomas Hardy* (Cambridge, 1999), p. 114
2. See Hans Robert Jauss, *Toward an Aesthetic of Reception*, trans. Timothy Bahti (Minneapolis, 1982).
3. Jauss, *Aesthetic of Reception*, p. 15.
4. Jauss, *Aesthetic of Reception*, p. 23.
5. Jauss, *Aesthetic of Reception*, p. 39.
6. Charles Lock, *Thomas Hardy* (London, 1992), p. 2.
7. Virginia Woolf, 'The Novels of Thomas Hardy', in *The Common Reader: Second Series* (London, 1932), pp. 247–8.
8. John Bayley, 'Realism', in *Oxford Reader's Companion to Hardy*, ed. Norman Page (Oxford, 2000), p. 347.
9. Edward Neill, *Trial by Ordeal: Thomas Hardy and the Critics* (Columbia, SC, 1999), p. 16.
10. Nicola Diane Thompson, *Reviewing Sex: Gender and the Reception of Victorian Novels* (New York, 1996), p. 3.
11. *Critical Heritage*, pp. 1–2.
12. *Critical Heritage*, pp. 3–4.
13. *Critical Heritage*, p. 2.
14. *Critical Heritage*, pp. 3–4.
15. *Critical Heritage*, p. 4.
16. Michael Millgate, *Thomas Hardy: A Biography* (New York, 1982), p. 135.
17. *Critical Heritage*, pp. 6–7.
18. *Critical Heritage*, p. 9.

19. Richard L. Purdy, *Thomas Hardy: A Bibliographical Study* (1954; Oxford, 1979) p. 7.
20. Michael Millgate, *Thomas Hardy: His Career as a Novelist* (1971; London, 1994) p. 42.
21. *Critical Heritage*, p. 11.
22. *Critical Heritage*, p. 13.
23. *Critical Heritage*, pp. 15–16. This review, unlike the previous two in the *Saturday Review*, was not written by Horace Moule. Much to Hardy's shock, he committed suicide on 21 September 1873.
24. *Critical Heritage*, pp. 32–3.
25. *Critical Heritage*, p. 20.
26. *Critical Heritage*, p. 22.
27. *Observer*, 3 January 1875, Quoted in Graham Clarke, ed., *Thomas Hardy: Critical Assessments of Writers in English*. 4 vols. (Mountfield, East Sussex, 1993), Vol. I, p. 72.
28. *Critical Heritage*, p. 31.
29. *Critical Heritage*, p. 56.
30. *Critical Heritage*, p. 49.
31. *Critical Heritage*, p. 53.
32. *Critical Heritage*, pp. 73, 75, 77.
33. *Critical Heritage*, p. 134.
34. *Critical Heritage*, p. 138.
35. *Critical Heritage*, pp. 142–3.
36. *Critical Heritage*, p. 247.
37. *Critical Heritage*, p. 249.
38. *The Bookman* (New York), January 1896; Clarke, *Critical Assessments*, I, p. 268.
39. See Richard le Gallienne's comment that the 'study of French authors seems to be having a strong influence on Mr. Hardy's work just lately. Realism as a theory seems in danger of possessing him at times, though happily but intermittently.' *Critical Heritage*, p. 79.
40. *Critical Heritage*, p. 257.
41. Quoted in James Gibson, ed., *Thomas Hardy: Interviews and Recollections* (New York, 1999), p. 136.
42. *Letters*, 1I, p. 28.
43. Lock, *Thomas Hardy*, p. 45.
44. 'The Profitable Reading of Fiction', New York *Forum*, March 1888; Harold Orel, ed., *Thomas Hardy's Personal Writings* (London, 1967), p. 111.
45. *Personal Writings*, p. 112.
46. *Personal Writings*, p. 125.
47. 'Candour in English Fiction', *New Review*, January 1890; *Personal Writings*, p. 127.
48. *Personal Writings*, p. 127.
49. *Personal Writings*, p. 128.
50. *Personal Writings*, p. 129.
51. *Personal Writings*, p. 129.
52. 'The Science of Fiction', *New Review*, April 1891; *Personal Writings*, p. 134.
53. *Personal Writings*, p. 134.

54. *Personal Writings*, p. 135.
55. *Personal Writings*, p. 136.
56. Simon Gatrell, 'Wessex', in *Cambridge Companion*, p. 19.
57. Michael Millgate, *Testamentary Acts: Browning, Tennyson, James, Hardy* (Oxford, 1992), p. 112.
58. Millgate, *Testamentary Acts*, pp. 112–13.
59. Along with Gatrell's article 'Wessex', see his *Hardy the Creator: A Textual Biography* (Oxford, 1988).
60. Gatrell, 'Wessex', p. 29.
61. Penny Boumelha, *Thomas Hardy and Women: Sexual Ideology and Narrative Form* (Madison, 1982), p. 28.
62. Millgate, *Testamentary Acts*, p. 118.
63. Millgate, *Testamentary Acts*, p. 119.
64. *Personal Writings*, p. 44.
65. *Personal Writings*, p. 46.
66. *Personal Writings*, p. 44.
67. *Personal Writings*, p. 45.
68. *Personal Writings*, p. 44.
69. Millgate, *Testamentary Acts*, p. 119.
70. *Critical Heritage*, p. 319.
71. *Critical Heritage*, p. 332.
72. Gibson, *Interviews*, p. 187.
73. *Critical Heritage*, p. 436.
74. *Critical Heritage*, p. 437.
75. *Personal Writings*, pp. 48–9.
76. *Personal Writings*, p. 49.
77. *Personal Writings*, p. 49.
78. Millgate, *Thomas Hardy*, p. 542.
79. *Personal Writings*, p. 55.
80. *Personal Writings*, p. 55.
81. *Personal Writings*, p. 56.
82. Gibson, *Interviews*, p. 112.
83. Gibson, *Interviews*, p. 147.
84. Millgate, *Testamentary Acts*, p. 120.
85. Millgate, *Testamentary Acts*, p. 164.
86. Lock, *Thomas Hardy*, p. 98.
87. F. R. Leavis, *New Bearings in English Poetry* (Ann Arbor, 1960), p. 59.
88. F. R. Leavis, 'Hardy the Poet', *The Southern Review*, 1940–41, Vol. 6; Clarke, *Critical Assessments*, II, p. 228.
89. Neill, *Trial by Ordeal*, p. 35.
90. Quoted in Millgate, *Thomas Hardy*, p. 110.
91. Linda M. Shires, 'The Radical Aesthetic of *Tess of the d'Urbervilles*', in *Cambridge Companion*, p. 147.

3
hardy and biography

ralph pite

Hardy, when he died in 1928, was a very famous man. He had been awarded the Order of Merit in 1910, by which time he had already turned down a knighthood. In 1923, the Prince of Wales visited him at Max Gate. He received honorary degrees from several prestigious universities, including even Oxford – the institution which *Jude the Obscure* had so fiercely attacked. Public recognition of this kind had been long in coming and Hardy undoubtedly cherished it. For both his first and second wives, the consequences were less happy and more arduous. They had to play hostess to a stream of admirers, some fawning, some pushy and some exploitative. As far as Hardy was concerned, however, the only serious drawback was the attention of biographers, attracted by so great (and lucrative) a potential subject.

From roughly the time of his sudden rise in popularity in 1891–92, when *Tess of the d'Urbervilles* was published, Hardy began to be bothered by interviewers and reporters, seeking not only news of his work but details of his life and background as well. By temperament, Hardy was unusually private and he found such inquiries into his personal life intrusive. Also, Hardy's background was modest. He took great pride in his family in some respects. Their self-sufficiency and decency were virtues he emulated. Yet to outsiders his parents were little better than peasants. If that view of them became widespread, Hardy's standing would be damaged and his loved ones would be humiliated. This made him very touchy on the subject and he started to employ two apparently opposite tactics when fending off questions. Either he would try not to answer and so leave the matter obscure or he would provide a full answer that was not open to further questioning. In other words, he would give no account or he would try to exert complete control over the account of his family that entered the public domain.

As he grew older and his fame extended around the turn of the century, Hardy started to contemplate the prospect of full-length biographies being written about him. There were not only occasional journalists now; there were full-time scholars as well, probing his novels for secret autobiographical references. His response to this development followed the same pattern as his earlier defensive tactics. Either he said nothing or he said 'everything' – not literally everything, of course; far from it. Hardy was persistently secretive. Again, though, there would be either no account at all or there would be a version authorised and controlled by Hardy himself. The result of this approach was Hardy's strange, yet characteristic adaptation of Victorian and Edwardian biographical conventions, *The Life of Thomas Hardy*, which was published in two volumes, in 1928 and 1930, soon after his death. The book has continued profoundly to influence accounts of Hardy's life up until the present day. The difficulties it has caused Hardy's biographers are symptomatic, moreover, of difficulties the genre always faces, though usually in a less extreme form – difficulties surrounding the process of separating a person's life from their own account of that life, of disentangling their personality from their self-image.

Famous Victorians often had their lives written by family members or close friends. Christopher Wordsworth, William Wordsworth's nephew, published the life of his uncle; Hallam Tennyson wrote his father's biography, *Tennyson: A Memoir* (1897). Hardy's friend, Edmund Gosse, now famous for his in many ways unflattering record of his father published in *Father and Son* (1907) also wrote the much more conventional and laudatory 'official' version, *The Life of Philip Henry Gosse, F. R. S.* (1890). Similarly, it was Dickens's trusted friend, John Forster, who wrote Dickens's life, while Carlyle's biography was written by his disciple, James Anthony Froude. These books were normally eulogistic, even hagiographic. Weighed down by detail, they provided, nonetheless, only a discreet insight into their subjects.

There were particular social and cultural circumstances that encouraged this protective form of biography. Victorian writers were more liable to be turned into celebrities even than their Romantic predecessors. Biographies contributed to that elevation and public exposure, while also attempting to counter it. In that respect, the form reflected a paradox governing Victorian writers' relation to their popularity: it constrained them yet was also their lifeblood. Writers were required to perform a social function – to uplift and reassure their audience as well as entertaining them. They were supposed to be exemplary. So they had constantly to give the impression of personal presence while also ensuring that anything dubious in their personal life remained unknown. They had to be intimate with their audience without ever fully confiding in them.

It was a situation that created a lot of psychological pressure. One solution was to become extraordinarily self-controlled. You might then maintain in private the ideal behaviour that was required in public and leave nothing scandalous for the biographer to unearth or disguise. All Victorian public figures, to a greater or lesser degree, experienced this pressure to make their entire lives morally impeccable. It was not simply fear of scandal that drove them. Rather, declining religious faith led to the search for human instead of superhuman or supernatural heroic figures. Because the human was the clearest – to some, the only – manifestation of the divine, the human must not lapse.

At the same time, accurate biographical representation was increasingly seen to depend upon simply relaying exactly what happened. Carlyle influentially argued in his essay 'Biography' that by presenting all the events of a life, a biography would 'decipher the whole heart of [the subject's] mystery'. For Carlyle, biography should not present exemplary nor recognisable types; instead it should offer to the reader unique individuals. Their uniqueness, paradoxically, meant they could become sources of unity: 'feeling with the heart of every neighbour, [the Lover of Biography] lives with every neighbour's life, even as with his own. Of these millions of living men each individual is a mirror to us.' Carlyle included in the essay a quotation from an imaginary professor: 'wherever there is a Man, a God also is revealed, and all that is Godlike: a whole epitome of the Infinite, with its meanings, lies enfolded in the Life of every Man'.[1]

Consequently, Victorian biography (like its subjects as they lived) had continually to find a balance between disclosure and discretion. The idea was that by saying all, all would be revealed – the Godlike would emerge from the smallest as well as the largest actions of the man. On the one hand, there was no justification for keeping things secret while, on the other, it was often necessary to do so. Otherwise the devilish or just the sordidly human would peep out from the heroic image. A god would not be revealed so much as an imp or a fool. And, unable to justify their omissions, biographers could not very easily let on about them. The genre was forced to become secretive about its secrets.

Virginia Woolf described the result as 'like the wax figures now preserved in Westminster Abbey ... effigies that have only a smooth superficial likeness to the body in the coffin'. Similarly, Freud remarked that biographers would tolerate in their subjects 'no vestige of human weakness or imperfection. They thus present us with what is in fact a cold, strange, ideal figure, instead of a human being.'[2] The form, in other words, became structured around the mixture of eulogy and erasure that made Lytton Strachey's task so easy when, in the anti-Victorian backlash of the early twentieth century, he decided to debunk the 'eminent Victorians'.[3]

So, although the Victorian period was in some ways the heyday of biography, it was also a time when official and unofficial lives diverged most markedly. And by the end of the century, the High Victorian model was starting to break down. Carlyle was himself the most high profile victim of the changing genre. Froude, instead of glossing over the problems in Carlyle's marriage, as would have been usual, told more of the uncomfortable truth and went as far as suggesting that Carlyle was impotent. The result, when the book was published in 1882–84, was a furore which caused lasting damage to Carlyle's reputation. In the same period, new forms of biography began to be written. The *Dictionary of National Biography*, edited by Leslie Stephen, began in 1882, concurrently with the 'English Men of Letters' and 'Great Writers' series – comparatively short biographies of famous writers (Gosse wrote lives of Thomas Gray and William Congreve) in which life-writing was combined with literary criticism.[4] Both the *DNB* and the 'English Men of Letters' series sought to establish national pantheons – one celebrating all areas of excellence, one seeking to enhance the reputation and status of writers particularly. A successful novelist, such as Hardy, could expect to join such elevated company and as he or she did so their life would come under scrutiny. It would also be connected more intimately than before with their works.

Carlyle's chastening example and these developments in biography both exacerbated Hardy's wariness of the form. The old Victorian model seemed more fragile and also more necessary, if you were to avoid both scandal-mongering and, to Hardy's mind, the intellectually dubious business of interpreting an author's psychology from his or her output. So, around 1916, when Hardy was already in his mid-seventies, he began to compose his own biography. He went through his old notebooks and letters and selected from them suitable, interesting passages. These he then strung together with a narrative, written in the third person, in which he speaks of himself as 'Hardy'. The narrator purports to be Hardy's second wife, Florence. She was helping him with the book, admittedly, though mostly in the same way as a secretary would have done. She helped him transcribe notebook entries; she typed things up. Hardy, however, maintained the fiction that this was Florence's account of him and the books appeared over her name. It was quite some time after his death that the true sequence of events and the true authorship of the books came out.[5]

By then, Hardy had given to posterity an autobiography disguised as an 'authorised' biography. That mask lent his version of himself a degree of authority and objectivity that would never have been granted to an autobiography – a form of writing that is confessedly biased. And he had largely avoided the danger that a trusted keeper of the flame might turn out to be unreliable: the loyal friend or family member was himself. In a few significant ways, Florence altered Hardy's typescript before publishing it. She tended to do down her predecessor, Emma Lavinia Hardy, whose memory had overshadowed her own marriage, and she cut some of Hardy's references to the society people he met in London in the 1890s – references that consisted mostly of lists of names.[6] Nevertheless, the *Life of Thomas Hardy* remains substantially a life *by* Thomas Hardy. Moreover, he destroyed the rest of the evidence either himself or by proxy after his death. For many parts of his life, especially the early years, the *Life* is very nearly all we have. Where other records of him do survive, they are dwarfed by his own work. So, as in the 1890s, Hardy wants conflicting versions to be silenced and his own version to stand alone, authorised and authoritative. Connections between his life and work are pre-empted and/or discouraged. His history is made suitable for inclusion in the most stringently respectable of pantheons.

Naturally, though, the *Life* is a highly selective work – partial and personal. In some areas, the selectivity is manifest. The gaps in Hardy's life-story have been explored by subsequent biographers, often illuminatingly. Yet in other ways, the portrait Hardy gives of himself has survived unquestioned. The biographer's role has been reduced, for a large proportion of the time, essentially to that of providing annotations to Hardy's version of his life. Filling in gaps, expanding allusions, drawing thumbnail sketches of friends and relations – all these activities have usefully gone on and yet left Hardy's self-descriptions unchallenged. This is true, I think, of Michael Millgate's *Thomas Hardy: A Biography* (1982), whose extraordinary scholarship rarely challenges established views of Hardy. F. B. Pinion's more recent *Thomas Hardy: His Life and Friends* (1992) follows a similar pattern.

The two other major biographies of Hardy published since the war are Robert Gittings's *Young Thomas Hardy* (1975) and *The Older Hardy* (1978) and Martin Seymour-Smith's *Hardy* (1994). They both dispute Hardy's view of himself in different ways. Their difficulties in doing so reveal other consequences of Hardy's self-protectiveness. That is to say, although Florence had little power to influence the *Life* itself, she remained the principal means of access to Hardy for the ten years or so after his death. She controlled not only his papers (in conjunction with Sidney Cockerell, who shared her role as Hardy's literary executor), but she also enjoyed a position of authority. After all, she had known Hardy intimately for more than 20 years and been married to him for nearly 15. Her recorded conversations became highly influential, the more so because so little else apart from the *Life* was forthcoming. And Florence's views – especially about Emma Lavinia and Emma's family – have been disproportionately influential down the years.

Florence's power in this area reveals the success with which Hardy suppressed alternate pictures of him and shows how, in the absence of documents, the other sides of Hardy have taken on a ghostly existence, fuelled by speculation and hearsay. The *Life* clearly is not the whole story. Readers sense this sooner or later. Yet there is little else to go on, so even the most uncertain testimony becomes extraordinarily important to a biographer. And, as with Florence, the purveyors of that testimony (who can be the biographers themselves) have acquired almost a free hand. Hardy's insistence on control has been, to some, a liberation.

This is most obviously and notoriously the case with Lois Deacon. Her studies of Hardy and Tryphena Sparks, culminating in *Providence and Mr. Hardy* (1966), which was co-written with Terry Coleman, originate in the uncorroborated testimony of a single, ageing person. From this basis, Lois Deacon has maintained that Hardy had a child by Tryphena and that Horace Moule, Hardy's closest friend as a young man, also fell in love with her. Losing Tryphena to Horace was the bane, Lois Deacon argues, of Hardy's life, as well as contributing to Horace Moule's suicide.

These opinions have provoked outrage and received acclaim. Yet they are not so unusual. Other famous people have had their personal affairs speculated about by biographers in similar ways. What was really going on between Dickens and Ellen Ternan? Did Wordsworth have an incestuous affair with Dorothy, his sister? Can we trace Shakespeare's illegitimate son among the minor poets of the seventeenth century? These questions are part of biography's stock-in-trade. The distinctive thing, perhaps, about Hardy and Lois Deacon is the sense of her having revealed the key to the mystery. For a time, probably ten years or more, Hardy students and Hardy enthusiasts divided up into those for and those against Lois Deacon's account of him. That was partly the result of the way she presented her work. She came across as a detective filled with missionary fervour. It was also, however, the consequence of the special situation Hardy had created for his biographers. They had either to accept the limits of what he had told them or venture out into almost uncharted waters.

These limits, as set up by the *Life*, are most influential where they are least visible. The opening sections of the book make few references, for example, to Hardy's love affairs as a young man. Hardy remarks in a studiedly off-hand tone that 'it may as well be mentioned here among other trivialities, he lost his heart for a few days to a young girl' and 'In this kind there was another young girl':

> Yet another attachment, somewhat later, which went deeper, was to a well-to-do farmer's daughter named Louisa. There were more probably. They all appear, however, to have been quite fugitive, except perhaps the one for Louisa, which may have lasted a year or longer, since he used to meet her down to his 23rd or 24th year on his visits to Dorset from London. (*Life*, p. 30)

With these words the first chapter closes. The rhetoric guides the reader towards discounting these matters at the same time as the passage acknowledges them. The third-person stance is very useful to Hardy here and in similar passages because it allows him to provide as much or as little evidence as he wants, then to suggest that anything further is pure speculation and finally to do the speculating himself. 'They all appear, however, to have been quite fugitive', he asserts, apparently offering a judicious summary of a body of evidence, some reliable and some dubious.

When you know this is Hardy's own text, then its self-distance feels odd. It is hard to imagine speaking of oneself so dispassionately. Yet this may reflect some of the strangeness of old age, when you find yourself looking back on times long gone and growing vague – when the self you recall seems to have little in common with the self you have become. The more striking quality, however, in these passages is their devious mixture of disclosure and secrecy. 'There were more probably', Hardy airily concedes, daring the prying biographer to find them if he can and posing as the biographer who has already done his best but found nothing specific, nothing incriminating.

Nonetheless, this is one of the moments when the curtain is visibly lowered. It signals its discretion. According to established precedent, it is saying (among other things) that Hardy had all the natural 'instincts and affections' of a young unmarried man and that these did not lead him into anything scandalous. You need, dear reader, dear biographer, look no further. The passage also reveals a less obvious and more pervasive mode of restricting inquiry. The tone is gently condescending to the young man. It assumes that youth is full of folly. The narrator treats him with the kindly amusement of settled maturity. No doubt Hardy felt something of this about his past life, particularly his early days, when he wrote about them in 1916. But this was not his only feeling, as the poems he wrote at the same time bear ample witness.

The *Life* always tends to edit out Hardy's anguish and regret about his past. That was one aspect of its desire to present a respectable image of the great man. Hardy's stance as his own narrator and the tone taken by that narrator both encouraged the impression that his past contained nothing to fear. It could all be easily handled, attractively packaged and deftly downplayed. But where there was nothing to fear, there was little to love either. Hardy's youthful self is hard to discern. He is modelled so closely on what Hardy later became that things become impossibly consistent. Judging from the *Life*, Hardy had *always* wanted to be a poet really and never rated his novels highly. Architecture had, similarly, never been a passion, only a source of income. He had always felt and thought roughly what he felt and thought in his maturity, so that the view of life expressed in the major novels and, especially, *The Dynasts*, was one he had held from early on, even if as a young man he did not have the intellectual and literary expertise to express it so well.

All of these particular claims are easy to dispute, even to dislodge. Even if, for instance, his first love was poetry, his commitment to his novels during the 1870s and 1880s was extreme. He had clear and grand ambitions for them. 'Ever since I began to write,' he said in a letter of 1891, 'I have felt that the doll of English fiction must be demolished, if England is to have a school of fiction at all.'[7] It is not surprising, of course, that Hardy should have been so intently focused on what he could achieve as a novelist. It would have been bizarre for him not to be. Yet the *Life* frequently pretends otherwise, as if he had always been the dedicated poet of his later years, financially secure, philosophical and melancholy.

This tactic in the book restricts access to the earlier self not by silence so much as by imposing a single voice. That is the more difficult tactic to resist because it creates coherence rather than gaps; it answers all our questions instead of raising any. And, in many important areas, that coherent picture has gone unchallenged. The *Life* describes Hardy as unusually youthful in 1862 when he first moved to London. The account of his arrival gives the impression of happenstance assisting the dreamy youth to find work and lodgings in the alien world of the capital. That image suits Hardy's consistent depiction of himself as unmotivated by ambition, unworldly and 'poetical'. It is a good story – amusing, sweet and familiar – and it continues the *Life*'s trick of making the young man a little foolish in order to maintain the status of the older man.

Gittings as well as Millgate repeat this image. 'Hardy's unfledged appearance, his youthful and abnormally boyish expression, were evidently plain to see', Gittings asserts. He was at the time, according to Millgate, 'not an especially prepossessing young man ... sadly lacking in worldly experience and social assurance, and unmistakably countrified'. Not until Martin Seymour-Smith was this impression countered in a biography:

> It is clear that those to whom he introduced himself, and who were to be useful to him, liked him. His social accomplishments cannot have been all that poor. And he was qualified in his profession.
> He was by no means nothing, then, when he arrived in London.

He had, moreover, two letters of introduction – one to Benjamin Ferrey, a rising star in the profession who had known Hardy's father, and a second to John Norton, who was a pupil of Ferrey's and a friend of Hardy's Dorchester employer, John Hicks. The letter to Norton was written by Hicks, and Norton, unlike Ferrey, proved able to help Hardy get settled. Seymour-Smith does not emphasise this side of the story so much as Hardy's gifts, including his 'iron determination to succeed' and 'his private confidence in his abilities'.[8]

There certainly was such determination in Hardy's makeup. Seymour-Smith gives it such emphasis because he is trying to correct, fundamentally, not so much Millgate's errors (which he tends to harp on) as Hardy's own self-representation. That creates an exaggerated insistence on Hardy's will to the neglect, in this instance, of his reliance on Hicks. Millgate quotes a story dating from conversations between Hardy and Sidney Cockerell in 1916 in which Hicks is reported as thinking that Hardy would fail in

London and come home soon enough. The story enables Millgate to admire Hardy's triumphant success in finding work with Norton and soon afterwards Arthur Blomfield. Yet, as Millgate also informs us, Hicks wrote the letter of introduction. Hardy in later life would have wanted to deny his earlier dependence – the journey to London was, as he saw it, his first entrance into the world. It was the opening of his independent life. But, probably, he went there partly at Hicks's suggestion and certainly with Hicks's support. It was good experience for him. He would improve as an architect and that would be likely to help Hicks later on, assuming that he returned, as was likely and as in fact happened five years later. It was not, therefore, either naive whimsy nor iron determination which took Hardy to London. It was a shrewd and sensible move, encouraged by his employer.

Biographical accounts of this incident reveal the pervasive impact of Hardy's self-portrait in the *Life*. Most have repeated the emphases of Hardy's narrative and those who have differed have been contesting that emphasis, albeit in Seymour-Smith's case at one remove. And other key moments have been persistently seen in a Hardyan light. Hardy's return to Dorset in 1881, after his illness, and his move back to Dorchester itself, two years later, are treated by Gittings, Millgate and Seymour-Smith with remarkable consistency.

Each view the decision to leave London as a moment when Hardy's deepest, most natural instincts reasserted themselves, with beneficial consequences. That point of view also regards Hardy's greatest artistic achievements as his novels of rural life. He began these in 1873 and 1874, so this narrative asserts, with *Under the Greenwood Tree* and *Far from the Madding Crowd*. A number of unsuccessful experiments followed for the next ten years, with the solitary exception of *The Return of the Native* in 1878. Then, when Hardy got back to Dorchester, a series of great novels were written: *The Mayor of Casterbridge* (1886), *The Woodlanders* (1887), *Tess of the d'Urbervilles* (1891) and *Jude the Obscure* (1895).

This has been, until recently, the standard line to take and has reflected the critical consensus on his work. The curious thing is that although the *Life* allows such a reading, it does not insist on it. Hardy's text implies several different feelings about his return to Dorchester. On this occasion, the biography unsettles the picture. Consequently, the incident suggests that the *Life* should not always be taken at face value and that its apparent endorsement of biographical conventions is, in fact, no more than apparent. Reading the *Life* in different ways may therefore become emblematic of how biography may be read and written differently.

Hardy states in the *Life* that the decision to leave London 'and establish their home in the country' was made in the spring of 1881. The country was preferable:

> both for reasons of health and for mental inspiration, Hardy finding, or thinking he found, that residence in or near a city tended to force mechanical and ordinary productions from his pen, concerning ordinary society-life and habits. (*Life*, p. 154)

The qualification that he introduces – 'finding, *or thinking he found*' – might seem the result of natural vanity. He is reluctant to say that any of his novels were, in truth, 'mechanical and ordinary', so he suggests it was only his opinion at the time. The admiring reader is welcome to oppose that view and heap praise on *The Hand of Ethelberta* or *A Laodicean*. The parenthesis has another effect as well, however.

By the early twentieth century, Hardy was widely celebrated as the novelist of Wessex. He had encouraged this image of himself and his work. Among other things, he had entitled his collected works, the 'Wessex Edition' in 1895–96. It had been a useful marketing ploy, if nothing else, and it was so useful in part because it reflected one genuine quality in his writing and sensibility. He was deeply attached to his home county, to its way of life and to the feeling that rural experience offered benefits which the city did not. Still, 'Wessex' was always only a part of his project as a writer and part of the purpose of the *Life* was to suggest other interests as of equal importance. Hence, it laid great emphasis upon the poetry and *The Dynasts* especially – Hardy's epic poetic drama about the Napoleonic Wars. Hardy was not, the *Life* claimed, someone you could conveniently (or condescendingly) pigeonhole as a rural novelist. He had many other strings to his bow. And, in 1881, he was not defeated by the city, as would have been suggested had the clause 'or thinking he found' not been included in the sentence. Instead, Hardy decided that London was not doing him any good and moved elsewhere.

It is characteristic of the book to imply a few doubts about the accepted picture of Hardy. In some ways, this is another distancing device. Because Hardy discourages any alternative view from coming to light, the accepted picture gains in authority. Yet that accepted picture is made to appear an image that has been imposed on the true Hardy, obscuring the real person beyond recovery. As with several of Hardy's heroines, from Elfride to Tess, who are destroyed by being defined, so with Hardy. The *Life* does no more than hint that a nebulous, elusive person has been confined within Hardy the writer and public figure. The true person remains invisible and this fact proves, among other things, the superficiality, even the pointlessness of biography. So, often, the *Life* reads like an elaborate, rather dry joke. Hardy writes of his move with Emma to Dorchester that

> This removal to the country-town, and later to a spot a little outside it, was a step they often regretted having taken but the bracing air brought them health and renewed vigour, and in the long run it proved not ill-advised. (*Life*, p. 167)

The careful balancing here of pros and cons leads to an appropriately measured conclusion in the form of a double negative: 'in the long run it proved not ill-advised'. Wordsworthian, this way of talking may be; helpful, it isn't. It is a moment that contributes to the book's indirect attack on the conventional view of Hardy as happily rustic. Yet it makes that point by an equally indirect assertion that nothing really can be known about Hardy's feelings. The reader may start to wonder how far this is a parody of decorous, formal, discreet biographical writing.

These techniques also allow, however, for a reading of the *Life* in which hints are followed by guesses. Hardy may be ultimately elusive but he leaves a few traces that the reader may follow. One example will have to do. The move back to Dorset in 1881 came in the wake of Hardy's suffering a serious illness that had confined him to bed between October 1880 and April 1881. There have been several medical explanations offered. He may have had a kidney stone and the treatment prescribed by his doctor probably prolonged his physical weakness. Biographers, though, have frequently suggested that nervous strain contributed to his collapse. He had been working very hard for the previous two years; his marriage was becoming uneasy. There are signs in his letters of increasing anxiety. Seymour-Smith says boldly that 'the severity of the illness, at least, was of psychosomatic origin'. Gittings allows that 'Stress, worry, fatigue, a very damp house ... would all predispose' Hardy to physical ailments. Millgate and Evelyn Hardy connect the illness more specifically to Hardy's recent visit to Cambridge: 'his illness was presaged', Evelyn Hardy, 'by the weird shapes which he saw in the guttering candles of King's College Chapel'. Millgate goes one step further: Hardy's 'fascination with the shapes' he says, 'must have been stirred by recollections of the "shroud" formed by Moule's candle during their last evening together'.[9]

Millgate is alluding here to Hardy's late poem, 'Standing by the Mantelpiece', published in his last, posthumous collection, *Winter Words*.

Its subtitle, '(H. M. M., 1873)', refers to Horace Moule, who committed suicide in Cambridge in September 1873. Hardy had last met him on a visit to Cambridge in July. The *Life* does not mention the poem (which may not have been written when the *Life* was compiled). It does, however, suggest the connection made by Evelyn Hardy and Millgate. Chapter X ends with Hardy's note about the candles: they 'guttered in the most fantastic shapes I ever saw', and, he concludes, 'Wordsworth's ghost, too, seemed to haunt the place, lingering and wandering on somewhere alone in the fan-traceried vaulting' (*Life*, p. 145). He introduces this note by saying that after a day or two in Cambridge, 'he felt an indescribable physical weariness, which was really the beginning of the long illness he was to endure'. Chapter X ends Part II of the book; Part III is entitled 'Illness, Novels, and Italy'. In between these two references to his illness comes this passage about the candles, implying some link between the two events. Moreover, King's Chapel has been mentioned before, again at quite a prominent point in the story, the end of Chapter VI:

> Next morning went with H. M. M. to King's Chapel early. M. opened the great West doors to show the interior vista: we got upon the roof, where we could see Ely Cathedral gleaming in the distant sunlight. A never-to-be-forgotten morning. H. M. M. saw me off for London. His last smile. (*Life*, p. 96)

Reading the *Life* through brings out the link. You remember Moule as you read about the candles; you remember the roof as you look up with Hardy into the vaulting. The book encourages that comparison and leaves the reader to draw out what it might imply: that, perhaps, visiting Cambridge brought back memories of Moule and re-awoke Hardy's grief at his loss – grief that, in 1873–74, he had suppressed beneath intense work on *Far from the Madding Crowd* and preparations for his marriage. Such grief would, of course, have been partly a result of Hardy's identifying with Moule – his starting to fear at this point in his life that his career was foundering as Moule's had, and that melancholy was taking him over in the same way that depression had destroyed his friend. Wordsworth's ghost, therefore, is both Moule's ghost and the ghost of Hardy's youth, when he had written Wordsworthian poems and aspired to enter Cambridge.

These are not, of course, the only set of implications one can draw from the juxtaposition Hardy's structure creates. Yet something is implied.

The book tacitly invites speculation; it suggests, as it were privately, that the illness was, indeed, partly psychosomatic. And a wider feature of the *Life* becomes evident from this. Hardy collected inside the book the notes from his notebooks that he wished to preserve. The notebooks themselves were then almost all destroyed. This process kept potentially scandalous material out of harm's way forever. The resulting book, though, is multiple. It declares through its narrator control over the material and over Hardy's past selves. The material itself survives, not always submitting to that control, not always endorsing the narrator's point of view. And as in this instance, the narrative's decorous silence about the sources of Hardy's illness competes the structure's offer of possible explanations to the alert reader.

Naturally, because the structure is Hardy's, the possibilities available to the reader remain more fully under his control than would be the case if excerpts from the notebooks and letters had simply been left in an archive. Even so, the *Life*'s intricacies allow, surprisingly, for what Liz Stanley has advocated in her discussions of biography. Stanley prefers forms of biographical writing that are both reflexive – presenting the reader with the writer's uncertainties and changes of mind – and open-ended – allowing the several interpretative possibilities to remain for the reader to choose between in a process she calls 'active reading'. By this means, the complexity of the biographical subject will survive into the biographical account instead of being lost in biography's 'spotlight approach'. Similarly, the sociality of the subject will be reflected in the process of interpretation. The biography will be written so that its subject can be read differently by a potentially infinite number of different readers in the same way that the subject lived 'enmeshed with other lives which give hers the meaning it has'.[10] This form of address to Hardy has been made easier recently by James Gibson's volume in the 'Interviews and Recollections series'.[11] That series, like Stanley's work and like the forthcoming anthologies *Lives of Victorian Literary Figures*, reflects a widespread movement towards modes of biographical writing that disturb the authority of the biographer and challenge the singularity of the biographical subject.[12] Hardy's biographers, up until now, have operated in more traditional ways, yet Hardy himself (who thought deeply about the constructedness, artificiality and transience of the human self) produced a biography that is much more responsive to 'active reading' than to any other kind.

notes

1. Thomas Carlyle, 'Biography', *Fraser's Magazine* (April 1832), pp. 253–60 (pp. 253, 256).
2. Virginia Woolf, 'The Art of Biography', in *The Death of the Moth* (London, 1981), p. 121; Sigmund Freud, 'Leonardo da Vinci and a Memory of his Childhood', Penguin Freud Library, general editor Angela Richards, Vol. 14, p. 223.
3. Strachey's *Eminent Victorians* (London, 1918) was followed by his irreverent life of Queen Victoria: *Queen Victoria* (London, 1921).
4. See David Amigoni, *Victorian Biography: Intellectuals and the Ordering of Discourse* (Hemel Hempstead, 1993).
5. R. L. Purdy, *Thomas Hardy: A Bibliographical Study* (London, 1954) proved Hardy's authorship beyond doubt. The idea had first been put forward by E. L. Tinker in the *New York Times Book Review*, 12 May 1940, p. 25. See p. xxvii.
6. Millgate's edition of the *Life* restores the original text and shows, via appendices, Florence's excisions.
7. Hardy to H. W. Massingham, 31 December 1891: *Letters*, I, p. 250.
8. Robert Gittings, *Young Thomas Hardy* (London, 1975), p. 27; Michael Millgate, *Thomas Hardy: A Biography* (New York, 1982), p. 75; Martin Seymour-Smith, *Hardy* (London, 1994), p. 61.
9. Seymour-Smith, *Hardy*, p. 265; Robert Gittings, *The Older Hardy* (London, 1978), p. 22; Evelyn Hardy, *Thomas Hardy: A Critical Biography* (London, 1954), p. 176; Millgate, *Thomas Hardy*, p. 214.
10. Liz Stanley, *The Auto/Biographical I: The Theory and Practice of Feminist Auto/Biography* (Manchester and New York, 1992), pp. 14, 175–7, 255.
11. James Gibson, ed. *Thomas Hardy: Interviews and Recollections* (London and New York, 1999).
12. *Lives of Victorian Literary Figures*, series editor, Ralph Pite (London: Pickering & Chatto, 2003–). The first three volumes in the series are on George Eliot, edited by Gail Marshall; Charles Dickens, edited by Corinna Russell; and Alfred, Lord Tennyson, edited by Matthew Bevis. Further volumes, on the Rossettis, Robert Browning and Elizabeth Barrett, the Brontës and others will follow in 2004 and 2005. For other discussions of alternative forms of biography, see Carol Gilligan, 'Remapping the Moral Domain: New Images of the Self in Relationship', in *Reconstructing Individualism: Autonomy, Individuality, and the Self in Western Thought*, eds Thomas C. Heller, Morton Sosna, and David E. Wellbery (Stanford, California, 1986), pp. 237–52; Carol Gilligan, *In a Different Voice: Psychological Theory and Women's Development* (Cambridge, MA, 1982), and James Clifford, '"Hanging Up Looking Glasses at Odd Corners": Ethnobiographical Prospects', in *Studies in Biography*, ed. Daniel Aaron, Harvard English Studies 8 (Cambridge, MA, and London, 1978), pp. 41–56.

4
editing hardy

rosemarie morgan

Hardy's novels have a complex publishing history. All but the two earliest, *Desperate Remedies* and *Under the Greenwood Tree*, were published first in serial form, often substantially revised from the manuscript to comply with the demands of nervous editors, followed by a series of volume editions, in which the text was typically brought closer to its earlier manuscript form, and then in two collected editions, with further revisions, in 1895–96, and in 1912. The textual changes made at these various stages are sometimes odd and quirky, sometimes inspired, occasionally ill-considered, often retaliative, frequently jaded, fanciful, and even commercially driven. But Hardy never ceased to experience the changes superimposed on his original, holographic text as a bowdlerisation of a work for which the world was not yet ready. Whether imposed by editors or self-inflicted in order to circumnavigate the same, bowdlerisation remained, for Hardy, an act of mutilation which he was never able to reconcile with the art of free self-expression in imaginative literature. He regarded censorship by editors as paralyzing, the pirating (in the US, mainly) of his texts as irremediable and the freehanded rewriting of entire episodes and other unorthodox marketing practices, particularly by some American editors, as a 'sharp practice in literature which ... perfectly astonishes me'.[1] He revised his own prose and verse over and over – the creative mind cannot simply cease upon the hour – but as often as not with as much humility, indecision and doubt as pride and satisfaction. The case of *Far from the Madding Crowd* is in many ways typical. In the post-publication era of revisions at the turn of the century, notably the attempt to render a certain uniformity to the Wessex Editions of his novels, Hardy reflected on the *Far from the Madding Crowd* of some 40 years earlier and saw it to be the work of 'a much younger man'. Historicity remains, in this context, unimpeachable, whether or not the older Hardy approved or thought he could improve upon this work of a 'much younger man'.

The millennium years have seen a turn towards the holographic manuscript and the first edition, following intensive academic studies into the so-called 'definitive' text provided by the 1912 Wessex Edition. There is little doubt that Hardy's late revisions frequently harmed the integrity of his original texts.[2] Not only were these shaped by post-publication attempts to forge a coherent 'Wessex' topography which, in many cases, scatters the form and content of the novel in unfortunate ways, but many changes were also provoked by critical commentators. The return to the manuscript and/or the first edition escapes most of these hazards, although in the case of the metamorphic text such as *Tess of the d'Urbervilles*, which went through several permutations in the four years prior to the first edition and further substantial changes the year following its 1891 publication, students and scholars would be advised to study the textual variants, particularly in the one-volume edition of 1892.[3]

The time is long overdue to abolish the concept of the definitive text. The act of interpretation is all, and this should not be made subject to the limits imposed by editors. In the event of a lost manuscript the first-volume edition succeeds in retaining the freshness and authenticity of the holograph text, and goes a long way to providing readers with a work that is a product of a unique authorial sensibility and a specific historical time, and innocent of the accretions of any other.

Recent editors have commented on some controversy over Hardy's implied intentions regarding the punctuation and paragraphing in his holograph manuscripts and later revised texts. 'Implied intentions' is itself a spurious concept. Anyone studying a Hardy manuscript is struck by one aspect that remains a critical constant: the cancelled words. What Hardy might have 'intended' on Tuesday is revoked on Wednesday, reinstated on Thursday and revised on Friday. To assume authorial intention is to assume a stasis of thought, methodology, epistemology and vision that is nowhere to be found in Hardy's art. However, an authorial preference for one style over another, for one methodology over another, is an entirely different matter. A preference *can* be determined: first and foremost, and by definition, it is distinguishable from other preferences; it will, most likely, be variable, but unlike intention it remains an act of choice implying other choices and may well be riven with incertitudes, ambivalence, uncertainty – but never 'stasis'. The nature of choice itself implies an alternative, a road not taken. 'Intention', on the other hand, indicates a mind firmly fixed upon something; invariable and certain. Unless Hardy specifically indicates such a purposeful act I doubt that scholars should step into his shoes and provide such an indication on his behalf.

But the vexed question, for some editors, remains: does Hardy's conspicuously light punctuation and idiosyncratic use of accidentals imply an 'authorial intention', or are these simply inconsequential, to be left to compositors who would in any case superimpose the preferred house style of the publishers? In terms of preference, Hardy clearly favoured, in composing his manuscripts, minimal punctuation, colons over semicolons, abundant dashes, exclamation points over commas and question marks, and this is what he attempted to restore in later revisions. But – and this is an important exclusion – at the manuscript stage of writing against the clock for serialisation, he often omitted quotation marks (speech marks, inverted commas), and frequently formed speech phrases in an impromptu style, dashed off with incomplete punctuation or none at all. He knew full well that compositors would go their own way when preparing the manuscript for serialisation or first edition. House style was and is a particularity, a signature almost, of individual publishers and, as fashion prevails, there would be variables over the decades. Such a variable is most evident in the instance of the copious capitalisations in early Victorian letters which rapidly went out fashion during the latter half of the nineteenth century: one might speculate that a 'levelling' of 'case' reflected the proletarianisation (or impending socialistic formation) of the culture.

Why didn't Hardy, in making post-publication revisions to punctuation, alter the compositor's quotation marks? Because there was no need. There was no discrepancy, no anomaly involved: these matched what he customarily employed in everyday (relaxed) writing – his letters, his private note-taking, his textual emendations. None of these show any irregularity in the use of quotation marks. If he was inclined to omit them in the manuscript writing this is understandable; he was working at high speed for serialisation and knew compositors would insert them anyway; they would render all accidentals uniform whatever Hardy produced at the stage of composition. In sum, it would be fair to say that the circumspect editor would follow the manuscript for the majority of accidentals and the first edition for speech marks. It is a sophistry to say that the manuscript version should provide the copy text in this instance just because 'it is *all* authorial', and that 'non-authorial punctuation [should be] excluded even if the author passed it in proof'.[4] The truth is that what Hardy passed in proof, and let remain in later revisions, not once or twice but over and over again, has to be a preferred punctuation: it must surely represent the typesetting closest to manuscript usage; if it is never revoked at any point in post-publication revisions there is no valid reason for holding it to be 'non-authorial'.[5]

But what about other late systematic revisions? Do they also bear out a return to manuscript preferences? Dialectal revisions, for example, have much in common, in principle, with revisions to punctuation insofar as they follow the painstaking practice of Hardy's manuscript composition. Both manuscript and proofs of *Far from the Madding Crowd*, a representative seminal text, show, from the day of origination to the 1912 revision, a continuing adjustment to dialect, each and every item so carefully adjusted – from say, "ee' to 'you' and 'you' to "ee' – that, at first sight, the impression is one of a fanatical mind at work. Later in Hardy's career these adjustments may be additionally spurred by critical complaints that his rustics sound too educated, but the perpetual struggle with fine-tuning of this kind serves to establish a balance in usage, that is to say, a dialectal equilibrium between the traditional homespun wisdom and folk culture of the partly real, partly dream world and Hardy's ethical concerns regarding the rural workforce – the proud dignity of the agricultural labourer. Hardy abhorred the 'Hodge' stereotype and fought hard and long to abolish it in his fiction, evidently making a lifetime commitment to marrying vernacular usage with artistic form.[6] In this respect *Tess* can be taken as representative of some of Hardy's ethical concerns: Dorset dialect and Standard English coexist in the most humble cottager's home – a linguistic duality that is both flexible and sensitively negotiated and at all times underscored by his painstaking revisions to the most minute aspects of the vernacular. This is a meticulous balance sustained at all times and in all of his works, even as late as *The Dynasts*.[7]

Systematic revisions also include those to topography. However, unlike revisions to punctuation and dialect these do not show a return to the manuscript text. On the contrary, they stem from a hindsight evaluation of a Wessex which, within half a century, had broken the boundaries of art to become a commodity in its own right. By 1912, some 40 years after composing the first of 15 novels, the heartland of Hardy's imagination was already a tourist industry. Based on his own birthplace at Bockhampton and its environs (the earliest inspiration of the 'Wessex' microcosm), Hardy's first Wessex settings had not originally signified, either to reader or author, a 'universe' about to be created. This was still very much a world in the making even at the time of his sixth published novel, *The Return of the Native*. Who could have foretold, in the early 1870s, that, in the literary sense, Wessex would become a vast imaginative construct and that, in the actual, geographical, cultural and historical sense it would become the world that the real-life Hardys would inhabit for their entire lives together?[8]

It is generally held that the 'imaginative construct' of Wessex itself first comes into being in *Far from the Madding Crowd*. Even Hardy himself seizes upon this notion, with strategic hindsight, later in life.[9] To be sure, the manuscript does name 'Wessex' (later revised to South Wessex) in the final chapters of this novel, and for the very first time in Hardy's work, but it is introduced as a historical region, a country of ancient kingdoms, solely to emphasise the ageless, time-worn tradition of the agricultural fair at prehistoric Greenhill. To give further emphasis to this site of great antiquity Greenhill is aligned here with Nijnii Novgorod (Nizhni Novgorod) in Russia. Now renamed Gorki, Nijnii Novgorod flanks the Volga river and trade fairs had been held there for hundreds of years. The city attracted visitors from across the globe in huge numbers annually. However, like its micro-counterpart, Greenhill, Nijnii Novgorod remained a remote destination to all but traders and travellers, whereas 'Wessex' was to emerge from obscurity, with some force, within a decade or two of the publication of *Far from the Madding Crowd*.[10]

Aside from their emphatic support of Hardy's 'pastoral' evocations, editors played a lesser part in shaping his Wessex than, say, his treatment of human relationships, class issues and sexuality. When Leslie Stephen commissioned *Far from the Madding Crowd* for serialisation in the *Cornhill* he had been hoping for a rural idyll along the lines of *Under the Greenwood Tree*. This novel, he told Hardy, had utterly delighted him. He now sought something similar to delight the *Cornhill* reader in turn. The 'delight', for Hardy, however, was to come at some cost to his crusade against the strictures of a puritanical culture and what he held to be its pernicious class divisions. As an editor Stephen certainly put Hardy through his paces. Despite giving the impression, in his letters and, no doubt, face to face, that the author should have the final say on stylistic and ethical concerns, Stephen would put his pencil through neologisms, sacrilegious rustic dialogues, light oaths such as invoking the name of the devil, sexually transgressive words (no bovine 'buttocks' allowed) and passages mentioning, say, Bathsheba's 'wanton' thoughts or Fanny's illegitimate baby.[11] Nor was Bathsheba permitted any anger: words such as 'vexed' were preferred by an editor who felt strongly that young female readers should, wherever possible, be edified with womanly models of 'feminine' passivity and submissiveness. Frequently Hardy only saw Stephen's deletions and alterations for the first time when reading the *Cornhill* version in print. For example, and at a relatively innocuous level of discourse, it was not until he picked up the first *Cornhill* instalment of *Far from the Madding Crowd* on a bookstall that he noticed his Fanny Robbin was now 'Fanny Robin.' And there was absolutely nothing he could do about it. It was now in print, henceforth, 'Robin' it would have to be. This is but one of many instances that urges upon us the manuscript version of the novel as the only version that bears true witness to the emergence of the candid, experimental, iconoclastic Hardy. Whether it is names and places, character delineations or plain old punctuation, there is no other text that can legitimately be named 'authentic'. Next in line is the first edition: thereafter the 'line' becomes, at various levels of severity, corrupted.

The designation 'Wessex' had come into common parlance soon after the publication of *Far from the Madding Crowd*, largely due to Charles Kegan Paul's article entitled 'The Wessex Labourer' in which Hardy's intimate knowledge of rural culture and country life had been enthusiastically praised.[12] Two decades later, and evidently bemused by the escalation of his 'Wessex' as a cultural artefact, Hardy observed to his editor, Frederick Macmillan, when negotiating cheaper editions of his novels, that 'The curious accident of a topographical interest having arisen in "Wessex" also helps the vitality of the volumes.'[13] Hardy was, at that point, insisting that 'Wessex' should figure in the series title although, curiously, Macmillan had not been inclined to do so. Unfortunately, the whole Wessex construct had, by this time, become something of an obsession with Hardy and not only did he drive himself into the ground to revise his life's work on the novels for the 'authoritative' Wessex Edition but in doing so he made 'improvements' to the topography of his novels that led to very many anomalies. It was not until recently, however, when Penguin reissued the first editions of the Wessex novels that these anomalies drew the attention of scholars in a serious way. *Desperate Remedies*, *The Hand of Ethelberta* and *A Laodicean* suffered particularly severe distortions of space and time in this 'improving' process. But the problem is widespread. For instance, *Far from the Madding Crowd* now had its distances adjusted to their requisite mileages, to accord with other Wessex novels, with the result that some of the inner workings of the plot were distorted. To take one typical example: Bathsheba's ability to overlook to see and hear clearly the children playing in the churchyard beneath her window is now implausible with a quarter of a mile to gaze over instead of the original 100 yards. Hardy, wretchedly overdriven in his late revisions, evidently remained unaware of this anomaly. However, when it came to working on topographical revisions for the *Harper* (1901) edition he abandoned most of them at the end of the day. Perhaps it was, after all, an impossible task. One particularly tricky episode will put this in perspective: Bathsheba's elopement to Bath. Originally, with no idea of a coherent 'Wessex' in mind Hardy had driven his speedily written plot towards the dramatic events involving his characters and not towards an accurately mapped terrain. In making topographical adjustments some 30 years after composition, had he gone on to revise the actual distances between Weatherbury and Bath he would have had to rewrite not only the events of Bathsheba's night flight to meet Troy but also the activities of the Weatherbury folk who were tracking her. All in all a daunting prospect. Better perhaps to allow his readers the possibility of discovering discrepancies in mileages rather than risk anomalies in character, event and plot? For whatever reason, many late revisions to the *Harper* edition were not incorporated into the so-called 'definitive' Wessex Edition of 1912.

Later substantive revisions would result in similar problems but none were as incongruous as those imposed by some of his contemporary editors. Henry Holt, for example, had earlier imposed textual variants which Hardy clearly could not sanction. Holt had requested, in November 1874, an advance copy of the last chapters of *Far from the Madding Crowd* for American book publication, but since Hardy had lost sight of his finished manuscript earlier in the summer and had completed the final November proofs the previous August he had nothing to offer. It has been suggested that Hardy supplied Holt with an alternative draft at this time but this is highly unlikely. To begin with Hardy had been writing against the clock for the *Cornhill* publication and was still correcting proofs when Holt's request arrived. In addition, he had recently become a married man and had a new bride, a new life and a newly rented house in Surbiton to take care of; moreover, he was already preparing notes for his next novel, *The Hand of Ethelberta*. Most important, he had every good reason for distrusting Holt who had already made cavalier adaptations to *Far from the Madding Crowd* without his permission. In fact Hardy tried to cut off relations with Holt altogether four years later in 1878. That he might have gone out of his way to supply him with an alternative draft when labouring under so many pressures and in the knowledge that this 'improving' editor had no qualms about falsifying an author's work appears deeply improbable. In fact, some of his letters reveal the angry frustration he felt upon learning of Holt's clumsy changes, but none specifies the instances.

Here are a couple of examples of Holt's 'improvements'. Boldwood, during his mental breakdown, had attached 'as much importance to a crease in the coat as to an earthquake in South America', thus pointing to the seriousness of his suicidal depression. This fastidious man has become obsessive. Under Holt's pen, however, he attaches 'as much importance to a crease in the coat as to an earthquake in the Mediterranean' which no longer points to a man, crazed in mind, obsessed with minutiae but to a non-event: earthquakes in the Mediterranean being both rare and unlikely. And that Holt should 'improve' Oak – toward the end of the novel – turning him into a churchwarden, remains, piety for piety, a reflection of a puritan culture and not of Hardy's own Oak who enjoys singing lustily in the church choir but otherwise displays no inclination to be approved by the incumbent vicar for church duty.

Overall, Hardy was well rewarded by the publication of *Far from the Madding Crowd*. Typical of the marketing of most of the Wessex novels that followed, it was serialised in the United States in four separate publications, *Every Saturday*, *Littell's Living Age*, *Eclectic Magazine* and the *New York Semi-Weekly Tribune* between the years 1874 and 1875. The large German publishing house of Tauchnitz was, by contrast with Holt's mangled edition, thoroughly reliable. In 1878 Baron von Tauchnitz brought out a two-volume edition accurately based on the Smith, Elder 1877 text and, better still, Tauchnitz paid copyright fees (not internationally mandated at this time), unlike those of his American counterparts who not only bowdlerised but also pirated the work of foreign authors. After numerous reprintings and as late as 1939 *Far from the Madding Crowd* still featured on Tauchnitz's '500 Best Titles' list.

Stephen promptly asked for another story to begin in the *Cornhill* as early as possible in 1875. Hardy, despite his new-found confidence, felt this to be precipitate:

This was the means of urging Hardy into the unfortunate course of hurrying forward a further production before he was aware of what there had been of value in his previous one: before learning, that is, not only what had attracted the public, but what was of true and genuine substance on which to build a career as a writer with a real literary message.[14]

Nevertheless, he had had sufficient time to glean that it was the aspect of 'pastoral idyll' in *Far from the Madding Crowd* which had so delighted his readers. Likewise, he had also had sufficient time in which to become extremely touchy about being mistaken for George Eliot in his depiction of rural life and rustic characters, and touchier still about his own humble origins which were now public property to be toyed with by the media; one report that shocked him had claimed that 'the author of *Far from the Madding Crowd* [has] been discovered to be a house-decorator' (*Life*, p. 105). Thus, less encouraged by the 'pastoral idyll' acclaim than discouraged by what he regarded as slurs upon his family and upon his art, a highly defensive Hardy abandoned the woodland story he had in mind (later to become *The Woodlanders*) in favour of making 'a plunge in a new and untried direction', not having, he says, 'the slightest intention of writing for ever about sheepfarming':

> Hence, to the consternation of his editor and publishers, in March he sent up as a response to their requests the beginning of a tale called *The Hand of Ethelberta – A Comedy in Chapters* which had nothing whatever in common with anything he had written before (*Life*, p. 105)

Stephen's dismay, and his misgivings on behalf of the publishers, Smith, Elder, was not immediately communicated to Hardy unless, perhaps, inadvertently, via his delay in responding to the rough draft of the first part of *Ethelberta*. Hardy had waited anxiously for several weeks and eventually wrote a slightly irascible letter to Smith, Elder expressing his concern which met with a tardy 'go-ahead' a week or so afterwards. Settling on £700 for English serial and volume publication Hardy also negotiated with the *New York Times* for serialisation of *Ethelberta* in the United States whereby he would supply advance proof sheets and would be paid £50 for each *Cornhill* instalment. The upshot was that, ironically, Hardy was paid for this – what, with hindsight, he called a 'frivolous' work – three times as much as he was paid for *Far from the Madding Crowd*.

Hardy did not succeed in 'keeping his hand in' with Stephen. And paradoxically, just as the serialisation and volume publication of *Ethelberta* had heaped on him more financial rewards than had the greater novel, *Far from the Madding Crowd*, so the serialisation of *The Return of the Native*, one of his finest works, offered him a good deal less. The very spareness of Hardy's account betrays something of his chagrin:

But his main occupation at Riverside Villa … was writing *The Return of the Native*. The only note he makes of its progress is that, on November 8, parts 3, 4 and 5 of the story were posted to Messrs. Chatto and Windus for publication in (of all places) *Belgravia* – a monthly magazine then running … (*Life*, p. 120)

'The only note', in all its brevity, is indeed a bitter one. The now cautious, and undoubtedly forearmed, Leslie Stephen had rejected *The Return of the Native* out of hand. No sooner had he read the opening chapters sent to him by Hardy than he feared that the relations between Eustacia, Wildeve and Thomasin might develop into something 'dangerous' for a family magazine, and he refused to have anything to do with it unless he could see the whole work.

Anxiety now urged Hardy to search for other publishers. He approached John Blackwood, editor of the prestigious *Blackwood's Magazine*, which paid well but whose readership had been drifting, increasingly, towards the *Cornhill*. Offering a serial story, as yet incomplete, Hardy stirred Blackwood's interest. The reply was favourable. Accordingly, in April Hardy sent in the first 15 chapters of *The Return of the Native* with an accompanying note to the effect that any bowdlerisation the editor might like to impose on the text would be in order. How desperate can an author get?

Unfortunately, as Hardy's ill-luck would have it, Blackwood declined the novel, saying, with the utmost courtesy, that the magazine was fully booked up. He then tried the editor of *Temple Bar* – who declined. Eventually *Belgravia* accepted it. 'Of all places', *Belgravia*, which had until 1876 been edited by the novelist Mary Elizabeth Braddon, whom Hardy liked but whose 78 works of fiction and nine plays were under constant attack for 'blasphemy, irreligion, low-class origins, obscenity and plagiarism'.[15] *Belgravia* bore nothing of the star quality that had distinguished the *Cornhill*, but remained, even after Mary Braddon's departure, notorious for its cheap sensationalism. As Swinburne bluntly put it, '*Belgravia* stinks.'[16] One of Hardy's best friends among the literati, the irrepressible Mrs Procter, at finding 'the divine Hardy' no longer in the *Cornhill* but, rather, in the pages of *Belgravia*, expostulated: 'I suppose Hardy could not stand Leslie Stephen … I could not.'[17]

No wonder Hardy elides details of the *Belgravia* episode in the *Life*. Disappointment heaped upon disappointment. Hardy seems, at this time, to have lost interest in *The Return of the Native* altogether, if his revisions for the 1878 and 1880 three-volume editions, published by Smith, Elder (at £200 for 1,000 copies), are illustrative. Tony Slade, in his Notes to the recent Penguin edition, points to only three or four substantive changes from serial to volume publication. However, latterly, Hardy's interest revived and in preparing the 1895 edition for Osgood, McIlvaine & Co. his revisions included the fine-tuning of characterisation, clarifying moral attributes and placing greater emphasis on class background.

On the other hand, the map of Egdon Heath Hardy had sketched and drawn upon for the serial version, and had subsequently refined, offering it to his publishers for inclusion in the 1878 edition, did not thrive. Hardy held that 'nothing could give such reality to a tale as a map of this sort'. Yet 'real' it is not. The sketch depicts a relief map of an imaginative kind in which the three 'real' (existing) barrows on the periphery of the south Dorset heathlands have been replaced by one central barrow. In the serial this is named Black Barrow, and later Rainbarrow. Then there is the Bloom's End house which is shown as situated where the Bockhampton birthplace stands in relation to Shadwater weir. Hardy himself admits in the 1912 Postscript that 'In some other respects also there has been a bringing together of scattered characteristics.' If reality' it is then it is presumably the 'reality' of a dream world – a claim borne out by the fact that some interpretations take the map's abstract representation of Egdon's 'convexities' and 'concavities' to be diffused images of male and female genitalia. Oddly, the map prominently displayed as a frontispiece in 1878 later vanishes altogether – removed from all future editions.

Over one and only one imaginative construct Hardy forbade all editorial intervention. This was *The Dynasts*, his *magnum opus*. He had worked, off and on, on *The Dynasts* from the 1860s through to 1908, 50 years in all, and he was more passionately committed to it than to any other single major work. In many ways, his epistemology in *The Dynasts* was rehearsed in the composition of *A Laodicean*: bedridden for months on end, he had been dictating the novel to the patient and forbearing Emma:

> By spinning out the architectural 'business,' therefore, by introducing a series of more or less melodramatic plot developments, and by exploiting the notes he had taken during his French and German travels, Hardy was able to stay the course and fulfil his contract to the satisfaction of Harper & Brothers – if not, perhaps, to their unqualified delight.[18]

'Spinning out the architectural "business"' was evidently one way of staying the course; that this was something of a pragmatic 'way' induced by his state of invalidism, is evidenced by the fact that in revising the 1896 edition Hardy made hundreds of deletions to all those spun-out architectural details. Aside from these reversals and, of course, the requisite late-century construction of 'Wessex' (including the introduction of dialect) – an anomalous emphasis as it happens because *A Laodicean* is not a 'Wessex' novel by any stretch of the imagination[19] – the most significant revisions Hardy made to this 'Novel of Ingenuity' are the alterations to Paula Power's characterisation. Hardy's revisions to the proof sheets for the serial publication underwent some considerable toning down of her more unconventional aspects; in common with Bathsheba before her, Paula Power's unrestrained behaviour and 'unwomanly' outbursts of anger had to be muted, and like Tess after her, Paula's sensual awareness and proactive response to the physical world required 'correcting'. It was critically important to preserve the impression that Hardy was not a 'fleshly writer'.[20]

Remote as this might seem from *The Dynasts*, the long confinement in bed and the 'spinning out' processes of composition actually gave Hardy dreaming time for his as yet unfulfilled ambition, an epic work in verse to be based on the Napoleonic Wars. But, in the meantime he had a living to make; accordingly, once up and about, he set about *Two on a Tower* – 'the actual writing was lamentably hurried', he told Edmund Gosse.[21]

This was now two novels written in mid-career in a highly unsatisfactory manner, in Hardy's view. Fortunately his editor at this time happened to be a principled man of renowned integrity, and despite being exceedingly wary of matters 'fleshly' where Hardy was concerned, the strictly puritanical Thomas Bailey Aldrich – editor of the *Atlantic Monthly* and publisher of *Two on a Tower* – did not bowdlerise Hardy's work in any way. He intervened not at all except to remark somewhat dolefully that whereas he had been looking for a 'family story' he seemed to have been given 'a story in the family way'.[22]

If Hardy in his invalidism and recuperation had felt out of sorts in composing *Laodicean* and *Two on a Tower*, his next novel, *The Mayor of Casterbridge*, caused him even greater stress. Well accustomed by this time to working to strict deadlines he was disconcerted to be offered, on this occasion, an exceptionally long lead time. According to his editors and *Graphic* proprietors, Arthur Locker and W. J. Thomas, *The Mayor of Casterbridge*, begun in 1883, would not commence serialisation until it was completed (thus it would also be ready for book publication by Smith, Elder in two volumes the same year). January 1886 was to be the serial commencement date:

> The novel ... was not concerned with sexual relations, but even so he [Hardy] would be troubled by censorship ... [the] editor and proprietor of the *Graphic*, badly wanted a Hardy story to grace their pages; but knowing that he was 'dangerous', they made sure that they would have plenty of time to slice out whatever might offend their readership.[23]

'Not concerned with sexual relations' is not entirely accurate. One 'slice out' was occasioned by Lucetta's sexual relationship with Henchard. Hardy was told to mute this 'dangerous' item. Self-imposed bowdlerisations of this kind invariably disrupted the flow of continuity and creativity, and Hardy floundered; he inadvertently created what he called some 'improbabilities of character' (*Life*, p. 183), and was filled with chagrin. Nor did his troubles end there. When it came to reworking the bowdlerised sections for volume publication in May of the same year Hardy felt the revisions were strained; he was plunged into deep depression and a total loss of inspirational energy.

Thus it was, paradoxically, that the abundance of time allowed for the composition of *The Mayor of Casterbridge* may have benefitted the publishers but did not sit at all well with Hardy:

> Later in the year he confessed to William Dean Howells that he had failed to realize on paper the story 'as it existed in my mind', adding: 'I ought to have improved it much – for the greater part was finished in 1884 – a year & half before publication. But I could not get thoroughly into it after the interval.'[24]

Hence, in the uncomfortable intervals between bouts of composing *The Mayor of Casterbridge*, the distracted, enervated author decided to embark on yet another novel: *The Woodlanders* began appearing in *Macmillan's Magazine* at the same time as the volume edition of *The Mayor of Casterbridge* (May 1886).

Hardy still suffered from severe bouts of depression – he could not shake them off. These factors in themselves might have led him to feel, as he certainly did feel, that his revisions to serial and book editions of *The Mayor of Casterbridge* were confused and strained.[25] To aggravate things further, the commissioning publisher for *The Woodlanders* had been *Macmillan's Magazine* with Mowbray Morris as editor (replacing John Morley) who had apparently told Frederick Macmillan that whereas he had 'no desire to edit' Hardy's work in any 'impertinent way' he had, in fact, marked up one or two items in the proofs.[26] Sunk as he was in moods of despondency and despair Hardy promptly started to slash his text so that by the time Morris wrote to warn him not to allow any impropriety into the relationship between Fitzpiers and Suke Damson the bowdlerisation had already taken place.

Clearly Hardy's psychological state at this time was not wholly attributable to the intervention of editors and the paralysing effects of censorship. The harsh reality of a marriage in which both parties are trapped in mutual misery – a 'reality' Hardy had wanted to make more of in the stark denouement of *The Woodlanders* (but was thwarted by Morris) – and the suicidal ending of 'The Withered Arm' (1887: rejected by Longman's as too grim), were realities only too miserably familiar to Hardy and Emma.

Perhaps this background of domestic turbulence also contributed to the utter chaos of the production of *Tess*. But the trials and tribulations of the publishing world certainly took their toll. From cancelled contracts from Tillotson's who, too late, found the work deeply offensive, to Hardy's confusion in sending his manuscript to two other publishers at the same time and compounding the confusion by submitting it to a third, Mowbray Morris, *Tess of the d'Urbervilles* was pitted against a precarious world from the outset. Morris rejected it on the grounds of 'too much succulence' and Edward Arnold found it gave 'frequent and detailed reference to immoral situations'.[27] Bitterly forearmed by the time the *Graphic* finally agreed to publish it, Hardy had already grimly excised large portions. The notorious baptism scene was one such. This was published separately in the *Fortnightly Review*. The Chase scene, depicting Alec's appropriation of Tess's body, was also cut. This, in turn, was revised and published separately in the *National Observer*. There were several other major deletions and alterations: Hardy, understandably, preferred to mutilate his text himself rather than allow editors this doubtful privilege; self-bowdlerisation also made it easier to restore the original passages to the novel in volume publication. Hardy nowhere offers an explanation for the chaotic publication negotiations with *Tess*. Juliet Grindle and Simon Gatrell, in their 1983 critical edition, argue that Hardy was preoccupied with preparing the ground for his essay on 'Candour in English Fiction' (published in January 1890). Tim Dolin, almost as unconvincingly, suggests that payment was an issue. As for Hardy himself, taking one last depressed and despairing look at a situation he had only known to be a 'nightmare' (as he spoke of it to Gosse), he decided that this was the beginning of the end of his career as a novelist.

It was only with the first volume edition of *Tess* that Hardy insisted upon the subtitle 'A Pure Woman'. This bespeaks a grim determination on his part not only to retain some kind of control over his creation but also to stand in defiance of social mores (and periodical editors) – a defiance writ large. Ironically, despite censors, the 'nightmare' and the 'beginning of the end of his career as a novelist', when *Tess* was published in November, 1891, it attracted mixed reviews but unexpectedly huge sales. The novel sold out by the end of the year and was reprinted in 1892; it then went through five impressions and 17,000 copies within a year.

Hardy's sense of the 'paralysis' he endured at the hands of his editors and the more censorious reviewer is reflected in the *Life*, where he speaks of closure in his title opening to Part V, of '*Tess*, *Jude*, and the End of Prose'; the chapter on the writing of *Jude* is entitled 'Another Novel Finished, Mutilated and Restored'. Could there be anything more bitterly disillusioned than these words uttered by a world-class novelist as his thoughts turn upon his last great prose manuscript? Early on with *Jude*, in the process of composition, Hardy had already felt that it was moving in the wrong direction and that he should withdraw from his agreement with *Harper's Magazine* to submit it for serial publication. Could he bear yet another extended period of cutting his novel to pieces, of excising its vital parts, of destroying its central movement, its imaginative dynamic, its essential energy? As it happened *Harper's* turned down his proposal to withdraw.

The serial cuts to *Jude* were extensive. For example, Sue and Jude remain merely cousinly, their children are adopted and the sexual content is radically diminished. These cancellations severely undermine the serial's justification of the novel's plot.[28] However the volume edition reinstates the essential elements from the manuscript – another example of the benefits of forestalling editors by self-bowdlerisation. Even so, Hardy was exhausted and confused by this seemingly endless restoration work. In August 1895, he told his publishers:

> On account of the labour of altering 'Jude the Obscure' to suit the magazine, and then having to alter it back, I have lost energy for revising and improving the original as I meant to. (*Life*, p. 286)

The Dynasts – now *Europe in Throes* – resurfaced to dominate Hardy's thinking. His return to poetry was by now well in the ascendant:

Perhaps I can express more fully in verse ideas and emotions which run counter to the inert crystallized opinion – hard as a rock – which the vast body of men have vested interests in supporting ... to put it in argumentative prose will make them sneer, or foam, and set all the literary contortionists jumping upon me, a harmless agnostic, as if I were a clamorous atheist, which in their crass illiteracy they seem to think is the same thing ... if Galileo had said in verse that the world moved, the Inquisition might have let him alone. (*Life*, p. 302)

Thus, with abandonment of the novel ever-present in his mind, when Hardy revised for volume publication the book which in 1897 became *The Well-Beloved*, he made extensive revisions together with a completely rewritten ending, but his heart was not in it. He had already moved on. This is evinced in the *Life*, where he speaks dismissively of *The Well-Beloved* as belonging to an earlier period, sketched many years ago 'when I was comparatively a young man, and interested in the Platonic Idea'. His main concern, he says, is to tell the reader that 'this fantastic tale of a subjective idea' is 'exemplified in a poem bearing the same name, written about this time and published with *Poems of the Past and the Present* in 1901' (*Life*, p. 303).

Having now spurned prose (with the exception of a handful of short stories already commissioned), Hardy rationalised the move away from the novel with a forgiving eye:

The change, after all, was not so great as it seemed. It was not as if he had been a writer of novels proper, and as more specifically understood, that is, stories of modern artificial life and manners showing a certain smartness of treatment. He had mostly aimed at keeping his narratives close to natural life and as near to poetry in their subject as the conditions would allow, and had often regretted that those conditions would not let him keep them nearer still. (*Life*, pp. 309–10)

He had been writing poetry, on and off, since 1865 but, possibly for reasons of his relative obscurity, published little. Topically speaking, *The Dynasts* still remained his greatest passion – an attempt to 'put forth a complete "philosophy of life"',[29] mirrored in the short pieces he now gathered for publication such as 'The Peasant's Confession', 'Valenciennes' and 'The Sergeant's Song'. Taking these short war poems together with many earlier verses Hardy produced, in 1898, his first volume of poems,

Wessex Poems and other Verses. The following year found him pursuing similar themes and now publishing, without difficulty, in newspapers such as the *Daily Chronicle*, the *Graphic*, the *Westminster Gazette* and the *Cornhill*, those poems responding to the South African campaign – 'The Going of the Battery', 'The Dead Drummer' ('Drummer Hodge'), 'A Christmas Ghost-Story' and 'The Souls of the Slain' – which he would collect in 1901 as *Poems of the Past and the Present*.

Now famed as the author of 'The Wessex Novels', Hardy no longer had to endure the censorship of market-minded, 'improving' editors and promptly returned, *Dynasts* in hand, to the house of Macmillan who had, to his ever-loyal mind, earned an important place in his career by showing a genuine interest in his early work. Frederick Macmillan responded eagerly to this 'return' and assured Hardy he would never regret his choice. Royalties were agreed upon (one-fourth of the selling price, with some sale-price modifications) and it was a relatively unburdened Hardy who now gave himself up to the 'theosophic'[30] passion of his life: *The Dynasts*.

For the last 20 years of his life Hardy enjoyed an ease of publication undreamed of in his youth. His poems and *The Dynasts* encountered few obstacles in terms of commissioning editors, although criticism still raged from those who regarded some of his iconoclastic poems, such as 'The Wood Fire', as sacrilegious. 'A Sunday Morning Tragedy' – a rare example – *did* in fact give him trouble with the editor of the *Fortnightly*, who felt he could not print such a poem (which treats openly with abortifacients) in a 'family' magazine. But in the main the roles of editor and author were now reversed: editors sought to please Hardy; Hardy set down his own terms for editors. In the case of *The Dynasts*, for example, although Frederick Macmillan had assured Hardy that he would never regret his return to that firm, Macmillan himself was not to be so reassured. The first part of *The Dynasts* appeared in December 1903[31] and met with respectful but puzzled, sometimes diffident reviews. Macmillan was not thrilled. The second part was presented to him in 1905: Macmillan was filled with gloom:

> writing to the firm's New York office, [he] observed that it would have to be published, despite the 'disastrous' commercial failure of Part First, since they could not afford to 'disoblige an author of Mr. Hardy's standing'.[32]

Hardy had anticipated an unfavourable reception. *The Dynasts*, after all, was based on the assumption that the old theologies were defunct, 'So that one must make an independent plunge ... But I expect that I shall catch it hot & strong for attempting it' (*Life*, p. 344). He took the precaution, cleverly, of gaining some favourable responses by sending copies to several of his literary friends including Clodd, Florence Henniker, Gosse, Arthur Symons, Henry Newbolt (one of Hardy's greatest admirers) and Leslie Stephen's successor as editor of the *Dictionary of National Biography*, Sidney Lee. When, in the winter of 1907 Part Third of *The Dynasts* was in its final stages of completion Hardy – unlike Macmillan – felt he would miss it sadly when it was all over. It remained not only the most sizeable of his poetic works but had also taken the longest time to compose. It had been gestating for nigh on 50 years before it was brought to completion over the course of the first seven years of the new century. A life-work indeed!

By now newspaper and periodical editors were clamouring for contributions and Hardy, still sensitive about the social acceptability of his topics or, rather, his treatment of them, had learned a new form of tact. He submitted the rather obscure and clumsy alternative title, 'The Funeral of Jahveh', to the *Fortnightly Review* only to have it promptly dismissed (as he had hoped) by the editor in favour of the original title, 'God's Funeral'. Hardy was extremely sensitive about having his agnosticism misunderstood. Finding that he was all too often accused, by 'invidious critics' of being a 'Heretic', 'Immoralist', 'Pessimist', 'Infidel' and 'Atheist', he not only wrote a watered-down version of his outrage in the 'Apology' prefixed to *Late Lyrics and Earlier* (1922) but also a candid diatribe in the *Life* where he speaks of a 'fiery-faced and tyrannous' God 'who flies into a rage on the slightest provocation' and who, 'after some thousands of years of trial, produced the present infamous state of Europe' (*Life*, p. 406).

His public persona remained, however, discreet and his dealings with editors, agents and critics, diffident. Thus when the director of the Fitzwilliam Museum, Cambridge, Sydney Cockerell, approached him about endowing his manuscripts to deserving museums Hardy said he preferred to have no say in the matter but promptly handed them over to Cockerell to do as he wished with them.[33]

After following the fortunes of his beloved *Dynasts* through its re-publication in 1919 in Volume II of his *Collected Poems*, to its many theatrical productions, Hardy experienced a memorable event. Oxford University reassembled after the war at a time when the future of the

Oxford University Dramatic Society was in 'low water' (as Hardy put it) and to his astonishment *The Dynasts* was nominated as the first annual play in the new series, chosen to set the Dramatic Society on the road to success. This episode is lengthily recorded in the *Life*, most of the account being supplied by Charles Morgan, Manager of OUDS. Of particular note is the fact that *The Dynasts* was nominated by an undergraduate who 'had to defend it against those who objected that it was not Shakespearean and that Shakespeare was a tradition of the Society'. Moreover, the cost of production would be high. Last but not least of the problems was that the play was copyright and it 'seemed probable that Hardy would refuse permission to perform [being] an old man ... [not] troubled with our affairs ... forbidding and formidable' – too formidable to approach. Not only did the undergraduate win his nomination, and not only was the financial difficulty overcome by personal guarantees, but all other hazards also vanished in the instant that Hardy was approached and 'gave his play to us, not grudgingly nor with any air of patronage, but with so gracious a courtesy ... genuinely pleased to find young men eager to perform his work' (*Life*, pp. 524–5).

Hardy was almost 80 years old. He had struggled with rejections from editors, their intervention and castigations. He might not live to see the day, in the millennium years, when his first editions and manuscripts would supersede the gamut of various 'eclectic' texts pressured into existence by ambitious editors, well-meaning publishers and the hand of a 'much older man', but he had now experienced the greatest achievement of all: the fervent admiration of young poets. He now knew, on this day, *The Dynasts* to be 'unique in literature, an epic-drama without predecessor in its own kind ... its subject ... closely linked with the tragedy in which nearly all the players had participated' (*Life*, p. 524). This last was perhaps more deeply poignant in its imprint on Hardy's heart than anything he had ever known. And, to be sure, it was on this same momentous day, when contemplating his life's work, that he turned to his companion and said, with serene finality, 'My stories are written.'

notes

1. *Letters*, I, p. 28. In a subsequent letter he adds that 'American usages are very perplexing': *Letters*, 1, p. 29.
2. See Rosemarie Morgan, ed., *Editing Hardy* (New Haven, 1999).
3. For further details see Tim Dolin's 'History of the Text' in his edition of *Tess of the d'Urbervilles* (London, 1998), pp. xliv–lxviii.

4. Quoted from Simon Gatrell's Introduction to *Under the Greenwood Tree*, in Morgan, *Editing Hardy*, p. 26.

5. Dale Kramer shares this view in his edition of *The Woodlanders* (Oxford, 1981).

6. See Rosemarie Morgan, *Cancelled Words: Rediscovering Thomas Hardy* (London, 1992) for a detailed discussion of Hardy's revisions to dialect. If this 'balance' is not immediately apparent to readers of the novels it may be self-evident to readers of his verse.

7. Dialectal formations in *The Dynasts* warrant a separate study altogether. The manner in which linguistic usages shape the dramatic form of the work is complex and extraordinary.

8. *Wessex Tales* was published in 1888; the first volume of *Wessex Novels* was published in 1895; *Wessex Poems* was published in 1898.

9. Hardy's first mention of 'Wessex' to his publishers is in a letter to Edward Marston (c. 1888): 'Could you, whenever advertising my books, use the words "Wessex novels" at the head of the list? I mean, instead of "By T.H.", "T.H's Wessex novels", or something of the sort? I find that the name Wessex, wh. I was the first to use in fiction, is getting to be taken up everywhere: & it would be a pity for us to lose the right to it for want of asserting it. It might also be used on the paper covers of the novels.' *Letters*, I, p. 171.

10. Curiously, today's *OED* does not list 'Wessex' whereas *Webster's* has two entries, one devoted almost entirely to Hardy.

11. Of note here is the fact that Paterson's illustration of Fanny Robbin on her way to the workhouse for the birthing of her baby depicts a young woman with a nineteen-inch waist! For fuller details, see Morgan, *Cancelled Words*.

12. *The Examiner*, 15 July 1876.

13. *Letters*, III, p. 12

14. *Life*, p. 105.

15. See Tony Slade's 'Note on the History of the Text', in his edition of *The Return of the Native* (London, 1999), pp. xxxix–xlv.

16. Robert Lee Wolff, *Sensational Victorian: The Life and Fiction of Mary Elizabeth Braddon* (New York, 1979), p. 179.

17. Michael Millgate, *Thomas Hardy: A Biography* (Oxford, 1982), p. 188.

18. Millgate, *Thomas Hardy*, p. 218.

19. See John Schad's Introduction and Notes to his edition of *A Laodicean* (London, 1997).

20. In 1871 Robert Buchanan had attacked the poetry of (especially) D. G. Rossetti in an article on 'The Fleshly School of Poetry'. See Martin Seymour-Smith, *Hardy* (London, 1994), p. 280.

21. *Letters*, I, p. 114.

22. Seymour-Smith, *Hardy*, p. 280.

23. Seymour-Smith, *Hardy*, p. 320.

24. Millgate, *Thomas Hardy*, pp. 268–9.

25. See Keith Wilson's note on the text, in his Penguin edition of *The Mayor of Casterbridge* (London, 1997).

26. Millgate, *Thomas Hardy*, pp. 273–4.

27. See Tim Dolin's 'A History of the Text' in his edition of *Tess*.

28. For further details see Dennis Taylor's 'Note on the History of the Text' in his edition of *Jude the Obscure* (London, 1998), p. xxxix.
29. Seymour-Smith, *Hardy*, p. 577.
30. Hardy's word: see *Life*, p. 343.
31. According to Hardy (*Life*, p. 318); Millgate, however, has January 1904.
32. Michael Millgate, *Thomas Hardy*, p. 441.
33. Under Cockerell's auspices, the manuscripts of *The Dynasts* and *Tess* went to the British Museum, *Time's Laughingstocks* and *Jude* to the Fitzwilliam, and *Wessex Poems*, one of Hardy's favourites and the only volume of his poems illustrated by himself, to Birmingham. Upon request from Dorset County Museum Hardy did, himself, donate the manuscript of *The Mayor of Casterbridge*. The manuscript of *Far from the Madding Crowd*, missing since the day Hardy first serialised it, was found in the publisher's vaults in 1918 and sold, with Hardy's approval, to raise funds for the Red Cross. Today it is held by the Beinecke Rare Book and Manuscript Museum at Yale.

5
hardy and class

roger ebbatson

When the publisher Charles Kegan Paul referred to Thomas Hardy, in the *British Quarterly Review* of 1881, as one 'sprung of a race of labouring men', the novelist corrected him with a touchy punctiliousness:

> my father is one of the last of the old 'master-masons' left ... From time immemorial – I can speak from certain knowledge of four generations – my direct ancestors have all been master masons, with a set of journey-men masons under them: though they have never risen above this level, they have never sunk below it – i.e. they have never been journeymen themselves.[1]

Hardy's claims for his father's status represented a slight deviation from the truth; however that may be, the writer incontrovertibly was born into an era of momentous social change. During the 1830s and 1840s the passing of the Reform Act, the Swing riots, the repeal of the Corn Laws, introduction of the New Poor Law and the growth and collapse of the Chartist movement were expressions of conflict between newly emergent classes. By the time Hardy was in his teens, the eighteenth-century notion of hierarchy had been partially replaced by a tripartite class structure (upper, middle and lower) which became progressively stabilised. Whether or not this model is entirely valid, it is clear that the entire British social order was being vigorously politicised at this juncture, following the industrial and agricultural revolutions which left their mark even in a remote county like Dorset. The language of class was increasingly pervasive as the old hierarchies were unsettled or left behind, and though it may be tendentious to characterise the era as that of the 'making of the working class' (or of the middle class), it is true that a stable and settled sense of hierarchy was being undermined whilst, at the same time, the importance of the middle echelons of Victorian society was being stressed in a rhetorical strategy aimed at securing the hegemony of these powerful groups. In Hardy's boyhood years, competing visions of how British society was constituted were a topic of vigorous debate: the Corn Law agitation alluded to in the Preface to *The Mayor of Casterbridge* was motivated by an animus against 'aristocratic misrule' and in favour of middle-class requirements. Disraeli's famous formula of the 'two nations' might have been applied with equal justification to the division between middle and upper-class groups at this time. However, the notion of monolithic socio-economic blocs was a drastic oversimplification as regards a complex and shifting situation of which both right (Disraeli and Young England) and left (Marx and Engels) were sometimes guilty. England remained a society constituted by complicated hierarchies of status in which nuances of accent, deportment and rank were crucial but ever-changing signifiers: it was the double-edged achievement of the young Hardy to negotiate his way through such treacherous zones towards a higher status.

In considering Hardy's career, then, we need to set aside a conventionally organised model of upper, middle and lower classes, since this masks and distorts the social realities of the period. Marx concluded that the Victorian middle classes in later decades had confined their energies to business and commerce (like Farfrae), and had failed to capture the real levers of power from the gentry and aristocracy, but in practice the boundaries between such 'classes', or between middle and working classes, were difficult to define. In any case, the simplistic contrast between the rich and the poor remained perhaps more visible in the burgeoning industrial centres than in the countryside, which retained a greater element of the feudal in its structure and practice. At this historical moment, society was seen as a series of social gradations or pyramidal ranks, but much ink was devoted to the issues of ascending such a pyramid, from the self-congratulatory and evangelical tone of Samuel Smiles's *Self-Help* (1859), to the tensions and self-questioning satire of *Great Expectations* (1861). Indeed, during Hardy's years as a young adult making his way in the world, the language of class was predominantly deployed to characterise the troubled decades of social upheaval during the 1830s and 1840s: class, that is to say, was opposed to the more stable notion of hierarchy. Despite the 'leap in the dark' of 1867, when the vote was awarded to a proportion of the working class, social hierarchy based in possession of land retained its hold on the British social structure. Lady Catherine de Burgh, in *Pride and Prejudice*, remarked trenchantly that she wished to have 'the distinctions of rank preserved', and this desire held good for most of her fellow-citizens throughout the century. The majority of Victorians believed, rightly or wrongly, that theirs was a stable and viably hierarchised society, and that individual identity was to be defined in terms of notions of superiority and subordination. This was a belief which Hardy, in his life as in his work, both endorsed and subverted.

In contemplating the issues raised by considerations of class in Victorian England, it is worth recalling E. P. Thompson's proposition that class is a relationship, and not a thing. Under this analysis, class is defined by men and women living their own history, and the concept of class was only realised in the conditions of nineteenth-century capital. Classes are not to be conceived of as static 'entities': they are the product of struggle or conflict, and it may be argued that Hardy's fiction demonstrates increasing awareness of this factor as a determinant in his characters' lives. The great transformation that took place within Hardy's adult life was the progressive commodification of money, land and labour, and it is this, rather than any metaphysically defined 'tragic vision', that marks the crucial distinctions between early novels such as *Under the Greenwood Tree* or *Far from the Madding Crowd* and later works such as *Tess of the d'Urbervilles* or *Jude the Obscure*. Hardy's novels trace and refract a national experience whereby work leaves the home, cross-class households are dispersed, and residential communities become segregated through the indices of class.

There is significant separation between home and work in this period (contradictorily experienced by Hardy's both living and working at Max Gate). Parallel to this is the fact that class relations are experienced not only at work but also at home. Classes are formed by groups with shared dispositions, whether of the 'rustics' of Weatherbury, the slum-dwellers of Mixen Lane, or the middling people such as Bathsheba or Clym Yeobright. Class, as Thompson remarks, is a 'junction term', uniting structure and process; the kind of structural changes to which Hardy bore witness in his movement away from a village economy give rise to a radically changed experience of life. As Hardy remarks in his essay on 'The Dorsetshire Labourer',[2] change is also a sort of education, and for Hardy, this is an education not only in class but in gender. In his fiction and poetry Hardy is alert not only to general questions of class formation but also to sexual difference, conceived not simply as 'natural' but read as socially implicated with gender, sexuality and the family. Inequalities of class are matched and echoed, in Wessex as elsewhere in Victorian society, by inequalities of gender. A nuanced reading of, say, *The Hand of Ethelberta* or *Two on a Tower*, offers a counterbalance to readings of class and gender as a universal set of categories, and it is part of the project of *Tess* or *Jude* to rescue the late-Victorian woman from invisibility. Class is also inseparable from language, and the range and variety of language types assembled by Hardy bears witness to his fine ear for this type of registration. In general, it may be suggested, his novels handle dialect and other class-marked forms with increasing gravity and seriousness: there is a resonance in the dialogue of the rural population of *The Mayor* or *Tess* which is absent in the diatribes of William Worm (*A Pair of Blue Eyes*) or Joseph Poorgrass (*Far from the Madding Crowd*). Hardy's attention was increasingly concentrated upon what we might term the 'true people' of England, those who had been exiled from their birthright, and whose culture was embedded in dialect patterns and folklore customs. Tess may not represent the death of the peasantry, as Arnold Kettle proposed,[3] but she does represent and embody the cultural memory of a dispossessed class fraction.

Consideration of class in Victorian England needs to bear in mind that, although that society was subject to crucial and far-reaching transformations, the extent of the change was more limited than at first appeared. Older patterns of behaviour and value retained their validity, as the nation never acquired a clearly identifiable bourgeois or industrial elite. Accommodations between aristocracy and bourgeoisie meant continuous adaptation, whilst the retreat of the aristocracy was more political than psychological, the landed gentry giving way only slowly to the newly empowered industrialists. The raw industrialisation of the early nineteenth century was humanised and contained by ruling groups with an interest in land and property, and subordinate fractions such as the provincial middle class would internalise the values of their 'betters' by increasingly abandoning the prior culture of the countryside with its roots in oral tradition and folk festivities, matters which were to gain a good deal of Hardy's attention.

In *Young Thomas Hardy*, Robert Gittings uncovered a lower-class network of relations which he argued Hardy had deliberately suppressed or censored – 'labourers, cobblers, bricklayers, carpenters, farm servants, journeyman joiners, butlers ... cooks, house-servants, [and] ladies' maids'. Hardy's claims about his father's status appear to have deviated from the fact: Thomas Hardy senior was, when his son was born in 1840, a self-employed mason; by 1850 he had become a bricklayer employing two fellow-labourers. It was not until 1860 that he was to be designated master-mason, now employing six labourers. At the time of his death in 1892, as Gittings notes, Hardy senior possessed some considerable property in the local area.[4] Certainly Hardy's fiction and his autobiography reveal that the focus of his interest is in the 'metamorphic classes of society', as he calls them in *The Hand of Ethelberta* (chapter 39) – that class fraction of village artisans, neither farmers nor labourers, to which his own family belonged. As the child of a small-time master-mason and a woman who had been raised on parish relief, Hardy had been something of an autodidact, disabled from university education but raising himself into professional ranks first as an architect and subsequently as a writer, and marrying a woman whose self-consciously genteel origins were within the professional middle class. Hardy was reluctant to discuss his own social origins, and this censorship is mirrored in protagonists such as Stephen Smith and Ethelberta Petherwin: the young architect Smith is rejected by the Rev. Swancourt when he turns out to be 'the son of one of my village peasants', and Ethelberta, who through her storytelling and then through marriage gains entrée to the upper class, is habitually secretive about belonging to a family of servants. Hardy's background was similarly humble, and like Smith, he was to rise through marriage. In his fiction generally, marriage is often an instrument of social advancement, and it is notable that his lost first novel, 'The Poor Man and the Lady' (significantly 'by the Poor Man'), was concerned with a love affair between an heiress and a son of the soil. This was a situation the youthful Hardy had experienced when, as a boy, he was taken up by the plutocratic Julia Augusta Martin of Kingston Maurward House, in an act of semi-maternal patronage broken off by Jemima Hardy. It was Hardy's apprenticeship to a local architect which first enabled him, unlike his brother Henry, to transform his unpromising social origins, but it was the assumption of authorship that ultimately translated him into the middle class. Indeed, the years of his maturity were marked not only by an abandonment of his early socialistic ideals but by a fascinated involvement with aristocratic circles in the London season. Behind the eminent author, it may be, there lurked the ghosts of those lower-class relations consigned to silence. For Hardy, the issue of class is therefore intimately entwined with his problematic entry into the Victorian literary field: a zone, as Pierre Bourdieu has argued, that possesses its own laws and structures.[5] Writers at this juncture possessed a changeable and precarious status relative to their competitors and to the field of literary production.

Hardy, for instance, experienced a rapid accession of cultural authority from the publication of *A Pair of Blue Eyes*, by the unscrupulous William

Tinsley, to that of *Far from the Madding Crowd* under the auspices of the eminent man of letters, Leslie Stephen. Publishers invested their books with prestige in a process Bourdieu nominates 'symbolic production', and this is how cultural status is conferred upon a text. Writers, under this analysis, are implicated in a network of values which is grounded in the social structure of the field: the writer is thus always entangled in class movement and currents, his/her status ineluctably tied to the work of cultural production. For Hardy, as for other writers of this period such as Gissing, James or Sarah Grand, there is a conflict between large-scale (popular) production and restricted (aesthetic) production, a conflict exacerbated by the practice of magazine serialisation. Writing as a commercial activity is thus contrasted with writing which has a specific aesthetic value.

Hardy attempted to negotiate this complex terrain by abandoning the large-scale field of fiction for the aesthetically 'purer' field of poetry, in a move which is itself resonant with class aspirations and motives. A writer's origins clearly influence his/her conduct as a holder of a specific position, and Bourdieu's concept of 'habitus' (a socially learned second nature) is of value here. As an autodidact moving from the rural sub-class of his relatives, Hardy was compelled to learn a cultural language that was foreign to him, as it was not, for example, to Henry James or Oscar Wilde. Hardy's literary career, in which he traced a trajectory from popular sensation forms (*Desperate Remedies*) through rural realism towards purist aestheticism (*The Well-Beloved*, the poetry), reduplicates or refracts his changing class position: writer as storyteller is replaced by writer as bard. In his measured revolt against what Edmund Gosse termed 'the disease which we may call Mudieitis', Hardy ranged himself with the avant-garde whilst continuing (as in the amendments to the serial version of *Tess*) to compromise and to ally himself with the popular market: like his heroine, Tess, we might say, Hardy spoke the two languages of culture, the popular and the elite. As a writer dedicated to the representation of a changing rural world, Hardy repeatedly re-enacts scenarios of his own class and class-fraction positions; his practice in relation to the signifying system of class relations in the late-Victorian countryside is fraught with inconsistency. Hardy's novels and poems are not totalising or rationalised responses to crisis personal and social, but fluctuating and fissured literary responses changing over the period of his long career, deeply rooted in class and family positions but never identical with them.

A number of Hardy's more radically minded critics have made significant contributions to the debate about class in Hardy's life and

work. In his complex study, *Thomas Hardy: The Offensive Truth*, John Goode argues that Hardy's work is centred on the act of writing, and that the writing age is one of dislocation and urbanisation. Writing gives access to knowledge for those previously culturally excluded and in this sense possesses a radical potential that, for instance, the story of Jude's career explores and defines. The key to Goode's dense analysis of the novels is the concept of ideology, predicated as a set of strategies of containment or as a language through which human beings live and survive. The phase of industrial capital in full swing at Hardy's birth is characterised by a co-ordination of nature and human experience. As Goode puts it:

> The self becomes decentered by history, by evolution, by the need to negotiate the complex demands of a social network which is alien but undeniable.[6]

Goode sees Hardy as a writer who co-operates with the literary market so as to gain professional success and 'rise' from his rural origins, but who simultaneously subverts the orientation of that market. This subversion is muted in early work such as *Far from the Madding Crowd*, but in its later counterpart, *The Woodlanders*, the 'communal nature of work is shadowed by actual conditions of production' so that 'the wheat actually embodies itself not as food but as its exchange value' (p. 97) – a remark that echoes Richard Jefferies's memorable formulation, in his bitterly ironic depiction of the living conditions of an agricultural labourer, that 'The wheat is beautiful, but human life is labour.'[7] This is the underlying meaning, for Goode, of the famous depiction of the woodland trees and their internecine struggle with each other. *The Woodlanders* is thus a novel in which, crucially, sexual politics cuts across class relations in ways dramatically exemplified by both Fitzpiers and Grace, and Goode goes on to develop this theme further in his extended polemical analysis of *Tess of the d'Urbervilles*. One strand of this novel, he suggests, is concerned with the way in which Tess 'is made to pay as a working-class woman for the desire of the middle-class males' (p. 128). The tendency of the final sequence of the novel, Flintcomb-Ash, the Lady Day migration, or the allotment scene, is to put Tess 'in her class again'. The silencing of Tess is accompanied by the bestowal of a voice, the voice of a dispossessed *class*, upon the reader; the work of reading, that is to say, '*puts the reader through* the primary working-class experience': 'Prostitution is the ultimate capitalist relationship for the woman' (p. 131). The logical outcome of such a theme, Goode argues, is *Jude the Obscure*, which he re-reads as a political intervention in the key issues – marriage law, theology, education and class – of the 1890s. If education and the family form the Althusserian frame of late-capitalism, the peripatetic structure of Hardy's final novel serves to enforce dis-location and arbitrariness: both Christminster and Marygreen are 'about the condition of the working class' (p. 142), whilst Melchester and Shaston concern themselves primarily with training and marriage. Jude's career, thus, refracts that of his creator: as Goode perceives it, Hardy's relation with writing is dialectical, 'both an institution which has to be negotiated and an agency of self-improvement' (p. 142). Even the sacred writing of the New Testament is reinflected in this novel, citation of the epistle to the Corinthians, for instance, operating 'as a document of human experience that privileges love, sex and the resistance to oppression' (p. 144). The 'educated proletariat' invoked in H. G. Wells's review of *Jude* is a contradiction in terms: 'to be educated (led out) is to cease to be proletarian' (p. 145). In *Jude the Obscure* may be heard the 'heterodox voice that is the voice of the future tied dependently into the discourse of the present' (p. 170), in an entanglement of class, religion and sexuality so complex that Hardy could never again return to large-scale fiction. As Goode remarks, *Jude* 'is a novel which calls for a reply, and still awaits it' (p. 170).

In his equally fertile study, *The Hidden Hardy*, Joe Fisher adopts a different strategy, focusing upon the market potential of Hardy's texts and their insertion into the literary industry. The principal means of such insertion is the exploitative concoction of 'Wessex', a device which allows Hardy to participate ambivalently in the commodification of literature. Serial publication, and the censorship involved in this process, enable a capitalist form of control over the production of texts, but Hardy attempts to participate in a 'disruptive moment of class struggle' by making his texts both obedient to, and subversive of, 'the hegemonic authority of library buyers and magazine editors'.[8] Hardy, that is to say, 'trades' on the raw material of Wessex, thereby acquiring cultural power and a kind of political platform. Whilst Hardy necessarily achieves his project by largely silencing the emergence of a working-class consciousness in Dorset at this time of the Great Depression, his disruptions proceed stealthily to undermine current ideology. There is therefore, in Fisher's analysis, a perceptible and telling gap between the 'traded' and 'narrated' texts produced by a subtle process of self-subversion. The 'hidden Hardy' of his title is a writer who produces cartoons of a 'Swiftian brutality' (p. 8) overlaid by a more acceptable veneer of material in a contract with the reader that is essentially patriarchal: 'Both women and workers are commodities presented as objects of consumption and control' (p. 10). Within such an equation, sexuality stands for the working class whilst femininity is middle class. But whilst female sexuality is replaced, in this fiction, by a more acceptable male voyeurism, the 'insistent presence of sexuality and the self-consciousness of the erotic surveillance become an ever-present subversion' (p. 13). The enforced deferences of gender and class mean that Hardy's use of the (concealed) sexual act 'becomes an attack on the naturalised alienation and deference of the workfolk and small traders he uses to represent the "natural" and "organic" Wessex' (p. 13). The writing of woman and the writing of landscape are clear equivalents here, both 'equally and transparently artificial' (p. 14), yet simultaneously such texts as *Far from the Madding Crowd* or *Tess* contain 'the machinery of a counter-text which subverts and contradicts [their] "traded" and more easily visible narrative surface' (p. 15).

Hardy in History, Peter Widdowson's defining essay on class in Hardy's writing, largely concurs with this analysis since, as he argues, 'the pressure, and suppression, of acute class consciousness are intimately related in Hardy's work'. He goes on:

> Hardy's social origins in a specific class fraction in mid nineteenth-century Dorset are, of course, important, but only within the frame of the upwardly-mobile professional writer operating in a metropolitan, upper-class dominated, social and literary culture.[9]

Widdowson pertinaciously traces Hardy's class origins, locating him accurately within that 'intermediate class' of rural artisans and craftsmen, and noting his mother's pauper background and autodidactic motivation. The 'complex and shifting composition of the class of Hardy's origins' (p. 131) meant that he had connections with labourers, craftsmen, and with other more upwardly mobile elements within the village economy. But it is Hardy's role as writer that ultimately defines his position, and the tension between this and his rural origins marks all his work. If education proved to be an escape route for Hardy, his failure to enter Cambridge left him with a sense of 'being only partly educated in terms of conventional, upper-class criteria' (p. 133). It was literature rather than architecture which offered him a career structure not pre-determined by class factors, but it was still a field dominated by educated upper-middle-class 'gatekeepers' such as John Morley and Leslie Stephen, two of Hardy's early mentors. In becoming a writer, Fisher suggests, Hardy 'had a careful eye on the market and its requirements' (p. 134), exemplified in both his accommodation with, and protests against, the moral and aesthetic pressures of periodical publication. In his disguised autobography Hardy (mis)represents himself, after the success of *Far from the Madding Crowd*, as 'literary man-about-town and the familiar of noble people', now that he has effectively joined 'that other class, the Victorian intelligentsia' (p. 137), and one consequence of this is his increasing concern to conceal his class origins. Paradoxically at this point in his career he produces the anti-pastoral *The Hand of Ethelberta*, a novel 'obsessively concerned with class relations, with class deception, and with his heroine's upward social mobility assisted by the composition of "fictions"' (pp. 137–8). The contradictions involved in the production of the later novels of social critique exemplify, for Widdowson, the way Hardy 'lies athwart the whole system'; in this light he is

> the lower-class rural man who has entered the educated and privileged domain of a metropolitan cultural class, and cannot admit his origins; the poet who is forced to be a novelist in order to succeed, and who becomes popular and respected as the latter; the serious and radical writer of fiction who must accommodate his work to the commercial and ethical pressures of late-Victorian serial publication. (p. 138)

The literary result is that 'clash of modes' which many readers of Hardy have noted; but more specifically Widdowson goes on to propose that the *Life of Thomas Hardy* is a fiction passed off under the name of the writer's second wife. This is a work of such elaborate 'deception' as to be resistant to interpretation, a presentation of Hardy for posterity 'as he wishes to be regarded' (p. 140). This is especially the case in the revealingly small space Hardy allocated to his early years, since 'as a *petit-bourgeois arriviste*, he could not speak of his social origins' (p. 141). Thus we have that telling insistence, in the *Life*, on the Hardys as a family of long-standing yeoman stock which is now in decline. Widdowson deals trenchantly with the sins of omission here, and connects them with the author's insistence on the absence of autobiographical elements in the fiction. It is notable, for example, that Stephen Smith, Clym Yeobright or Jude Fawley are emphatically claimed to be 'unlike' their creator. This is balanced by the often 'tedious' catalogues of the Hardys' noble or famous acquaintances, whilst the writer constantly stresses his disdain for social climbing – all classic symptoms, in Widdowson's account, of 'an inferiority complex, in which a disdainful superiority protects Hardy from admitting the desired participation' in a constant process of 'many-layered and schizophrenic

deception' (p. 147). The absence of any definable political position in
Hardy's work, producing a 'passive, apolitical alternativism (characteristic
of liberal humanism)' (p. 149), is equally symptomatic of the confusions
in Hardy's sense of class allegiance: the homely system-building that
produces the Immanent Will and the Chorus of the Pities emanates
from that depoliticised eclecticism so evident in the literary notebooks.
Widdowson also traces the impact of Hardy's career trajectory on his
treatment of women both fictional and real, which he sees as a mixture
of fascination and contempt, and on his presentation of himself as poet
rather than novelist: 'the image of "the poet" is more suitable than that
of the toiling novelist sweating away in the commercial purlieus of the
publishing trade':

> When Hardy could afford to stop writing fiction, he did; and *The Life*,
> in its incessant obsession with class and status, constructs an image of
> the true poet, 'instinctive and disinterested', freed now from even the
> taint of writing fiction (tainted, because it had been the escape route
> from his class origins). (pp. 153–4)

In contrast with Widdowson, in a fertile Bakhtinian discussion of
the language of gender and class in Victorian Britain, Patricia Ingham
perceives a linguistic differentiation in representations of the working
class, which projects them as improvident and dependent, indeed
animalistic in character. This strategy of subordination was reinforced by
the 'sign' of a model of womanliness notably absent from the squalor and
promiscuity ascribed to the lower orders. The constitution of the middle-
class home as a 'haven' removed from the (masculinist) marketplace led
to the phenomenon of 'the Angel in the House', a creature of sensibility,
selflessness, tepid asexuality and weak intellect. Thus, 'the signs for
middle-class femininity/domesticity and for the fallen woman hold
together a coding of society in which the working classes are represented
as irrational, immoral and in need of restraint'.[10] As the century proceeds,
these ideological codings begin to come under strain, and traces of this
collapse are especially located in the narrative voice of Victorian fiction;
in fact we should more properly see the novel in Bakhtinian terms as
a 'multi-voiced' form, and nowhere more so than in the fiction of the
1890s which focuses and refracts the contentious issues surrounding
the New Woman and the fears attendant upon the emergence of an
'intermediate sex'. For Ingham, the guiding voice of *Jude the Obscure* is
no longer a middle-class one:

He does not condescend to the working class. They are no longer
treated as a group but as individuals with different stories, against
which dominant ideologies can, dangerously, be tested. (p. 164)

A number of Hardy's novels are significantly marked by an equation
between talented working-class males (Stephen Smith, Egbert Mayne,
Swithin St Cleeve) and all women. *Jude* shows how the church underpins
and manages class distinctions, and the conventions of the period connive
in this attempted restriction of opportunity. The Smilesian principle
of advancement which was such an evident motivation in Victorian
society is blocked and traduced here not only by economics but also
by the traditional classics-based educational curriculum Jude's bitterly
disappointed expectations run parallel to Sue's in her struggle with the
social and marital role of women, a struggle parodically shadowed by
Arabella. Whilst it is Tess's fate to subsume 'in her identity all members
of the working class', Sue 'challenges the divisions between the classes as
well as the complementarity that defines women and men' (p. 182).

   This group of critics, along with others writing in the wake of the rise
of critical theory, have implicitly or explicitly rejected the 'cosmic' or
'tragic' readings of Hardy proposed by earlier readers, favouring instead
a critique founded in historical process and accentuating the social and
material bases of his writing project. For critics of this school, influenced
by Raymond Williams's key work in the field, *The Country and the City*
(1973), analysis begins with history; only through such an approach can
the complexities of the text and the implications of the author's own
class position be productively interrogated. It is therefore the case, for
instance, that neither nature nor mechanisation of themselves cause
Tess's sufferings; on the contrary, the Flintcomb-Ash scenes of the novel
represent a 'calvary of labour' (in Merryn Williams's telling phrase)
because of the prevailing relations of production.[11] A fully responsive
and responsible reading of *Tess of the d'Urbervilles* needs therefore to take
account of the contradictions inherent in agrarian capital The romantic
model of an arcadian nature disrupted and destroyed by an invading
urbanisation obfuscates what Hardy's writing is doing: Talbothays dairy,
for example, has been compelled to become a capitalist enterprise tied
to the London milk market, and throughout the novel Tess functions
not as a peasant rooted in the local soil but as a proletarian who must
travel to sell her labour. It is the separation of trade and labour which
Hardy often delineates in ways that reveal his unconscious affiliation with
the village artisan class formation, an element of the village economy

that was of itself a recent development in nineteenth-century England. The craftsmen lose their base in the village economy and progressively move to the town in a movement memorably chronicled in George Bourne's *Change in the Village* (1912). Hardy's novels are underscored by the conflict between agrarian capital and the small artisan in the countryside, and often refer to the displacement of cottagers and 'liviers' and the consequent new mobility in the labour force. The comments in Hardy's 1895 Preface to *Far from the Madding Crowd* are pertinent here; discussing the loss of community, he avers:

> The change at the root of this has been the recent supplanting of the class of stationary cottagers, who carried on the local traditions and humours, by a population of more or less migratory labourers, which has led to a break in continuity in local history, more fatal than any other thing to the preservation of legend, folk-lore, close inter-social relations, and eccentric individualities. For these the indispensable conditions of existence are attachment to the soil of one particular spot by generation after generation.[12]

Hardy's overview of the agricultural class was most usefully crystallised a few years earlier in his essay on 'The Dorsetshire Labourer', which appeared in *Longman's Magazine* in July 1883 as part of a series on contemporary rural conditions to which Richard Jefferies also contributed. Hardy argues here that the conventional image of 'Hodge' as a rustic boor does not coincide with reality and he urges the point that, 'although in their future there are only the workhouse and the grave', the labourers do in fact derive a degree of satisfaction from their existence: 'A pure atmosphere and a pastoral environment are a very appreciable portion of their sustenance which tends to produce the sound mind and body, and thus much sustenance is, at least, the labourer's birthright.' Hardy is especially anxious to establish the point, in this essay and elsewhere, that the Dorset dialect, 'instead of being a vile corruption of cultivated speech, was a tongue with grammatical inflection': 'Having attended the National School they would mix the printed tongue as taught therein with the unwritten, dying, Wessex English.' Hardy adopted a somewhat Darwinian view of this linguistic process, with all its ramifications as a class marker. In his selection of the poems of the dialect poet William Barnes, for instance, he claimed that in recent times 'education in the west of England as elsewhere has gone on with its silent and inevitable effacements, reducing the speech of this county to uniformity, and obliterating every year many a fine old local word'.[13] In the Dorset labourer essay, Hardy goes on to explain the false view of the agricultural worker that had arisen from the vantage point of 'philosophers who look down upon the class from the Olympian heights of society', often misconstruing cleanliness for dirt in the cottages they deigned to visit. To observe the labourer genuinely *in extremis*, Hardy contends, he should be viewed participating in a wet hiring-fair at Candlemas (2 February), and he provides a grim portrait of a superannuated shepherd hopelessly awaiting employment – a passage he would draw upon in the scene of Farfrae hiring the aged shepherd in *The Mayor*. He notes that the clothing worn at such fairs has become progressively darker and more uniform with that worn in towns, and he contrasts it with the smock-frock, shepherds' crooks and other more picturesque features of previous generations. At Old Lady Day (6 April) Hardy discerns a general post in the countryside, with the labourer's furniture, belongings and family piled up on the wagon sent by his new employer. At this juncture, the roads are full of movement, reflecting what the novelist perceives as a migratory increase throughout the rural economy. A loss of picturesque qualities generally is inevitable, he concedes, but he memorably insists, 'Change is also a certain sort of education': 'Many advantages accrue to the labourers from the varied experience it brings, apart from the discovery of the best market for their abilities.' The agricultural labourers are thus 'losing their peculiarities as a class' and the 'increasing nomadic habit' is necessarily leading to 'a less intimate and kindly relation with the land he tills'. On the other hand, this class is becoming more independent-minded largely due to the efforts of Joseph Arch, leader of the agricultural union movement. As a result of union activity, the wage of eight or nine shillings has been increased at a time of depression, a fact that demonstrates that the labourer 'must have been greatly wronged' in more prosperous days. In general, however, Hardy laments the depopulation proceeding apace in rural counties, a process, he argues, that has specially affected that 'interesting and better-informed class' of village artisans to which the Hardys belonged, whose life-holdings are falling into desuetude as part of the general drift to towns. His conclusion is that 'the question of the Dorset cottager here merges in that of all the houseless and landless poor'.[14]

In recent years the verisimilitude and reliability of Hardy's account of the field labourers in both his essay and his fiction, so widely accepted by his critics, has been called into question. The economic historian K. D. M. Snell has argued cogently that boundaries need to be carefully set as to what a writer 'may know and be able to express of his society and its social structure', in order to understand 'in what areas his knowledge is likely to be limited, occluded, or distorted'. Hardy's emphasis upon the newly migratory tendency in the lives of the fieldworkers is open to question in Snell's account, which argues that the system of annual hiring fairs had long provided 'an institutional nexus for mobility via the statute fairs'. It is thus possible that the alienation from a 'primal' place was 'based on a nostalgic fiction of the past', and Snell urges the point that Hardy's writing tends to efface the evidence that conditions in Dorset were 'about the most squalid and depressed living standards to be found in England', and went along with 'the most embittered class relations'.[15] In my own critique of the Dorset labourer essay, I have stressed the way in which Hardy 'is concerned largely to express a sense of inevitable process and change in which the field-labourers are ineluctably caught up'. By viewing social and linguistic change as dominated by Darwinian law, Hardy is blind to the sense that language is 'a site of conflict where different material interests state their separate claims to hegemony and meaning'. The essay, in its descriptive fluency, is 'visually submissive', tending to reify and silence the subjects of its discourse in a process which, I suggest, may be directly attributed to the contradictions inherent in Hardy's own class position. It is this that produces 'the fertile ambiguity of the fiction and the flawed weakness of the sociological essay'.[16] Hardy's portrayal of the rustic class is mediated by his internalisation of bourgeois values – he is sympathetic to their class subordination whilst at the same time distancing himself from them. The instabilities he attributes to late-Victorian rural society are largely those attendant on the threatened position of the class fraction of his own family – the hagglers, traders and artisans who were beginning to suffer loss of livelihood and a consequent move towards the role of itinerant worker. On the whole, the novels tend to endorse middle-class values by stressing the emotional and intellectual distinction of the middle-class protagonists who occupy that cultural, social and educational 'borderland' of which Raymond Williams wrote so eloquently. The overall, unconscious project of Hardy's writing career is thus to legitimise the cultural power of the middle class by contrasting it with upper-class reliance on land, money and title. Whilst he expands the boundaries of the Victorian novel by his inclusion of the rural workforce, his leading characters are marked by qualities of gentility and spirituality that elude this class. He set out to distinguish the rustics by emphasising their individuality – Leaf's simple-mindedness in *Under the Greenwood Tree* being contrasted with William Dewy's sagacity, or Worm's mental fish-frying in *A Pair of Blue Eyes* set against Mrs Smith's canny social ambitions, for instance. Whilst the overall effect is undoubtedly to imbue his narratives with enlivening local colour, such characters also serve to dramatise class issues and to retard or divert narrative trajectories – witness Poorgrass's drinking bout in *Far from the Madding Crowd* which leads to the discovery of Troy's affair with Fanny, or Christian Cantle's gambling away the spade guineas in *The Return of the Native* in a scene that will bring to a head the tension between Clym, Eustacia and Mrs Yeobright. Class conflicts, often treated comically in the early novels, carry a more bitter charge later: thus the proletarian skimmity-ride in *The Mayor* embarrasses Farfrae, exposes Henchard and effectively kills Lucetta. If these and other 'folk' actions, such as Susan Nunsuch's stabbing of Eustacia, are viewed in a Bakhtinian light as orchestrating, in the unconscious of the text, the claims of the 'grotesque body', they do not axiomatically endorse such claims. Rather, the tendency is for the 'rustic chorus' to be contrasted, in their humour and ignorance, with the more aspiring and upwardly mobile characters. Stephen Smith offers a telling instance of the fissures in Victorian constructions of class: as a product of a village culture who has trained as an architect, he is poised between classes in an awkward trajectory of self-improvement, an awkwardness tellingly examined when he returns home to be greeted by the celebratory but socially humiliating pig-killing ceremony. As an autodidact, like his creator, Smith finds his path strewn with difficulties in relation to the gentry society embodied in the snobbish parson, Mr Swancourt, whose hypocrisies are dramatically revealed in his own clandestine and materialistically motivated second marriage. This sense of a character shifting uneasily between class positions is developed with subtle variants in the later fiction, from Gabriel Oak through Diggory Venn to Grace Melbury. However, it is clear that *The Woodlanders*, along with Hardy's other late fiction, is more pessimistic about the process of social advancement: Melbury's scheme for his daughter's marriage backfires tragically, whilst she herself is able to embrace neither the vapidly empty life of the aristocratic Felice Charmond nor the working-class authenticity, harshness and physicality of Winterborne and Marty South. It is only in the final novels that Hardy allows himself explicitly to take the working class as his subject.

I turn, in conclusion, to a brief consideration of one major text, *The Mayor of Casterbridge* (1886), in order to tease out some of the implications of these class issues for Hardy's writing project. This is the one novel by Hardy in which class predominates over those questions of sexual relationship that so concern him, and it is a work that examines and illuminates a view of class which is both economic and ideological. From the dramatised scene of the wife-sale onwards, *The Mayor* repeatedly illustrates the governing principle of an emergent capitalist system founded in exchange and substitution – the exchange of Susan and her baby for Newson's five guineas, the substitution of the spoilt by the restored grain, the 'replacement' of one Elizabeth-Jane by another, Lucetta's transfer of favours from Henchard to Farfrae, the reinstatement of the mayor as Susan's husband, for example. The narrator's insistence that 'Character is Fate'[17] might be reinflected by a query of Walter Benjamin's:

> Isn't there a certain structure of money that can be recognised only in fate, and a certain structure of fate that can be recognised only in money?[18]

This 'fate' is embedded in the capitalist principle of exchange as neatly expounded by one of the onlookers in the tent at Weydon Priors fair:

> 'For my part I don't see why men who have got wives and don't want 'em, shouldn't get rid of 'em as these gipsy fellows do their old horses,' said the man in the tent. 'Why shouldn't they put 'em up and sell 'em by auction to men who are in need of such articles?' (I, p. 9)

But the drama of this scene of patriarchal divestment of responsibility gains its deepest resonance in the context of the massive social changes that the novel envisages, and in which it intervenes. Casterbridge is the second term of the title and provides the locus for the main action. Hardy describes its layout in attentive detail, and the marketplace, overlooked by High Place Hall, significantly forms the central arena of the action, 'like the regulation Open Place in spectacular dramas' (XXIV, p. 126). Exchange is at the heart of the economy and has led to the formation of the carefully registered social hierarchies that mark and designate the spaces of the town, notably in the case of the three hostelries: the King's Arms, literally and symbolically the highest, is the setting for the mayoral dinner, the initial meeting between Henchard and Farfrae, and the bankruptcy proceedings. The Three Mariners occupies a middling position, its regulars being 'of a grade somewhat below that of the diners at the King's Arms' (VI, p. 34), and is the favoured haunt of Christopher Coney, Solomon Longways and others who comment on the action. But even here there are class gradations of some nicety to be observed: the occupants, when Farfrae, Elizabeth-Jane and Susan first arrive, 'in addition to the respectable master-tradesmen occupying the seats of privilege in the bow-window and its neighbourhood, included an inferior set at the unlighted end' (VIII, p. 40). The Mariners is the venue for two contrasting episodes, the performance of Farfrae's sentimental Scottish songs and the doleful recitation of Psalm 109 which the newly alcoholic Henchard orders to be sung as a curse upon his rival. The third inn, 'the church of Mixen Lane', is Peter's Finger, haunt of the poachers and the down and out, where the skimmity-ride is planned. Even the two bridges preserve these class distinctions, the one closer to town being reserved for those of low estate whilst the more distant one is the haunt of more eminent townspeople fallen on hard times.

Although the town is thus riven with class dissension and difference, the narrative insists upon the organic connection between town and country:

> The agricultural and pastoral character of the people upon whom the town depended for its existence was shown by the class of objects displayed in the shop windows. Scythes, reap-hooks, sheep-shears, bill-hooks, spades, mattocks, and hoes at the iron-monger's, bee-hives, butter-firkins, churns, milking stools and pails, hay-rakes, field-flagons, and seed-lips at the cooper's ... (IV, pp. 24–5)

There is no abrupt transition from urban to rural; economically and culturally there is a fusion of interest, and ecological integration:

> Bees and butterflies in the cornfields at the top of the town, who desired to get to the meads at the bottom, took no circuitous course, but flew straight down High Street without any apparent consciousness that they were traversing strange latitudes. (IX, p. 46)

Despite this arcadian note, *The Mayor* lays bare those factors whereby the self-sufficiency of the rural economy is undermined by urban patterns of consumption, the static feudal order partly embodied in Henchard being dismantled by the free action of the exchange principle that he unwittingly sets in train at the wife-sale. Through such acts, Marx observed, 'all ties of personal dependence, distinctions of birth, education ... are in fact broken, abolished': 'The individuals *appear* to be independent ... appear to collide with one another freely, and to exchange with one another in this freedom.'[19] The newly created solitary individual – Henchard, torn from his family, the apparently rootless Farfrae, the seafaring Newson

– is the characteristic subject of modernity; indeed subjectivity is levelled out under the law of exchange, the more malleable Farfrae gaining gradual ascendancy over the obdurate mayor. Class in Casterbridge is ineluctably tied to those economic conditions whereby, as Marx phrases it, 'commodities are in love with money'[20] – indeed this may be termed the true love interest of a novel in which sexual passion is at a low ebb. The characters engage in a circular round of attachment and detachment which dazzlingly illustrates that 'conversion of things into persons and the conversion of persons into things' that Marx detects going on under capital, and which reaches its climax in Henchard's sighting of his own effigy at Ten-Hatches weir. In such a world, 'Circulation sweats money from every pore.'[21] The process of commodification affects all the characters indifferently, but none more so than Lucetta, a 'flighty and unsettled' individual (XXII, p. 116) who lives through flirtation and self-display. When the two dresses arrive from a London fashion house, Lucetta arranges them on the bed to suggest human figures, explaining to Elizabeth-Jane, 'You are that person … or you are *that* totally different person … for the whole of the coming spring' (XXIV, p. 127). In the skimmity-ride this self-projection is cruelly parodied. As the commentary of the two maids indicates, the skimmity figure is dressed 'just as *she* was dressed' (significantly at the theatre): 'She's me – she's me – even to the parasol – my green parasol,' cries Lucetta falling into a fit (XXXIX, pp. 210–11). As a type, Lucetta is symptomatic of a more general trend that the demise of Henchard serves to highlight – what may be termed an increasing impersonalisation that afflicts so many of the characters: Susan Henchard, Donald Farfrae, even Elizabeth-Jane, are all marked by a certain anonymity by comparison with the mayor in his rough-hewn integrity. In the nineteenth century, Walter Benjamin suggests

> the number of 'hollowed out' things increases at a rate and on a scale that was previously unknown, for technical progress is continually withdrawing newly introduced objects from circulation.[22]

The coming of the railway to Casterbridge and Farfrae's introduction of the seed drill are only the most notable instances of this general process. The model of a countryside invaded by technology needs to be modified in favour of a more nuanced interpretive strategy that would stress the way in which the expansion of a class based on trade in a predominantly agrarian society is to be equated with the expansion of capital. Henchard, we might claim, is a proto-capitalist in his transformation from day-labourer to corn merchant and mayor, whilst retaining elements of a feudal oral culture: thus, the narrator refers to Henchard as 'mentally and physically unfit for grubbing subtleties from soiled paper' (XII, p. 60), and notes how, with the installation of Farfrae as manager, the 'old crude viva voce system ... in which everything depended upon his memory, and bargains were made by the tongue alone' is swept away by the Scotsman's 'letters and ledgers' (XIV, p. 70). This attachment to the oral is part of a kind of heroic, animistic communal culture nicely embodied in Henchard's visit to Conjuror Fall, but the contradictions between town and country which in some sense the mayor and Farfrae embody are to be seen, in Marx's phrase, as 'the crassest expression of the subjection of the individual to the division of labour, to a specific activity forced upon him' in a general instantiation of class society.[23] By divesting himself of family ties Henchard transforms himself into a 'primitive' accumulator of capital: his career encapsulates within its span that large-scale trajectory whereby the characteristic relations of production of feudalism give way to those of capitalism, a peasant economy making way for a newly class-oriented social structure. Henchard's career, in its upward and downward movement, effectively enacts the Marxian principle that men make their own history, but they do so within those conditions studiously memorialised in the novel – the destruction of feudal bonds, the increasing dependence and self-aggrandisement of rural traders and commodity producers, and the contested establishment of principles of civic governance.

Casterbridge is, however, a contradictory space, conceived both as a site of modernity and respectability – the mayoralty, the visit of the royal personage, the policing of Constable Stubberd and the magistrates' bench – and at the same time what Buzzford characterises as 'a old, hoary place o' wickedness' (VIII, p. 42) with its roots in prehistory, its Roman remains, its pool for the disposal of bastard infants, and its ancient Ring overlaid by gruesome memories of public executions. The outburst of 'rough music' in the skimmity-ride may gesture towards popular carnival, a symbolic inversion and subversion of authority, but it is also an expression of class conflict, brief but potent resistance to the ideology of the market that has created the stratified society of the modern borough with its excluded and liminal annexe in Mixen Lane. The 'freedom' and 'equality' of the market, to which Farfrae will adhere, are specious or illusory forms of the social relations of production, a point neatly made when the Scotsman lowers his employees' wages. Henchard's spectacular failed gamble in speculating on harvest prices and scarcity is only the most obvious example in the novel of the way urban principles of capital infiltrate a rural economy in a process which culminates in the 'victory' of Farfrae. The events taking place in Casterbridge articulate and embody the principle that urbanisation and ruralisation are opposite sides of the same process of the capitalist division of labour, or, as Benjamin phrases it, 'There is an effort to master the new experiences of the city within the framework of the old traditional experiences of nature.'[24]

Henchard's rise in society, following the debacle of the wife-sale, is marked and fuelled by rigorous self-abnegation, his career aptly mirroring Marx's diagnosis of the way the 'cult of money has its corresponding asceticism, its renunciation, its self-sacrifice'.[25] This homology has been most suggestively traced by Max Weber in *The Protestant Ethic and the Rise of Capitalism* (1905) and elsewhere. Weber characterises the feudal, to which Henchard still partly adheres, as a 'sphere of strict traditionalism' paradoxically combined with 'free arbitrariness and lordly grace'.[26] Interestingly, recalling Henchard's visit to the Conjuror, Weber proposes that capitalism could not fully develop in an economic group that was 'bound hand and foot by magical beliefs'.[27] *The Protestant Ethic* propounds a sociological theory that may productively be related to the careers of Henchard and Farfrae, their opposing trajectories embodying new social patterns in which an 'old leisurely and comfortable attitude toward life gave way to a hard frugality in which some participated and came to the top'[28] (one recalls Farfrae's reluctance to search any further for Henchard since it would 'make a hole in a sovereign' (XLV, p. 249)). A previously 'idyllic state', Weber argues, 'collapsed under the pressure of a bitter competitive struggle' of the kind that erupts in the rival games, the royal visit, the wrestling scene and elsewhere. The earliest type of 'innovator' of capital was frequently subject to 'legends of mysterious shady spots in his previous life', such as the wife-sale or the affair with Lucetta that dog the mayor. In the circumstances, 'only an unusually strong character could save an entrepreneur of this new type from the loss of his temperate self-control'. It is not this kind of 'dare-devil' character who has instituted the principles of capital, Weber suggests, but rather men like Farfrae, who were 'calculating', 'temperate and reliable, shrewd and completely devoted to their business, with strictly bourgeois opinions and principles'.[29] The rival public entertainments bring to a head the distinctions between two ways of life in ways illuminated by Weber's argument:

Impulsive enjoyment of life, which leads away from both work in a calling and from religion, was as such the enemy of rational asceticism, whether in the form of seigneurial sports, or the enjoyment of the dance-hall or the public-house of the common man.[30]

It was indeed that 'continuous, systematic work in a worldly calling' embodied by Farfrae that provided 'the most powerful conceivable lever' for the 'spirit of capitalism'.[31]

Weber's thoughts on the 'charismatic personality' also shed light on the plot trajectory of *The Mayor*, and notably on the personality of Henchard. Charisma, Weber claims, 'is self-determined and sets its own limits'; it 'knows no formal and regulated appointment or dismissal, no career, advancement or salary'.[32] The charismatic leader rejects 'all methodical rational acquisition, in fact, all rational economic conduct', and his way of life 'rests upon heroism of an ascetic ... kind'.[33] Henchard's final journey across the roads of Dorset, ending in the 'humblest' of rural slum cottages, is illuminated by a further observation of Weber's:

> Every charisma is on the road from a turbulently emotional life that knows no economic rationality to a slow death by suffocation under the weight of material interests.[34]

Henchard's death-scene thus embodies that 'waning of charisma' which indicates 'the diminishing importance of individual action', Farfrae's final achievement of supremacy neatly signalling the fact that 'the most irresistible force is *rational discipline*'.[35]

Just before the end of the novel, the near-destitute Henchard acquires a goldfinch in a 'wire prison' (XLIV, p. 243) as a wedding present for Farfrae and Elizabeth-Jane. Entering their house modestly through a back door, he deposits 'bird and cage under a bush outside' (XLIV, p. 244). He then forgets it, and a month later Elizabeth-Jane discovers the 'new bird-cage' with its 'little ball of feathers' (XLV, p. 248). Towards the close of *The Protestant Ethic*, Max Weber writes eloquently of the transfer of the ascetic principle from the monastery to the 'technical and economic conditions of machine production'. In religious times, care for the world's goods, he observes, was 'like a light cloak': under the rationalised bureaucracy required of capital, 'fate decreed that the cloak should become an iron cage'. Whilst, as Weber claims, 'No one knows who will live in this cage in the future', it may that the characterisation of Donald Farfrae points rather chillingly ahead to a regime in which the newly dominant class may be defined and recognised, 'Spiritualists without spirit, sensualists without heart.'[36] Elsewhere in Weber's work, his prognosis offers a sociological summation of the dramatic truths embodied in Hardy's novel, with its intensely imagined response to the functional contradictions of class, economics and character in nineteenth-century Wessex:

Together with the inanimate machine, the living machine constructs the cage of future bondage. Perhaps men will be forced to fit themselves helplessly into this cage if a technically good, that is, a rational bureaucratic administration and provision of services, is to be the ultimate and only value.[37]

notes

1. *Letters*, I, p. 89.
2. *Longman's Magazine*, July 1883; reprinted in *Thomas Hardy's Personal Writings*, ed. H. Orel (London, 1967), pp. 168–89.
3. Arnold Kettle, *An Introduction to the English Novel*, 2 vols (1953; London, 1969), 2, p. 45.
4. Robert Gittings, *Young Thomas Hardy* (Harmondsworth, 1978), pp. 18, 23.
5. See Pierre Bourdieu, *The Field of Cultural Production* (Cambridge, 1993).
6. John Goode, *Thomas Hardy: The Offensive Truth* (Oxford, 1988), p. 63. Subsequent references given in the text. Much of the critique presented in this group of studies was indebted to the pioneering study by George Wotton, *Thomas Hardy: Towards a Materialist Criticism* (Dublin, 1985).
7. Richard Jefferies, 'One of the New Voters' (1885), *The Open Air* (London, n.d.), p. 107.
8. Joe Fisher, *The Hidden Hardy* (London, 1992), p. 4. Subsequent references given in parentheses in the text.
9. Peter Widdowson, *Hardy in History* (London, 1989), p. 130. Subsequent references given in parentheses in the text.
10. Patricia Ingham, *The Language of Gender and Class* (London, 1996), p. 26. Subsequent references given in parentheses in the text.
11. Merryn Williams, *Thomas Hardy and Rural England* (London, 1972), p. 176.
12. Preface, *Far from the Madding Crowd* (1895), ed. S. Falck-Yi (Oxford, 1993), pp. 4–5.
13. Preface, *Select Poems of William Barnes* (1908), in *Thomas Hardy's Personal Writings*, p. 76.
14. 'The Dorsetshire Labourer' (1883), in *Thomas Hardy's Personal Writings*, pp. 168–89.
15. K. D. M. Snell, *Annals of the Labouring Poor* (Cambridge, 1987), pp. 374, 387.
16. Roger Ebbatson, *Hardy: The Margin of the Unexpressed* (Sheffield, 1993), pp. 131, 148.
17. Thomas Hardy, *The Mayor of Casterbridge*, ed. Phillip Mallett (New York, 2001), p. 89. Subsequent parenthetical reference by chapter and page is to this edition.

18. Walter Benjamin, *The Arcades Project*, trans. H. Eiland ard K. McLaughlin (Cambridge, MA, 1999), p. 496.
19. Karl Marx, *Grundrisse*, ed. M. Nicolaus (Harmondsworth, 1973), p. 100.
20. Karl Marx, *Capital*, Vol. 1, trans. B. Fowkes (Harmondsworth, 1976), p. 202.
21. Marx, *Capital*, 1, pp. 209, 208.
22. Benjamin, *Arcades*, p. 466.
23. Marx, cited in Benjamin, *Arcades*, p. 432.
24. Benjamin, *Arcades*, p. 447.
25. Marx, *Grundrisse*, p. 164.
26. *From Max Weber*, ed. C. W. Mills (London, 1970), p. 217.
27. Max Weber, *General Economic History* (New York, 1966), p. 265.
28. Max Weber, *The Protestant Ethic and the Rise of Capitalism* (London, 1970), p. 68.
29. Weber, *Protestant Ethic*, pp. 68–9.
30. Weber, *Protestant Ethic*, pp. 167–8.
31. Weber, *Protestant Ethic*, p. 172.
32. Max Weber, *Economy and Society*, Vol. 2, ed. G. Roth and C. Wittich (Berkeley, 1978), p. 1112.
33. Weber, *Economy and Society*, 2, pp. 1113, 1116.
34. Weber, *Economy and Society*, 2, p. 1120.
35. Weber, *Economy and Society*, 2, pp. 1148–9.
36. Weber, *Protestant Ethic*, pp. 181–2.
37. Cited in Karl Lowith, *Max Weber and Karl Marx* (London, 1993), p. 74.

6
hardy, victorian culture and provinciality

mary rimmer

From his dates it seems abundantly clear that Hardy was a Victorian writer: born in 1840, three years after Victoria ascended the throne, he wrote all his novels during her reign, as well as a substantial body of poetry, and his second collection of poetry came out in 1901, the year of Victoria's death. That he also turned 61 in 1901 makes it hard to see him as anything but a Victorian writer, or at least a Victorian novelist, despite the poetic achievement of his last three decades. For much of the twentieth century, though, critics rarely approached him primarily as a Victorian, preferring to associate him with a rustic, isolated world untouched by history, or with a past far enough back to be almost atemporal, as in Lord David Cecil's assertion that Hardy 'was stirred primarily by the life he had known as a child'. For Cecil, that life, 'little touched by the changes of the great world ... revolved in the same slow rhythm as for hundreds of years past'.[1] Though Cecil goes on to discuss the 'age of transition' Hardy inhabited, the rustic writer of 'village tragedy', whose timeless characters battle an equally timeless 'omnipotent and indifferent fate', is the dominant presence in his influential *Hardy the Novelist* (1943).[2]

Many others followed in Cecil's wake, reading Hardy as an extra-cultural phenomenon, who emerged into novel writing from a mostly oral culture, presumably on what Charles Lock calls 'the assumption that Dorset was somehow impervious to printing'.[3] The New Critical readings dominant from the 1940s to the 1970s reinforced the habit of reading Hardy outside of print culture and history, since New Criticism tended to elide contexts in any case. Further, a Cecil-like reading of Hardy as village tragedian remained as a kind of background assumption in much critical writing, as in George Wing's description of him as writing 'from the earth, the soil, generally some cottage or purlieu of Wessex'.[4]

Those who did look at Hardy's contemporary connections tended to be looking for influences (material or intellectual) which 'explain' his pessimism, say, not examining the complexities of Hardy's relationships with contemporary culture.[5]

It was not until the late twentieth century that Hardy started to be read in more useful ways as a Victorian – a label which by that time connoted far more change and complexity than it had earlier in the century. Cultural contexts had by then begun to seem both more important and more complicated than they did to critics of earlier generations, and that shift in thinking produced renewed interest not only in Hardy's many points of contact with and divergence from his contemporaries, but also in his own approach to culture in his texts. Tracking all of this has been made easier over recent decades by biographical work and by the publication of Hardy's notebooks, commonplace books and letters, as well as the 1984 edition of his third-person, self-written *Life*.[6]

Victorian culture was already a site of change and conflict in 1840. There were the obvious technological developments such as the railway and telegraph, as well as a growing sense of Britain and especially its capital as a metropolitan hub of Empire, and a bewildering range of educational institutions and systems. The religious landscape included everything from radical dissenting sects and periodic evangelical revival movements (powerful forces even within the Church of England), to High Church ritual, Roman Catholicism, and rational scepticism and secularism. The trains, and the penny post introduced in 1840, made it possible to send letters and publications such as magazines cheaply and quickly to all parts of Great Britain. The market for fiction expanded with the booming magazine trade, and with the growth of literacy and communication networks, but it also came under increasing scrutiny from a variety of censors (publishers, churches, middle-class subscribers to periodicals and libraries) who tried to regulate the fictional representation of controversial subjects such as sexuality, gender, crime and unorthodox religious positions.

Hardy occupied a number of different places within this many-sided cultural landscape. He began by experiencing both the major educational networks set up in the nineteenth century to educate lower-class children, starting in a church-affiliated National School in his birthplace, Higher Bockhampton, and changing to a Noncomformist British School in Dorchester in order to get a higher standard of education and to take Latin as an 'extra'. Like many Victorians, he prized classical learning, still valued as a symbol of middle- and upper-class culture, though calls for more technically oriented subjects already threatened its curricular dominance. (A classical education was still crucial for some professions, notably the church.) He also read on his own, in English, Latin and Greek; the collection of books he acquired in youth and early adulthood and kept all his life speaks not only to his intensive reading and study in those years, but also to the value he placed on the printed word as a pathway into culture. Part of the vast contemporary market for educational materials and cheap reprints, he acquired some manuals of self-improvement in his teens, such as Cassell's *Popular Educator*; his mother had already given him a cheap edition of Dryden's translation of Virgil.[7]

It may be tempting to dismiss Hardy's painstaking attempts to 'get' culture, just as Matthew Arnold dismissed the culture of mere prestige, 'valued either out of sheer vanity and ignorance or else as an engine of social and class distinction, separating its holder, like a badge or title, from other people who have not got it'.[8] Yet it seems clear that Hardy was drawn to reading and study as a personal choice, not simply because the acquisition of socially defined 'culture' was the key to social advance. Involved in his mixed ambition was the equally mixed dream of going to Oxford or Cambridge and entering the church. Unlike many professions, the church required little capital, as long as one had the financial resources and the time to secure a classical education and an Oxbridge degree; the number of clerical poets over the centuries probably also suggested this as a profession congenial to literary pursuits. In an era which valorised the self-made capitalist, the church was a quixotic but expensive choice, not least because of the financially unproductive years that had to be devoted to securing the necessary education. A boy who began in a National School was certainly ambitious to aspire to it, in a sense, but the goal was remote from the main track of contemporary ambition. The young Hardy already defined self-advancement in cultural and personal rather than in more standard economic terms.

Though Hardy eventually had to face the collapse of his educational and ecclesiastical dream, he continued to orient himself towards cultural work as opposed to straightforward social advancement. His stop-gap career, architecture, was poised between the artistic and the practical; perhaps this fact explains why he found several other people in architects' offices who had pursued or were trying to pursue classical studies.[9] In the *Life* he carefully emphasises that he had little interest in the practical side of architecture, the side that might enable him to make a real career of it: he had 'neither the inclination nor the keenness for getting into social affairs and influential sets which would help him to start a practice of his own', so that his 'tastes reverted to the literary pursuits that he had been compelled to abandon' (*Life*, p. 49). Literature is a 'taste' that suits his 'inclination', and is implicitly contrasted with 'getting into social affairs and influential sets'. Hardy subtly positions himself as a gentleman of leisure here, the sort of leisure which enables cultural activity and a disdain for 'getting places' – but literature was to be a money-making profession for him, and one which would gain him entrée to the 'influential sets' he refused to cultivate for architectural business.

Hardy read widely in contemporary as well as older works; the young writer who in his twenties produced *The Poor Man and the Lady*, 'a sweeping dramatic satire of the squirearchy and nobility, London society, the vulgarity of the middle class, modern Christianity, church restoration, and political and domestic morals in general' (*Life*, pp. 62–3) may have been taking on too much in a first novel, but he was certainly immersed in the issues of the day. Moreover, he was alive to literature not only as a collection of texts which had to be mastered in order to make one's way, but also as a site of conflict: in the 1860s he was reading Swinburne, for instance, whose controversial impact he memorably registered in his poem 'A Singer Asleep' (1910). Advised by Meredith to withdraw *The Poor Man* so as not to '"nail his colours to the mast" so definitely' in a first novel (*Life*, p. 62), Hardy had his first personal encounter with the publishing business and its divisions between permissible and dangerous speech.[10] His surviving notebooks and records of his books reflect a still wider range of reading, particularly in periodicals, from at least the mid-1870s on.[11] Arnold, Macaulay, Carlyle, John Morley, Herbert Spencer are all prominent in the 'Literary Notes' commonplace books, but many other writers from his own era and earlier are represented.

Interestingly, novelists appear infrequently in the notebooks; Hardy's relationship to contemporary fiction often seems hostile, or at least guarded. He sometimes claimed kin with Fielding, Dickens, Defoe or Thackeray, all dead before he himself was a published novelist, but he disliked comparisons between his work and that of contemporaries, George Eliot especially. Even while still struggling to achieve critical and popular success as a novelist he was insulted rather than pleased by a critic's guess that *Far from the Madding Crowd* was by Eliot (*Life*, p. 100), and in 1895, during the controversy that followed the publication of *Jude the Obscure*, he objected to being compared to Zola, asserting that critics might have 'sneered at' the novel's 'coarse' scenes 'for their Fielding-ism rather than for their Zola-ism ... I am read in Zola very little, but have felt locally akin to Fielding' (*Letters*, II, p. 99). This sort of comment, of course, has made it easy to see Hardy as detached from his contemporaries, whether in England or further afield, and looking to writers of previous generations for models and affinities (at least when he was not simply writing 'from the earth'). Yet his move here is really more strategic than antiquarian, invoking inherited culture, and 'local kin' such as Fielding, as a way of fending off both competition (Eliot), and critics' efforts to place him within a school (Zola).

To see Hardy in a Victorian context should not mean seeing him as fitting in or agreeing with a large number of his contemporaries – who tended not to agree with each other in any case. A number of studies from the past few decades demonstrate the connections between Hardy's intellectual concerns and those of other Victorians, but they also make it clear that the directions he took were often idiosyncratic and ambivalent.[12] Although, as Raymond Williams has pointed out, Hardy had at least as much formal education as the majority of people in his era, and indeed in the twentieth century as well, much of the reading and study that deeply mattered to him was private and extra-curricular, and he was consequently free to make it his own and to decide his own approach to it.[13] He may have had such a notion in mind when he created Angel Clare's brothers in *Tess of the d'Urbervilles*, pilloried by the narrator as 'well-educated, hall-marked young men, correct to their remotest fibre; such unimpeachable models as are turned out yearly by the lathe of a systematic tuition'.[14] Contrasting sharply with such products of the lathe, Hardy takes an informed but critical, off-centre approach to culture, one that interrogates the very structures within which it moves. As John Goode has argued, the written for Hardy is 'a form of dislocation', even if it is also 'a mode of access to the culture and a career'.[15]

For Hardy himself, even 'Wessex', the concept often mobilised to turn him into a 'safe' rural chronicler, could serve subversive cultural ends. In an intriguing fragment of a letter (1909), he comments on Swinburne's death, the effect of Swinburne's radicalism in the 1860s, and the way that radicalism will now be buried under mindless praise for a dead celebrity:

> No doubt the press will say some good words about him now he is dead and does not care whether it says them or no. Well, I remember what it said in 1866, when he did care … .

The kindly cowardice of many papers is overwhelming him with such toleration, such theological judgements, hypocritical sympathy, and misdirected eulogy that, to use his own words ... 'it makes one sick in a corner' – or as we say down here in Wessex, 'it is enough to make every little dog run to mixen'. (*Letters*, IV, p. 15; *Life* p. 371)

Hardy here registers his scorn for literary pundits and their manipulations of cultural value – first by appropriating his dead friend s voice, and then by using a local phrase, as if to suggest that 'down here in Wessex' it is possible to see through pretentious posturing, to critique cultural arbiters. The radical Swinburne Hardy would later elegise in 'A Singer Asleep' as the irrepressible disrupter of Victoria's 'formal middle time', is here allied with 'Wessex': the cultivated radical and the 'provincial' unite, as it were, to resist cultural orthodoxy.

Perhaps the most revealing of Hardy's dialogues with his contemporaries is that with Matthew Arnold: an important cultural arbiter for Victorian intellectuals, a writer in whom Hardy had a significant interest despite their divergent perspectives and, interestingly, a persistent critic of 'provinciality'.[16] The Hardy–Arnold connection has attracted some attention: David De Laura explores one of the oppositions between the two, focusing on Hardy's quarrel with Arnold's 'neo-Christianity' – that is, the attempt to keep intact Christian morality (including the repressive attitude towards sexuality especially prevalent in most nineteenth-century Christian denominations) while leaving theological dogmas behind.[17] Although De Laura probably makes Hardy's opposition to neo-Christianity more thoroughgoing than the evidence warrants, his discussion is useful, especially in its attention to the complexities of Hardy's response to Arnold. Michael Millgate gives a fuller sense of these in *Thomas Hardy: His Career as a Novelist*, emphasising Hardy's and Arnold's divergent class positions. In Millgate's view, Hardy's 'social and intellectual insecurity' complicated his response to Arnold, whom he associated with 'Oxford and its values', and with the university education that Hardy himself wished for and never got; he read Arnold, absorbed and used many Arnoldian ideas, but was often critical of those ideas – and of Arnold himself.[18]

Very likely an association in Hardy's mind between Arnold and his old friend and mentor Horace Moule, who committed suicide in 1873, played a role in his response to the older writer. The two could hardly fail to be linked for Hardy; Arnold himself often invoked his Oxford background in his work, and though Moule (probably because of his alcoholism) had never managed to take a degree at either Oxford or Cambridge, he had attended both, and was 'charming, cultivated, scholarly, thoroughly at home in the glamorous worlds of the ancient universities and of literary London'.[19] The same could very well be said of Arnold, and though his personal impact on Hardy was smaller than Moule's, Hardy's interest in and resistance to his ideas may reflect memories of the friend who had impressed him, tutored him, served as his role model, and yet also snubbed him.[20]

In *Culture and Anarchy* (1867), Arnold famously defined culture as 'a study of perfection', and perfection as 'a harmonious expansion of all the powers which make the beauty and worth of human nature'.[21] *Culture and Anarchy* is a central text in the definition of Victorian culture; Marc Demorest argues that it virtually 'invented culture both for the Victorians and for modernism … fixing it as a defined theoretical object of a critical discourse'.[22] As Wotton points out, it appeared at a significant historical moment in Britain, 'on the brink of the transition from industrial to monopoly capitalism',[23] a transition linked to the extension of the electoral franchise, to imperialist expansion and to the consequent need for a cohesive national identity which would transcend class. Arnold deploys his newly codified 'culture' to do much of this ideological work. For him culture's responsibility is to improve each individual in the society; although to an extent this idea dovetails with the common Victorian notion of self-improvement, in Arnold's hands the standard of improvement becomes much more specific. Culture sets the terms; it fosters an 'expansion' of human powers, but insists that the expansion be 'harmonious', and consistent with an already defined 'perfection'. To Arnold, culture tries 'to draw ever nearer to a sense of what is indeed beautiful, graceful, and becoming, and to get the raw person to like that': the 'raw person' is emphatically an object here, not a subject.[24]

The concept of culture extending its influence picks up on an idea Arnold explored earlier, in 'The Function of Criticism at the Present Time' (1864), where the figure of the critic is identified as a secular priest of culture: the critic's function is to 'create a current of true and fresh ideas' which will slowly seep through the rest of the society, disseminating 'the best that is known and thought' from the intellectual elite down (eventually) to the society at large.[25] In both works the 'free play of the mind' is important, but in both that play leads towards a greater good, whether that good is defined as 'a current of true and fresh ideas' or as 'perfection'.[26] In either case, the mind is cultivated towards a fixed end, one with clear political ramifications: to this authority-centred (but avowedly classless) harmony, Arnold opposes the anarchic liberty that he sees as the product of unimproved democracy. *Culture and Anarchy* is haunted by the image of working-class crowds, putting 'in practice an Englishman's right to do what he likes ... hoot as he likes, threaten as he likes, smash as he likes'.[27]

That image encapsulates a common Victorian middle-class fear of the emergent working class – newly literate, newly enfranchised, and less readily absorbed into middle-class culture than the smaller groups of *arrivistes* who had acquired money, education and status in earlier eras. Despite being an *arriviste* himself and benefiting from the nineteenth-century expansion of education, Hardy was not immune to this sort of apprehension. In a note the *Life* ascribes to 1891, he records his reaction to working-class crowds he observed at the British Museum, passing 'with flippant comments the illuminated MSS. – the labour of years': 'Democratic government may be justice to man, but it will probably merge in proletarian, and when these people become our masters it will lead to more of this contempt, and possibly be the utter ruin of art and literature' (*Life*, p. 247). Even here, though, there is a subtle difference from Arnold: Hardy sees not violence in the crowd but a sort of cultural carelessness. Ominously for his own continued success as a producer of cultural goods, they do not value the intellectual labour which produces those goods.

Arnold's vision of culture has its fissures, then, in its attempt to draw a line between the 'best' ideas, which belong to culture and tend to perfection, and inferior ones, which do not. He insists that culture is a process, 'not a having and a resting, but a growing and a becoming', but his stance is teleological, and the destined end – the harmonious 'universal order' – governs the process.[28] Still, in many ways his order is a more open one than the 'close and bounded intellectual horizon' he and others saw as the mid-Victorian condition, and by the standards of his day he was even radical in his insistence that the English should lose their insularity and embrace the culture of Continental Europe.[29] Like Hardy, Arnold is wrestling with inherited concepts of culture which do not quite cohere in a society increasingly riven by class strife and other conflicts.

Arnold was a controversialist, and as he knew, the 'controversial life' obscures perception.[30] The self-contradictory statement in *Culture and Anarchy* that 'Culture hates hatred' suggests the ways in which his vision takes the imprint of the debate he is involved in.[31] He can never lose his consciousness of 'enemies' and the need to 'elude them'; in a sense, the 'ignorant armies' clashing by night which end 'Dover Beach' form a subtext in his essays.[32] Yet his rhetorical strategies mask their own operational problems and tactics; he is always striving to stabilize the concept of culture and to work towards 'harmony' and 'perfection'. Hardy's tendency, by contrast, is rather to expose gaps, conflicts and fissures. Hardy produces a much more angular cultural vision (one which can still seem angular even to twenty-first-century eyes). Indeed, one of his own most striking references to 'harmony' ironises the very concept: 'The new Vale of Tempe may be a gaunt waste in Thule: human souls may find themselves in closer harmony with external things wearing a sombreness distasteful to our race when it was young.'[33] A far cry from the 'Sweetness and Light' which is both chapter title and rallying cry in *Culture and Anarchy*, this passage from *The Return of the Native* effectively makes 'harmony' itself dissonant. Two sombre, gaunt entities 'agree' with each other, but only because both are out of sympathy with consonance and symmetry.

Despite their divergent attitudes, Hardy paid a great deal of attention to Arnold, perhaps more than to any other Victorian thinker, especially from the late 1870s on. Indeed, superficially Hardy's own long course of self-education resembles an Arnoldian project in which his youthful 'rawness' was tempered and shaped by culture. His lists of authors and painters, his arduous study of the classics in every spare moment and his notebooks can all be seen as attempts to identify currents of 'true ideas' and rid himself of 'provinciality'.[34] Hardy sometimes appears to lend support to this reading, as when he notes one of Arnold's many complaints about English provincialism, in 'The Literary Influence of Academies'. Hardy's note begins: '*On Style &c* – ... Get rid of provinciality', and goes on to record Arnold's contention that 'Provinciality is caused by remoteness from a centre of correct information'; he also notes Arnold's emphasis on 'urbanity', and on avoiding the 'eruptive and aggressive styles'.[35]

In the *Life* Hardy records an 1880 comment, probably made in response to this section of 'The Literary Influence of Academies'. The passage itself is not quoted in the *Life*, however, the comment being introduced simply as one 'on literary criticism':

> Arnold is wrong about provinciality, if he means anything more than a provincialism of style and manner in exposition. A certain provincialism of feeling is invaluable. It is of the essence of individuality, and is largely made up of that crude enthusiasm without which no great thoughts are thought, no great deeds done. (*Life*, p. 151)

The layers of response here are interesting. To begin with, Hardy paraphrases a long chunk of Arnold into a relatively short note: his paragraph-long paraphrase spans nine pages in the R. H Super edition of Arnold's works.[36] He also alters the emphasis. Arnold points to urbanity as a laudable quality of Newman's, remarking that 'to get rid of provinciality is a certain stage of culture', and uses a note about Alexander the Great in Palgrave's *Golden Treasury* as an example of 'a freak or a violence' which brings in the 'note of provinciality' by 'abandoning the true mode of intellectual action – persuasion' for violent contradiction of a received idea.[37] Hardy's note, by contrast, records a series of prescriptions, as though he were extracting rules to follow: 'Get rid of provinciality ... . Have *urbanity*: avoid the eruptive and aggressive styles ... . It is wrong to contradict without a word of preparation a fixed and familiar notion, right or wrong' (*Literary Notebooks*, I, p. 128). In effect, he highlights the coerciveness implicit in Arnold's tone, and may thereby register a resistance to it. Certainly resistance comes through in the comment recorded in the *Life*, even though he may seem to cede the point there as far as style is concerned; Dennis Taylor remarks uneasily that 'Hardy agrees with Arnold here more than he should'.[38]

The 'excessive' agreement with Arnold here is noteworthy. If Hardy opposes Arnold's concept of culture and urbanity his opposition is an informed one, unlike that of John Bright, the Radical Birmingham MP whom Arnold attacks in *Culture and Anarchy* for sneering at 'People who talk about what they call *culture*! ... by which they mean a smattering of the two dead languages of Greek and Latin'.[39] By contrast, Hardy's view of high culture, though often ironic, is not necessarily hostile; he expended considerable energy to acquire 'the two dead languages of Greek and Latin'. Yet his is still an outsider's view, something which may explain both his searching investigation of Arnold, and his championing of an off-centre 'provincialism of feeling'.

Hardy's record of his first meeting with Arnold in 1880 again suggests the mixture of attraction and reserve in his reaction to the older writer:

> Arnold 'had a manner of having made up his mind upon everything years ago, so that it was a pleasing futility for his interlocutor to begin thinking new ideas, different from his own, at that time of day'. Yet he was frank and modest enough to assure Hardy deprecatingly that he was only a hard-worked school inspector. (*Life*, p. 137)

Arnold is opinionated and condescending, yet also frank and modest. A little later he is said to make 'pronouncements' (a word which suggests pomposity); some of these are 'questionable' though others are 'undoubtedly true' (*Life*, p. 137). Curiously, the account closes with an anecdote about Arnold's teasing of the nervous and inexperienced young hostess: in response to her timid suggestion that it was time for the ladies to retire to the drawing room, Arnold 'put his hand upon her shoulder and pressed her down into her seat as if she were a child – she was not much more – saying "No, no! What's the use of going into that room. Now I'll pour you a glass of sherry to keep you here." And kept there she and the other ladies were' (*Life*, p. 138). Trivial enough in itself, the incident does hint at a nasty streak in Arnold, one which enjoys a joke at another's expense. Sensitive as he was to unease in social situations, Hardy likely bore the memory in mind, and his response to Arnold the writer may reflect his estimate of Arnold the dinner-table companion.

Most other references to Arnold in the *Life* are to his works rather than himself; Millgate suggests that Hardy's most intensive reading of Arnold was sparked by this first personal encounter.[40] The laconic remark in the *Life* that at their next meeting, in 1884, he liked Arnold 'better now than he did at their first' (*Life*, p. 173), reinforces the impression of an initial uneasiness. Both encounters, however, occurred at a time when Hardy was using Arnoldian themes and often direct references to Arnold in *The Return of the Native* (1878), *A Laodicean* (1880) and *Two on a Tower* (1882). He continued both to resist and to refer to Arnold, perhaps drawn by a sense of their shared uneasy agnosticism, haunted by the language of the Bible and the religious institutions in which both had been brought up – perhaps also impelled by a consciousness of Arnold as an adversary. In 1888, after reading Arnold's obituary, Hardy commented, 'The *Times* speaks quite truly of his "enthusiasm for the nobler and detestation of the meaner elements in humanity"' (*Life*, p. 216). Generous yet unspecific, and largely recorded from another source, this remark suggests Hardy's continuing reserve where Arnold was concerned.

Two Hardyan trajectories of acculturation, one from *The Hand of Ethelberta* (1876) and one from *Jude the Obscure* (1895), suggest the complexities that surround Hardy's cultural positioning and his deployment of the 'provincial' in his texts. Like their creator, Ethelberta Petherwin and Jude Fawley struggle for cultural belonging. Both attempt to rise via what the *Ethelberta* narrator calls 'the subversive Mephistophelian element, brains', but Jude never manages it, and Ethelberta's lasting success comes only via marriage.[41] Both novels enact the struggle for self-improvement central to much Victorian fiction as well as to Victorian culture in general, but instead of rewarding their protagonists with wordly and emotional success in the manner of a novel such as Dickens's *David Copperfield*, Hardy's plots give Ethelberta a parody of success in a wealthy, loveless marriage to a decrepit rake, and Jude a cumulative series of material and emotional disasters. Both plots repeatedly emphasise culture as contingent, mired in intransigent social and material circumstance, and very far removed from the culture that draws people away from contingency in an urbane, harmonious quest for perfection. Though the acquisition of culture fascinates Hardy, in his fiction at least his eye tends to fall not on the goal but on the process itself – on the 'raw person's' painful experience of acculturation.

Written before Hardy's first recorded responses to Arnold, *The Hand of Ethelberta* may help to explain their ambivalence. Criticism of the novel, as Tim Dolin points out, remained generally negative for a century after its publication, and tended to read the book's 'stylistic eccentricity ... as a symptom of its author's provincialism'.[42] But the provincial here, as so often in Hardy, is not so much a symptom as a concept the novel puts in play. Ethelberta the butler's daughter, having become a 'lady' herself, dreams not only of bringing her family with her into middle-class respectability, but also of cultivating them; she accordingly strives to give them a variety of cultural and social equipment, from books to read, French lessons and art gallery tours to hints on behaviour and dress. Accidents, she tells Christopher Julian, 'have split [them] up into sections' (p. 127), leaving some servants and artisans and others educated, potentially middle-class people. She seeks to reunite them, as if she herself were the embodiment of Arnold's culture, trying to draw her 'raw' siblings 'ever nearer to a sense of what is indeed beautiful, graceful, and becoming'. Because she straddles the raw/cultivated divide in her own person as both Berta Chickerel and the fashionable Mrs Petherwin, her career allows Hardy to examine the tensions and ironies of that divide.

Ethelberta, whom Dolin calls 'an expert interloper in male high culture',[43] can sound almost like a parody of Arnold. On one occasion, for instance, she seeks to bridge the family divisions by asking Gwendoline, her cook and older sister, for advice. Instead, she ends up instructing Gwendoline about the correct term for young onions. Her subsequent retreat from the kitchen and from 'the wretched homeliness' (p. 165) of her sister's mind recalls Arnold's remarks on 'hideous' lower-class names in 'The Function of Criticism'. Arnold too begins with an impulse to cross class boundaries here, moved by the case of 'Wragg', a girl arrested for child murder, and using her plight to critique complacent references to the 'unrivalled happiness' of English society. He accomplishes the critique, but the contemplation of Wragg's name distracts him into petulant fastidiousness: '... has anyone reflected what a touch of grossness in our race, what an original shortcoming in the more delicate spiritual perceptions, is shown by the natural growth amongst us of such hideous names – Higginbottom, Stiggins, Bugg!'[44] Indeed, it is almost as though the Chickerel family, marked physically and mentally by the operations of the economic and social order, are illustrations of the 'hideous' life of mass vulgarity Arnold recoiled from and tried to reshape. Sol Chickerel will later thrust his 'mis-shaped monster' of a hand under Ethelberta's eyes as he denounces her for marrying an aristocrat when her own brother is 'branded with work': 'That comes from the jack-plane, and my pushing against it day after day and year after year. If I were found drowned or buried, dressed or undressed, in fustian or broadcloth, folk would look at my hand and say, "That man's a carpenter"' (p. 376).

Ethelberta also differs from Arnold in crucial ways. Like Hardy, she cannot attach herself seamlessly to high culture. The gap between herself and most of her family pains her deeply, and each reminder of it brings back the 'old sense of disloyalty to her class and kin' she has lived with from the beginning of her social rise; there is 'no escaping it' (p. 166). Further, despite her desire to 'improve' her family, her methods are strategic, and her goals largely material, not intellectual or broadly social.[45] Rather than seeing culture in Arnoldian terms, as distanced from practical aims, Ethelberta must take culture as her arsenal. She becomes poet, public storyteller and social celebrity, scoring a victory that exposes but also exploits the commodification of culture. Her circumstances simply do not permit the degree of disinterested thought Arnold sees as a prerequisite for culture.

Ethelberta's less obviously materialistic work, interestingly, is markedly less successful than her cultural and social performances. The most detailed instance of her attempt to cultivate her family, the afternoon visit with her brothers to the Royal Academy, ends in disarray. She begins the afternoon confidently; at ease herself in the Academy setting despite the clothes she wears (ironically in order to pass as what she is, 'a respectable workman's relative'), she sets out, 'catalogue in hand', to expand her brothers' cultural awareness (p. 179). The lesson is consonant with many Victorian models of self-improvement and cultivation through art. Like Ruskin, and even like Arnold, Ethelberta believes in 'the kindly effects of artistic education upon the masses' (p. 179), in the ability of culture to raise the 'raw person' to a higher state of consciousness.[46] In the event, however, she meets with unexpected checks, and the episode ends up only adding another layer to the novel's edgily ironic commentary on the persistence of class and gender divides.

More respectful than the British Museum crowds Hardy observed 15 years after the publication of *Ethelberta*, Sol and Dan are still unpromising pupils. Though they tolerate Ethelberta's educational schemes, they maintain a clear sense of the social distinction between themselves and her. They often call her 'Mrs Petherwin', and although they will not '[break] faith with their admired lady-sister' (p. 179), they do insist on keeping her in that hyphenated role, and are at odds with the decorums of the art exhibit. Ethelberta must correct their untutored 'straying from the contemplation of the pictures as art to indulge in curious speculations on the intrinsic nature of the delineated subject, the gilding of the frames, the construction of the skylights overhead' (p. 180). She must also correct their social demeanour – their 'too reverential ... bearing' towards the 'well-dressed' crowd among whom they walk 'with the generally contrite bearing of meek people in church' (p. 179).[47] Acutely conscious of the social incongruities of the situation, her brothers cannot feel comfortable. The Academy show is clearly designed for members of another class, and requires a particular sort of learned response: paintings are to be seen as symbolically resonant forms, not as material objects framed by workmen, and not as illustrations which invite a viewer to move from painting to 'original'.

Yet 'art' refuses to remain a stable category here. The link between artwork and original has been crucial in the making and reception of the painting for which Ethelberta has modelled; both she and Ladywell the painter have profited from this packaging of her celebrated features. Accordingly, though she warns her brothers away from reacting to the painting as a representation of herself, two gentlemen looking at it pass quickly from artwork to 'original' as they begin discussing Ethelberta, and Alfred Neigh's assertion that he intends to marry her. Appropriate responses, it seems, are no more prevalent among those who 'belong' culturally than among uninstructed interlopers. This overheard conversation troubles Ethelberta's lesson by removing art from its supposedly serene niche above practical and social constraints: if it is not so enthroned, why should Sol and Dan, who reject social climbing as an end in itself, learn to decode it?

Though 'calm and compressed in manner' (p. 181), Ethelberta loses her serene pedagogical command from this point. Reminded of her own status as cultural commodity, she can no longer maintain the fiction that cultural improvement bridges social and material gaps. As a woman without property or a socially acceptable family, she must focus on the marriage market and investigate Neigh's claims as a suitor. This new emphasis on material exigency leaves her improving lesson to trail off into futility as Sol and Dan are 'left considerably longer to their private perceptions of the false and true in art than they had been earlier in the day' (p. 181).

As if to rub in the futility, Hardy goes on to parody the lesson at the end of the chapter, where Ethelberta and her sister Picotee go to examine Neigh's 'country estate'. There they find themselves gazing at a very different 'picture'. In place of the spacious manor house which 'by every law of manorial topography' (p. 185) ought to be visible from this vantage point, they see 'numerous horses in the last stage of decrepitude' (p. 186). Though it is not the 'prospect' they expect, this 'extraordinary group' is presented tableau fashion, much as if it were a work of art. The horses seem crudely drawn rather than simply emaciated, looking like 'specimens of some attenuated heraldic animal ... or enlarged castings of the fire-dog of past times' (p. 186). The sisters even look at the scene over a low rail fence, which suggests the barriers sometimes placed before larger canvases in galleries. Moreover, as they shift their gaze they seem to be looking at another in a series of pictures: the 'open-air larder' of horse meat prepared as food for hunting hounds is described as a 'chronological sequel to the previous scene' (p. 186). The familiar trope of the courtship novel, in which the pictorial 'prospect' of a suitor's estate reveals his true character, dissolves into grotesque laughter here, leaving Ethelberta and Picotee to confront a radically different sort of prospect. As Dolin suggests, the Harefield episode, especially in George du Maurier's illustration for the *Cornhill Magazine* serialisation of the novel, enacts a collision of artistic modes, in which 'two bemused, or vacant, *Punch* figures' stand in front of 'a kind of Goyaesque *chiaroscuro* – their bright fatuous world abutting a plainly moving and moralistic spectacle'.[48]

Jude the Obscure, written some 20 years later, deploys a much less distanced satire, mounts a more direct attack on the codes of high culture, and is more overtly concerned with Arnoldian ideas.[49] Nevertheless, *Jude* too turns on discoveries of the bad fit between individual cultural aspiration and the material barriers to it. Motivated by the desire to escape the provincial or 'obscure' circumstances he has been born into, Jude seeks to 'belong' to Christminster, the 'castle manned by scholarship and religion'.[50] He articulates a social ambition as well as an intellectual and religious one, and is 'startlingly aware' of the class element of his aspiration, as Patricia Ingham has pointed out.[51] Again like Ethelberta, who in her youth refuses to 'bend the knee' to the gentry,[52] Jude defines what he seeks as a refuge from the physical and psychological knocks he has received at the hands of the powerful; to him Christminster offers cultural space, 'a spot in which, without fear of farmers, or hindrance, or ridicule, he [can] watch and wait, and set himself to some mighty undertaking' (p. 25). Ironically, such a space of leisure and individual freedom is precisely what enables a 'cultured' perspective – and precisely what Jude lacks, as Hardy makes clear.

Jude is teacher and pupil both, and has the will to learn that Sol and Dan visibly lack, but material obstacles loom large for him from the outset – the first being his discovery that there is no easy 'law of transmutation' or 'patent process' for turning Latin and Greek into English, and that he must 'learn words one by one up to tens of thousands' (p. 31). After a while, this bitter setback does make learning still more desirable: 'The mountain weight of material under which the ideas lay in those dusty volumes called the classics piqued him into a dogged, mouselike subtlety of attempt to move it piecemeal' (p. 31). Interestingly, though, the narrator figures Jude's efforts as theft and subversion. Rather than scale walls like an invader – a successful invader, after all, would end up as owner – Jude creeps under the walls, unobserved, and begins to nibble away at the stores of the 'castle of learning', like a rodent of the kind his aunt would trap and kill if it got into her bakery.

As a 'hampered and lonely itinerant' (p. 32), Jude also needs a series of contrivances to make his work possible: an 'ingenious' strap to keep the book he is studying open, a dictionary balanced on his knees, a horse who knows the route well enough to need little direction. He has no other time for study, and he must interrupt his reading for each house where he delivers bread; he is also cautioned by a policeman, because neighbours see his combination of 'work and play' as a 'dangerous [practice] on the highway' (p. 33): the last circumstance makes his task more 'mouselike' than ever, since he must now hide his books when he sees anyone coming. Although his encounter with Arabella Donn and subsequent ill-fated marriage to her are the most obvious obstacles to his Christminster ambitions, the description of his early efforts makes the project seem doomed even before Arabella makes her first appearance.

Jude's own belief in his goal outlasts more than one disillusionment, though each one makes it harder for a reader to share that belief. When he finally arrives in Christminster and wanders the streets at night listening to the spectres his reading raises for him, he invokes many who implicitly critique his aspirations, notably Arnold, who comes in, with seeming fitness, to praise the city 'which, by her ineffable charm, keeps ever calling us to the true goal of all of us, to the ideal, to perfection' (p. 81).[53] But readers are more likely to see that Arnold does not include anyone like Jude in his 'us', a pronoun which implicitly suggests an audience of old Oxonians. He goes on to refer to himself as the university's 'unworthy son', whose institutional 'mother' will forgive him anything because he fights in her cause.[54] He belongs, so thoroughly that he can transgress in the confident expectation of forgiveness; Jude, meanwhile, has just been warned off the street by another policeman. Jude has earlier used mother/son language himself, though in a significantly different way. He borrows a biblical phrase to project his future as Christminster's 'beloved son, in whom she shall be well pleased' (p. 38) – just before Arabella hits him in the face with the pig's pizzle, indirectly initiating the collapse of his dreams and demonstrating that the filial status he has claimed is far beyond the reach of an obscure, 'mouselike' interloper. As Ingham points out, the culture that Jude attempts to appropriate reaches us only in allusions and quotations, remaining 'fragmented, useless, irrelevant to his dilemmas'.[55]

Neither Jude nor Ethelberta ever securely possesses knowledge; whether or not he intends it, Hardy's vision of culture as won 'piecemeal', by hard striving and clever strategy amid unpropitious circumstances, and sustainable only by the sort of elaborate manoeuvring Ethelberta has to master, forms a counter-statement to Arnold's. Harmony is costly, priced beyond the reach of the Judes and Ethelbertas. Jude dies alone and in despair; Ethelberta's final 'success' and her epic poem, in process as the novel ends, are presented only through hearsay, muted and off-stage. 'Provincialism of feeling' matters to Hardy because, among other things, it registers the gap between aspiration and fulfilment among the 'obscure', because it allows the dissonances of farcical rise and tragic fall to sound without being assimilated into harmony.

His intense awareness of the ways in which culture is contingent on class, on gender, on points of origin, made Hardy's own cultural space ineluctably liminal. He could not silence that awareness any more than Ethelberta can escape the conflict between family ties, education, and acquired middle-class status. It seems fitting that when Hardy finally returned to build a house in his native county of Dorset, he chose a correspondingly liminal physical space. Max Gate is within walking distance of the village of Higher Bockhampton where he was born, and on the edges of the county town of Dorchester where he began his transition into a metropolitan intellectual, and first felt the tension between a world 'which had advanced to railways and telegraphs and daily London papers' and one 'of shepherds and ploughmen ... where modern improvements were still regarded as wonders' (*Life*, p. 36). Dorchester was also the place where he lived 'a life twisted of three strands – the professional life, the scholar's life, and the rustic life' (*Life*, p. 36). Social stasis, social 'advance'; the rustic, the scholarly, the provincial, the cultured – for Hardy all these were not simply social categories but lived choices with different consequences. No wonder then, that his cultural positioning, like his house, remained off-centre, and that his fiction so sharply registers culture as contested ground. His readings of the cultural debates of his period are at once subversive and sympathetic, always attuned to discontinuities and conflict. Critical work which engages productively with these cultural currents and Hardy's relation to them is already appearing, and further explorations along those lines will enrich and complicate our sense of his contexts.

notes

1. Lord David Cecil, *Hardy the Novelist: An Essay in Criticism* (1943; reprinted London, 1965), pp. 18, 14.
2. Cecil, *Hardy the Novelist*, pp. 20, 17, 26.
3. Charles Lock, *Thomas Hardy*, Criticism in Focus series (New York, 1992), p. 102. Lock points out that many socialist critics, despite their political distance from Cecil, also present Hardy as almost wholly the product of a rural culture rooted in custom and orality (pp. 87–8). See for instance Douglas Brown, *Thomas Hardy* (1954; reprinted London, 1961), Arnold Kettle, *Hardy the Novelist* (Swansea, 1966) and Raymond Williams's chapter on Hardy in *The English Novel from Dickens to Lawrence* (Oxford, 1970), pp. 95–118. Lock overstates the case where Williams is concerned; Williams gives a nuanced reading of Hardy's conflicted social allegiances.
4. George Wing, 'Hardy and Regionalism', in *Thomas Hardy: The Writer and his Background*, ed. Norman Page (London, 1980), p. 77. Another example is Richard H. Taylor's *The Neglected Hardy: Hardy's Lesser Novels* (New York, 1982). Taylor sets out to give the 'lesser' novels their due, but tends to damn the comic or parodic ones with faint praise: a book like *The Hand of Ethelberta* is one that Hardy 'did not intend to be taken as seriously as the great tragic novels' (p. 57).
5. W. R. Rutland, *Thomas Hardy: A Study of his Writings and their Background* (1938; reprinted New York, 1962) is an honourable exception. The 'pessimism' studies include Albert Pettigrew Elliott, *Fatalism in the Works of Thomas Hardy* (1935; reprinted New York, 1966), and G. W. Sherman, *The Pessimism of Thomas Hardy* (Cranbury, NJ, 1976).

6. C. J. P. Beatty was the earliest in this field with his edition of *The Architectural Notebook of Thomas Hardy* (Dorchester, 1966). See also *The Personal Notebooks*, ed. Richard Taylor (London, 1978); *The Literary Notebooks of Thomas Hardy*, 2 vols, ed. Lennart Björk; *Thomas Hardy's 'Studies, Specimens &c.' Notebook*, eds Michael Millgate and Pamela Dalziel (Oxford, 1994).

7. *The Popular Educator*, Vol. I (London: Kent, 1855); Vol. II (London: Cassell, 1855); Vol. III (London: Cassell, 1856); John Dryden, trans., *The Works of Virgil* (London: Allman, n.d.). Hardy's copies are in the Dorset County Museum.

8. Matthew Arnold, *Culture and Anarchy: An Essay in Political and Social Criticism*, in *The Complete Prose Works of Matthew Arnold*, Vol. 5, ed. R. H. Super (Ann Arbor, MI, 1965), p. 90.

9. These included, for instance, John Hicks, the architect to whom Hardy went as an articled pupil, and Henry Bastow, also Hicks's pupil (Michael Millgate, *Thomas Hardy: A Biography* (Oxford, 1982), p. 55).

10. Joss Marsh, in *Word Crimes: Blasphemy, Culture and Literature in Nineteenth-Century England* (Chicago, 1998), notes that by the 1840s 'Literature' was being separated from self-taught 'literacy' and seen as a replacement religion, one protected by 'the literary property system and the operation of criminal law' (p. 107); in effect Meredith was steering Hardy towards 'Literature'.

11. Though the 'Studies, Specimens, &c' notebook, the Architectural notebook, parts of 'Memoranda I' and the 'Schools of Painting' notebook (the latter two are included in *Personal Notebooks*) date from the 1860s, the more general 'Literary Notes' probably start in the mid-1870s. See Björk's discussion of dating in the Introduction to the *Literary Notebooks* (I and II, pp. xxxvi–xl).

12. The first systematic attempt to look at Hardy in a Victorian context was Michael Millgate's *Thomas Hardy: His Career as a Novelist* (1971; reprinted London, 1994).

13. Williams, *The English Novel from Dickens to Lawrence*, p. 95. As Williams notes, the critical identification of Hardy, George Eliot and D. H. Lawrence as 'autodidacts' reflects the fact 'that none of the three was in the pattern of boarding-school and Oxbridge which in the late nineteenth century came to be regarded not simply as a kind of education but as education itself' (p. 96).

14. Hardy, *Tess of the d'Urbervilles*, eds Margaret Higonnet and Tim Dolin (London, 1999), p. 159.

15. John Goode, *Thomas Hardy: The Offensive Truth* (Oxford, 1988), pp. 2–3.

16. The following section of this chapter is indebted to the provocative discussion of Arnold in my graduate seminar, 'The Discourse of Class in Victorian Literature' (Fall Term, 2001), at the University of New Brunswick.

17. David J. De Laura, '"The Ache of Modernism" in Hardy's Later Novels', *English Literary History*, 34 (1967), pp. 380–99.

18. Millgate, *Thomas Hardy: His Career*, p. 177.

19. Millgate, *Thomas Hardy: A Biography*, p. 67.

20. Millgate (*Thomas Hardy: A Biography*, p. 71) suggests that 'the patronizing attitudes displayed by Henry Knight towards his protégé Stephen Smith in *A Pair of Blue Eyes*' owe something to recollection of those snubs.

21. Arnold, *Culture*, pp. 91, 92.

22. Marc Demorest, 'Arnold and Tyler: The Codification and Appropriation of Culture', in Patrick Scott and Pauline Fletcher, eds, *Culture and Education in Victorian England*, Bucknell Review (Lewisburg, PA, 1990), ɔ. 27.

23. Goode, *Thomas Hardy*, p. 31.

24. Arnold, *Culture*, p. 96.

25. Arnold, 'The Function of Criticism at the Present Time', *Complete Prose Works*, 3, p. 270. The notion of 'harmony' also appears earlier on, in Arnold's 1853 'Preface to Poems'. Peter Allan Dale, in *The Victorian Critic and the Idea of History: Carlyle, Arnold, Pater* (Cambridge, MA, 1977), suggests Schiller and Vico as possible sources for the concept of harmony (pp. 108–9).

26. Arnold, 'Function of Criticism', p. 270.

27. Arnold, *Culture*, p. 119. Marsh (*Word Crimes*, pp. 194–5) argues that Arnold has a specific 'hooter' in mind – Charles Bradlaugh MP, working-class leader and president of the National Secularist Society.

28. Arnold, *Culture*, p. 94.

29. Arnold, *Culture*, p. 92.

30. Arnold, 'Function of Criticism', p. 272.

31. Arnold, *Culture*, p. 112.

32. Arnold, *Culture*, p. 124.

33. Hardy, *The Return of the Native*, Book First, chapter 1.

34. Cf. Marsh, *Word Crimes*, on 'late-nineteenth-century bibliomania and book-collecting' (p. 193), which she associates with Literature's gradual acquisition of the cultural authority once held by religion.

35. *Literary Notebooks*, I, p. 128.

36. Arnold, 'The Literary Influence of Academies', *Complete Prose Works*, 3, pp. 244–53.

37. Arnold, 'Literary Influence of Academies', pp. 245, 253.

38. Dennis Taylor, *Hardy's Literary Language and Victorian Philology* (Oxford, 1993), p. 60.

39. Arnold, *Culture*, p. 87.

40. Millgate, *Thomas Hardy: A Biography*, p. 246.

41. *The Hand of Ethelberta*, ed. Tim Dolin (London, 1996), p. 241. Subsequent references to the novel in this edition are cited parenthetically in the text.

42. Dolin, Introduction to *The Hand of Ethelberta*, p. xxi.

43. Dolin, Introduction to *The Hand of Ethelberta*, p. xxiii.

44. Arnold, 'Function of Criticism', p. 273.

45. In his Introduction to *The Hand of Ethelberta*, Dolin also points out that Ethelberta's early acquisition of culture borders upon espionage and treason (p. xxix); in order to read she crouches under the library bookcases in the house where her father is butler, clutching matches and candle like a small Guy Fawkes.

46. Arnold's models of acculturation are more verbal and textual than visual, and in this sense Dolin is right to see Ruskin rather than Arnold as the guiding spirit of Ethelberta's art appreciation lesson (note to *The Hand of Ethelberta*, p. 425). Ruskin's influence helped to shape the Victorian middle-class belief in the morality of art, but the idea of using literature, art and other cultural forms to take the place of the eroded moral and spiritual power of religion was common to many Victorian intellectuals; it drove the substantial mid-

Victorian effort, especially at the Royal Academy, to increase working-class attendance at art galleries. See Paula Gillett, *The Victorian Painter's World* (Gloucester, 1990), pp. 217–18.

47. The sense of Sol and Dan as out of place is enhanced by the removal of 'generally' in the 1877 edition of the novel.

48. Dolin, Introduction to *The Hand of Ethelbert*, p. xxxiii. The illustration is reproduced on p. 187 of the Penguin edition.

49. Several critics have noted the Arnoldian elements, including Millgate in the *Jude* chapter of *Thomas Hardy: His Career*, and Ward Hellstrom, 'Hardy's Scholar-Gypsy', in *The English Novel in the Nineteenth Century: Essays on the Literary Mediation of Human Values*, ed. George Goodin (Urbana, 1972).

50. Hardy, *Jude the Obscure*, ed. Dennis Taylor (London, 1998), p. 26. Subsequent references to this edition cited parenthetically in the text.

51. Patricia Ingham, Introduction to *Jude the Obscure* (Oxford, 1985), p. xiii.

52. Sol Chickerel tells Christopher Julian that Ethelberta as a girl has resisted curtsying to the ladies and gentlemen, charging that 'bending your knees' implies more thorough submissiveness than the masculine 'equivalent' of merely touching the cap (p. 113).

53. Arnold, Preface to *Essays in Criticism, Complete Prose Works*, 3, p. 290.

54. Arnold, Preface to *Essays in Criticism*, 3, p. 290.

55. Ingham, Introduction to *Jude*, p. xvi. See also Marsh, *Word Crimes*, pp. 316–17.

7
hardy and science: a chapter of accidents
angelique richardson

Science was central to Victorian culture. Etymologically science means *knowledge*, and central to Hardy's work is the quest for knowledge in the broadest sense; for a deeper understanding of nature, of our place in it, and of ourselves, at a time when old certainties were crumbling, and new vistas of knowledge were jostling for attention. His notebooks are filled with discussion, comment and annotation of the new science.

In 1917 he declared:

> I have repeatedly stated in prefaces and elsewhere that the views in
> [my works of art] are *seemings*, provisional impressions only, used for
> artistic purposes because they represent approximately the impressions
> of the age, and are plausible, till somebody produces better theories
> of the universe.[1]

This foreshadows Thomas Kuhn's argument, some four decades later, that scientific truth is a matter of consensus and choice of theory among the scientific community.[2] It is in this light that one should read the disclaimer in the Preface to the 1912 Wessex Edition, in which Hardy pointed out that it was not likely

> that imaginative writings extending over more than forty years would
> exhibit a coherent scientific theory of the universe, even if it had been
> attempted – of that universe concerning which Spencer owns to the
> 'paralysing thought' that possibly there exists no comprehension of it
> anywhere … [T]he sentiments in the following pages have been stated
> truly to be mere impressions of the moment.

These impressions were no less truthful for their impermanence. Hardy desires, and desires to impart, *truth*: the truth of origins, of the material world and of mind, even if that truth turns out to be plural and shifting.

One major development in early nineteenth-century scientific thought, with profound social repercussions, was the publication between 1830 and 1833 of Charles Lyell's *Principles of Geology*, demonstrating that life on earth had not been created over the course of six days, but over millions of years. In the seventeenth century James Ussher, the Archbishop of Armagh, had dated the beginning of the world to the morning of 23 October 4004 BC; this idea could no longer stand. As the *Athenaeum* remarked, Lyell put man 'back on the huge dial of time'.[3] The theomorphic status of humanity, the idea that humanity has been created in the image of God, took a severe knock. The discovery of geological time not only unsettled the place of humans in the cosmos but formed part of a series of scientific discoveries that, over the course of the century, would call into question what it was to be human.

The social implications of science were to become increasingly apparent. 'Man – like *infusoria* in a drop of water under microscope', Hardy noted from Schopenhauer; and from Arthur Helps: 'My wonder is that our knowledge of astronomy ... gained in comparatively modern times, has not dwarfed & crushed ambition.'[4] Hardy described *Two on a Tower* (1882) as 'the outcome of a wish to set the emotional history of two infinitesimal lives against the stupendous background of the stellar universe, and to impart to readers the sentiment that of these contrasting magnitudes the smaller might be the greater to them as men'.[5] The life sciences, leading to Darwin's theory of descent through modification, had the most profound implications for the status of humanity. Satirical cartoons on 'the monkey theory' crowded into the periodical press, providing instances of bravado which were clear testimonies to self-doubt, and reluctant admissions of the decentrings of science.[6] As Grant Allen put it, 'it was not biology alone that [Darwin] was foredoomed to revolutionize, but the whole range of human thought, and perhaps even ultimately of human action'.[7] Darwin removed agency, purpose and teleology from the story of creation. However, while the idea of a purposive evolution was banished by his reason, it was continually readmitted through his language. Such readmissions are epidemic throughout the century, and testify to the difficulty of accepting that there might be no overall purpose to life on earth; no evidence for what Wordsworth, as Hardy recalled in *Tess of the d'Urbervilles*, had christened 'Nature's holy plan': 'some people would like to know whence the poet whose philosophy ⸬s in these days deemed as profound and trustworthy as his song is breezy and pure, gets his authority for speaking of "Nature's holy plan"'.[8] In 1900 Hardy cut out from the *Daily Chronicle* a piece on the German apostle of evolution, Ernst Haeckel:

> how far is the scientist justified in asserting that he utterly rejects 'teleology', when he can hardly open his mouth without speaking of organs which show 'provident arrangement' and 'excellent contrivance'? ... Professor Haeckel may hold to the conviction that 'teleology' is an outworn dogma, and that no one ought to speak of end or purpose in nature; but he does not make himself clear.[9]

Were the natural and social orders framed to any end (and was the social simply an extension of the natural), or were they the consequence of random chance?[10] There was the rub.

Alongside Darwin's story of process and development, which tended to be interpreted as a story of progress – though Darwin had made it clear in the *Origin of Species* that progress was no inevitable rule[11] – an alternative narrative was emerging; a narrative of death and decay taken up by the theories of degeneration at the *fin de siècle*. The process of 'entropy' was named in 1859, the same year that the *Origin* appeared;[12] three years later, William Thomson, later Lord Kelvin, basing his calculations on the rate of loss of radiant heat by the sun, warned that 'inhabitants of the earth cannot continue to enjoy the light and heat essential to their life, for many millions years longer, unless sources now unknown to us are prepared in the great storehouse of creation'.[13] Thomson's theory not only undermined the Victorian idea of progress, but directly challenged Darwin's theory of natural selection, which required far more time than Thomson's calculations allowed.[14] Relentlessly attacking the idea of natural selection, Thomson in fact offered a bleaker vision than Darwin's, though one more compatible with a religious view of the world. 'To those who fully admit the immortality of the human soul, the destruction of our world will not appear so dreadful', wrote Darwin in 1876, confessing that for him the idea that the sun would grow too cold to sustain life was 'an intolerable thought'.[15] Hardy was deeply attentive to such ideas. In 1875 his conversation with Leslie Stephen turned upon 'theologies decayed and defunct, the origin of things, the constitution of matter, the unreality of time and kindred subjects' (*Life*, p. 109). In his notebooks he copied a passage from James Cotter Morison's *The Service of Man. An*

Essay toward the Religion of the Future (1887): 'Decay & death stamped not only on man & his works, but on all that surrounds him. Nature herself decays – Alps – Sun himself – from the animalcule to the galaxy.'[16]

The new scientific ideas appear in Hardy's work in surprising, disjunctive, and provocative ways. Most famously, as Henry Knight, 'a fair geologist', hangs helplessly on a cliff face, and Elfride removes her underclothing to make a rope with which to rescue him, he comes face to face with 'an imbedded fossil, standing forth in low relief from the rock. It was a creature with eyes … Time closed up like a fan before him.' [17] There is no more striking evocation in fiction of geological time. In turn, astronomy is central to *Two on a Tower*. As Hardy wrote to Gosse, 'I send this particular book in the belief that you will perceive, if nobody else does, what I have aimed at – to make science, not the mere padding of a romance, but the actual vehicle of romance.'[18] The language of Darwinian evolution in its most sombre aspects pervades *The Woodlanders* (1887), upturning the comfort of pastoral:

> Here, as everywhere, the Unfulfilled Intention, which makes life what it is, was as obvious as it could be among the depraved crowds of a city slum. The leaf was deformed, the curve was crippled, the taper was interrupted; the lichen ate the vigour of the stalk, and the ivy slowly strangled to death the promising sapling.[19]

Volition and intention – of God and of humans alike – were also being eroded by mid-Victorian discovery. Darwin, while uncovering the animal origins and kinship of man, also brought to the fore the idea that chance might underlie regularity; that regularities might arise from distributions of events that were themselves the result of unfathomable, unmeasurable causes. In 1926 Hardy copied into his notebooks a quotation from George Bernard Shaw:

> As compared to the open-eyed intelligent wanting & trying of Lamarck, the Darwinian process may be described as a chapter of accidents. As such it seems simple, because you do not at first realize all that it involves. But when its whole significance dawns on you, your heart sinks into a heap of sand within you. There is a hideous fatalism about it, a ghastly & damnable reduction of beauty & intelligence, of strength & purpose, of honour & aspiration, to such casually picturesque changes as an avalance may make in a mountain landscape, or a railway accident in a human figure.[20]

Attempts were being made, predictably, to tame chance.[21] Appearing in the same year as the *Origin of Species*, a paper on kinetic theory by the Scottish physicist James Clerk Maxwell introduced the first foundational physical theory in which probability played a fundamental role.[22] In *A Laodicean* (1881) the roguish Dare seeks to learn and master the laws of chance, both to increase his earnings and to bring about the marriage of his father to the rich heiress Paula Power. At the beginning of Book the Second, he is seen 'thoughtfully' reading De Moivre's eighteenth-century *Doctrine of Chances*.[23] The subtitle to this seminal work is 'a Method of Calculating the Probabilities of Events in Play'. The *Doctrine of Chances* is not just about play; De Moivre uses a sustained analysis of the results of play to develop 'a Method of Calculating the Effects of Chance'.[24] One of his aims is that the *Doctrine* 'may serve ... as a fit introduction to the Art of Reasoning; it being known by experience that nothing can contribute more to the attaining of that Art, than the consideration of a long Train of consequences, rightly deduced from undoubted Principles, of which this Book Affords many Examples'.[25] Later in the novel, sitting in a Monte Carlo casino, Dare insists on the soundness of his theory of chances and recurrences: 'if I only persevere in my system, the certainty that I must win is almost mathematical'.[26] *A Laodicean* repeatedly draws an analogy between sexual relationships and games, suggesting that the rules determining both may be understood and mastered. When Dare refers to his grand matchmaking scheme as a game, he is alive to the role that probability could – and would – play in scientific and social calculation.[27] Darwin's cousin Frances Galton, the founder of eugenics, wrote in 1889 that the chief law of probability 'reigns with serenity and in complete effacement amidst the wildest confusion';[28] in the words of Ian Hacking, 'by the end of the century chance had attained the respectability of a Victorian valet, ready to be the loyal servant of the natural, biological and social sciences'.[29]

the irrepressible new

Hardy copied and underlined Matthew Arnold's observations on the complexity of modernity:

> modern times find themselves with an immense system of institutions, established facts, accredited dogmas, customs, rules which have come to them from times not modern. In this system their life has to be carried forward; yet they have a sense that this system is not of their

own creation, that it by no means corresponds exactly with the wants of their actual life, that, for them it is customary, not rational. The awakening of this sense is the awakening of the modern spirit.[30]

Modernity was defined in terms of an awakening, a need to adjust to and make sense of what Hardy called the 'irrepressible new'.[31] Working in the Platonic tradition, nineteenth-century scientists from John Herschel in his *Preliminary Discourse on the Study of Natural Philosophy* (1830) through Thomas Huxley to Karl Pearson in 1892 argued that science embodies an almost ideal way of knowing, of *interpreting*.[32] But science was at once a method of knowing, and a source of further confusion: 'modern science is literally bombarding us with new conditions – and new ideas'.[33]

Darwin's new creation story, *The Origin of Species*, explicitly a quest for origins, set in train among his contemporaries a new search for self-knowledge. Fear of the break up of social and political custom, of abandonment by God, of biological and moral degeneration, dogged the late nineteenth century. Hardy recorded in his notebooks: '"Man know thyself," a modern scientist once asserted, had been converted by the increase of knowledge into the gloomy advice, "Man, may thou never know what thou art".'[34] In *Jude the Obscure* Sue and Jude's own supersensitivity, their abnormal self-consciousness, is synonymous with modernity itself; they are supremely attuned to the transitional state into which they are born and for which they are at once unprepared and too ready. 'No poor woman has ever wished more than I that Eve had not fallen, so that (as the primitive Christians believed) some harmless mode of vegetation might have peopled Paradise', declares Sue, but it is clear from her language that she does not really wish this.[35] Free-thinking Sue, whose intellect scintillates like a star before she retreats into self-recrimination, convention and despair at the close of the novel, does not want to return to vegetative non-being. Nonetheless, she has a point. The tree of knowledge has its own torments. 'Don't suppose for a moment', said Hardy in 1904, 'that I am hostile to the Christian religion. I often wish that I had lived in the Middle Ages, when the Church was supreme and unquestioned.'[36] If the universe was not governed by God, then who or what was at the helm? In 'Nature's Questioning' Hardy framed the first cause as some 'Vast Imbecility'; at the close of the nineteenth century, it seemed that the President of the Immortals was sporting with humans, as Hardy puts it famously at the close of *Tess of the d'Urbervilles*; or worse, that there might be no president. Was the world, like the rudderless Durbeyfield ship that represents it – 'if the heads of the Durbeyfield household chose to sail into difficulty, disaster, starvation, disease, degradation, death, thither were these half-dozen little captives under hatches compelled to sail with them' (p. 61) – at the mercy of Godless chance and myopic human vision? This was the question that plagued the late Victorians, and to which science seemed to pose more questions than answers. 'If science ... augments the means of satisfying ancient wants, it involves also the creation of new wants.'[37]

feeling and freedom

Freedom and feeling are central to Hardy's work. '*Feeling* – the great motor force of human life', he noted from Comte's *Social Dynamics*, and his novels and poetry show a sustained exploration of the possibilities of, and constraints upon, free will.[38] Struck by the irony of the Darwinian psychologist Henry Maudsley in *Natural Causes and Supernatural Seemings* (1886), he copied the following into his notebooks: 'consciousness tells [the individual] indeed that he is a self-sufficing individual with infinite potentialities of freewill; it tells him also that the sun goes round the earth'.[39] Equally, he noted that 'others had said, determinism or freedom. K[ant] says determinism & freedom', and

> Haeckel's world, in which men are mere puppets and automata, is contrary to the daily evidence of our own experience. There is no living man possessed of personality who can deny that his own fate lies in his own hands. Instinctively we feel that we have the power to choose, and to choose between good and evil.[40]

The idea that the knowledge brought by scientific inquiry would not necessarily reduce possibilities for freedom clearly struck a chord with Hardy:

> we cannot, it is true, as yet logically reconcile this freedom of the will with the uniformity of the laws of nature or with such observed facts as heredity. But it cannot be doubted that as the human mind advances the formula will be found to reconcile them. Nor can those who adopt Haeckel's position ignore the fact that modern science is shaking the very foundations of their theories as to the indestructibility and permanence of matter.[41]

Hardy's desire for intellectual freedom promoted his interest in scientific inquiry and his desire for access to the latest scientific thinking. But his attitude to science remained ambivalent all his life. Fully conscious of the potential of science for good, he opposed any form of intellectual censorship, writing to Gosse in 1909 that the *Origin of Species* was one of those books that would have been banned if library censorship had its way, and pointing out 'the discriminator between the bad and worthless, & the startling & enlightening' was unlikely to be found 'in the ranks of busy librarians'.[42] Aged 19 when the *Origin* was published, he recorded that he had been one its 'earliest acclaimers' (*Life*, p. 158), and listed those who had had the greatest influence on him as 'Darwin, Huxley, Spencer, Comte, Hume, Mill'.[43] He attended Darwin's funeral at Westminster Abbey where, 46 years later, he too – minus his heart – was buried. He read and rubbed shoulders with scientists, drawing upon, and writing against them, in his fiction. In 1863 he even had his head examined by the same phrenologist, Cornelius Donovan, who had read the head of Galton in 1849: 'Dr Donovan the phrenologist gauged heads in the Strand, informing [him] that his would lead him to no good' (*Life*, p. 43). He knew the scientists James Crichton-Browne and Ray Lankester, took notes from a *Spectator* review of Galton's *Inquiries into the Human Faculty and its Development* (in which the term 'eugenics' first appeared),[44] attended at least one meeting of the Eugenics Education Society, where he heard Montague Crackanthorpe's Presidential Address, and corresponded regularly with the eugenist Charles William Saleeby. He also worked closely with the archaeologist General Augustus Pitt-Rivers on the digs at Max Gate.[45]

But Hardy was also aware of the potential for the abuse of scientific knowledge. He was struck by a disturbingly prescient prediction from the historian and essayist Arthur Helps:

> if scientific-men really give their minds to the destruction of their fellow-creatures they will invent something which will throw all your Armstrong guns into the shade ... . Some day there will come the knowledge of the means of creating a pestilence ... some vapour.[46]

In 1924, over half a century later, Hardy wrote: 'After two thousand years of mass / We've got as far as poison-gas.'[47] Science was potentially at odds not only with freedom but also with feeling. Hardy confessed in his autobiography in 1881 to 'infinite trying to reconcile a scientific view of life with the emotional and spiritual, so that they may not be interdestructive', but this trying only led him to conclude that 'the emotions have no place in a world of defect, and it is a cruel injustice that they should have developed in it' (*Life*, p. 153). What he really sought was a synthesis between science and imagination, lamenting the fragmentation that modernity brought in train. A note on the 'Spiritual movement' in the nineteenth century continued:

> the thought of the century ... all schools tended to the doctrine of philosophic unity, & that the principle of dualism was thoroughly discarded. Whether we take the Hegelian system, or the idea of 'a double-face' unity or the so called Philosophy of the Unconscious, or the idealistic Theism of some eminent thinkers, or the Spencerian philosophy of Evolution, – in all there is a strenuous attempt to reach a universal unity, a substance (in the sense of Spinoza) from which all phenomena take their origin.[48]

Likewise, Hardy noted, 'will not the men of the future look back with wonder on the ages in which religion, philosophy, & the science of nature were supposed to be at war, instead of being, as they will be then, one system?',[49] and urged an interchange between the disciplines of science and history:

> in the deplorable condition of our present historical & scientific training – history leaving out science, & science leaving out history – discoverers of equal or greater intrinsic merit than Harvey remain uncommemorated. Archimedes, Kepler, Huyghens, Lagrange, Lavoisier, Bichat, are names which though known to the many, are appreciated only by the few.[50]

mind and matter

Hardy had two careers, as an architect and a writer. From the age of 16 to 32 he worked in architecture, and his architectural notebook shows him to be an accomplished draughtsman and architect. As Sir John Summerson wrote in the 1966 foreword to this book, 'the sensibility to architectural forms and devices shown on some of these pages is a thing which, once acquired, can never be lost. Hardy had it and no study of him as a man, novelist and poet can be complete without recognition of this fact.'[51] C. J. P. Beatty notes that after a break of some eight or nine years, following his decision in 1872 not to return to working for T. Roger Smith (with whom he had been designing schools for the London School Board), Hardy continued to make use of his architectural expertise, at least in an advisory capacity, for the rest of his life.[52] His architectural skills were readily transferred to his writing career. He built structures out of his poetry and novels. 'Not only does Mr Hardy's scientific profession speak through the mouths of his characters, but old and beautiful buildings adorn his pages as they do the landscape he loves', observed the *Atlantic Monthly*, adding that Hardy not only drew on architecture for material for his novels, but that the intellectual appeal of his novels came largely 'from the architectonics of his literary structures. One never loses sight of Hardy the architect.'[53] This ability to embrace and to seek to unite science and art – what Hardy would call 'the science of fiction' in an article of this name in *The New Review* in 1891 – is evident in many of his fictional characters. In *The Well-Beloved* Pierston is an artist, but well-versed in geometry; Fitzpiers in *The Woodlanders* is both a medical doctor and an idealist; Farfrae in *The Mayor of Casterbridge* is a singer and master of machinery, and Jude a scholar, an idealist and a stonemason.

Hardy was deeply committed to things *in the world*, as well as in and of the mind. So who better than he to provide a way of seeing not only the tension but the essential connectedness of world and mind? In 1886 he noted an essay in the *Contemporary Review* by the physiologist George Romanes: 'Although all conscious volition is matter in motion ... it does not follow that all matter in motion is conscious volition', adding '[Qy. how much complication is necessary to produce consciousness].'[54] For Hardy the world is greater than the individual – the source of all Tess's woe, for example – even though on occasions the indomitable spirit of the romantics, of Victorian liberalism and individuality does break through and champion the value of the individual: 'upon her sensations the whole world depended to Tess; through her existence all her fellow-creatures existed, to her. The universe itself only came into being for Tess on the particular day in the particular year in which she was born' (p. 214). Ultimately, however, he remains committed to material forces in the world; he does not champion or even concede the absolute triumph of the individual, repeatedly underscoring the importance of community, and the power of environment, for good or bad, so that individual and society remain at odds through his work. In the words of Gosse, looking back from 1918,

we find in Mr. Hardy's earliest verse no echo of the passionate belief in personal immortality which was professed by Ruskin and Browning. He opposed the Victorian theory of human 'progress'; the Tennysonian sympathy and goodness of Nature, and was in revolt against the self-centredness of the Romantics.[55]

Darwin succeeded in integrating humans into the animal kingdom, an integration which frequently turns up in Hardy's notebooks: 'the first condition of happiness, he (T.) tells us, is that the link between man & nature shall not be broken'; 'in the eyes of science man is not "higher" than the other animals'; '*Man* – The very ground-thought of Science is to treat man as part of the natural order.'[56] Hardy is consistently aware of the interaction between individual and environment, profoundly committed to the power and importance of place, not simply in respect of regional attachment, but for its interactive influence.[57] He copied into his notebooks from an article in the *Fortnightly Review* by Leslie Stephen: 'history depends upon the relation between the organism & the environment'.[58] Equally, he noted from Herbert Spencer that 'the highest possible Life is reached when there is some inner relation of actions fitted to meet every outer relation of actions by which the organism can be affected',[59] and was struck also by Comte on the relation between organism and environment: 'Biological Dependence' – 'The nobler phenomena are everywhere subordinate to those which are grosser, but also simpler & more regular ... Man is entirely subordinate to the World – each living being to its own environment.'[60] This was an expression of Hardy's socialist politics no less than his adherence to evolutionary ideas. Environment, or circumstance, rather than heredity or breeding, are fundamental to the progress – or stagnation – of the individual, as his novels show: for example, in *The Hand of Ethelberta* Ethelberta is able to use the city to disguise her lowly origins and keep herself and her family in luxury. Jude knows the Nicene creed better than his rich counterparts, but the doors of Oxford colleges are closed to him; and while Marty South is denied opportunity for artistic creation by the harsh socio-economic circumstances in which she finds herself, 'the fingers which clasped the heavy ash haft might have skilfully guided the pencil or swept the string, had they only been set to do it in good time' (p. 48). The same politics lies behind his notebook comment on a piece by the poet and essayist Frederick Myers in the *Fortnightly Review*:

the drift of the article is that beings have a *multiplex* nature, human as other; that what we suppose to be choice is reflex action only – that by implanting impulses in hypnotic states they can be made part of the character. There seems reason in this, for physical development

– (e.g. of the hand) – can be produced (in other ways) (by labour say) – as well as hereditarily.[61]

For Hardy, London is a hotbed of environmental gloom; a city of 'four million forlorn hopes', where 'cabin'd, cribb'd, confin'd – in Whitechapel the density of population [gives] only 3 1/2 square yards of space for each person, air & water alike being impure'.[62] Through this emphasis on the environment Hardy embraces the central tenet of Darwinism, the interrelation of individual and environment, and, ultimately, the subordination of species to their surroundings; after all, the survival of the fittest (a term for which Herbert Spencer was responsible, but which Darwin then adopted) was the survival of those who were most *fitted* to their environment, or able to fit into it, to *adapt*. 'Variation', Darwin had observed in the *Origin*,

> would be taken advantage of by natural and sexual selection, in order to fit the several species to their several places in the economy of nature, and likewise to fit the two sexes of the same species to each other, or to fit the males and females to different habitats of life, or the males to struggle with other males for the possession of the females.[63]

Fitness was born of random variation, and bore no relation to moral goodness. It is no literary accident, though arguably a moral one, that Arabella Donn, Hardy's least loveable woman, adapts, and survives.

the scientific imagination

In 1876 Hardy copied from an article by the positivist John Henry Bridges:

> every great scientific effort demands ... the imaginative audacity to soar above the level of routine & prejudice, & to evoke ... from the unknown chaos unheard-of hypotheses, until one shall appear worthy of being confronted with the facts – capable of informing them with meaning.[64]

Some 30 years later he was struck by the remarks of Lafcadio Hearn on the importance of the scientific imagination to the creative process:

> In history I think one should only seek the extraordinary, the
> monstrous, the terrible; in mythology the most fantastic and sensuous,
> just as in romance. But there is one more absolutely essential study in
> the formation of a strong style – science. No romance equals it. If one
> can store up in his brain the most extraordinary facts of astronomy,
> geology, ethnology, etc., they furnish him with a wonderful and
> startling variety of images, symbols, and illustrations.[65]

Hardy gives us scientific images and explanations, but he also gives us
windows onto the supernatural; onto magical worlds in which the powers
of the mind, of dreams and fantasies overpower reason. often electing,
as Gosse noted in the *Edinburgh Review* in 1918, 'that the dream shall
hold the place of fact'.[66] In 'An Imaginative Woman' Ella Marchmill
inadvertently falls pregnant through sexual fantasy, assisted, it would
seem, by the presence of a photograph under her pillow.[67]

Hardy's commitment to rural life, as a ballast against the new, also
provides him with a storehouse of faith and magical thinking:

> You must not think me a hard-hearted rationalist ... Half my time
> (particularly when I write verse) I believe – in the modern use of
> the word – not only in things that Bergson does, but in spectres,
> mysterious voices, intuitions, omens, dreams, haunted places, etc.,
> etc. (*Life*, p. 489)

When these phenomena occur in Hardy they are nonetheless framed
by economic considerations, pointing to his abiding materialism, and
his commitment, ultimately, to the forces of mind and matter alike. As
Blackwood's Magazine noted in 1913, 'in the world of his painting the
"forecaster" still foretells the weather at a price, the quack-salver vends
his cheap cures, or offers for sale the love-philtres, which seemed of
efficacy in the golden age'.[68]

A growing scientific interest in the workings of the mind and the
unconscious allows Hardy to explore superstition without being
unscientific, and an understanding of his interest in the unconscious
extends what we may regard as science in his fiction. As he noted from
Eduard von Hartmann's *Philosophy of the Unconscious*:

> A number of the contrarieties & antinomies of earlier creeds & systems
> are reconciled by the adoption of ... the principle of the Unconscious
> ... There is a general tendency of thought towards this single principle.

In each succeeding chapter one piece more of the world crystallizes, as it were, around this *nucleus*, until, expanded to *all-unity*, it embraces the Cosmos, & at last is suddenly revealed as that wh. has formed the core of all great philosophies, the Substance of Spinoza, the Absolute Idea of Plato & Hegel, Schopenhauer's *Will*, & c.[69]

Hardy saw a need to expand the realm of science, noting the essentially scientific material that literature contained:

Strange to say it is where the data are fewest that the unwillingness to concede the title of Science is least. The word Anthropology is practically limited to the study of men of the tertiary or quaternary periods. The laws of mental & social development during the last 3000 years, where materials for forming a sound judgment are really at hand, are still very commonly regarded as lying outside the pale of science & as belonging to the domain of literature.[70]

The crucial relationship between science and the imagination was taken up by several scientific thinkers in the second half of the nineteenth century. A paper by John Tyndall on 'The Scientific Use of the Imagination' is a case in point; Darwin found it 'grand and most interesting'.[71] The idealist philosopher and founder of biometrics Karl Pearson, Britain's first professor of Eugenics, referred readers of *The Grammar of Science* (1892), his most widely read book, to Wordsworth's Preface to the *Lyrical Ballads* as an example of the parallel between the aesthetic and the scientific judgement. He went on to show the integral role of the imagination to science, observing that the laws of science

are products of the creative imagination. They are the mental interpretations – the formulae under which we resume wide ranges of phenomena, the results of observation on the part of ourselves or of our fellowmen ... it is necessary to strongly emphasize this side of science, for we are frequently told that the growth of science is destroying the beauty and poetry of life.[72]

Pearson warned against the assumption of opposition between the aesthetic and scientific judgements: 'the fact is, that with the growth of our scientific knowledge the basis of the aesthetic judgment is changing and must change'. In Hardy's fiction science and the aesthetic are closely bound.

the unconscious

Current scientific debate on the nature of consciousness argues that the self is an illusion born of biochemical reactions or 'neurone firing'. Steve Jones, in his 1997 introduction to James Watson's *The Double Helix* (1968) writes: 'Darwin knocked mankind off his pinnacle. DNA grinds his face into the biological mud.'[73] The nature of mind came under close scrutiny in mid-Victorian Britain:

> phenomena of will ... can only be considered as the last transformation of the great natural forces of light & heat & electricity, passing through the mysterious involvements of the human nervous system. Conscience merely makes the last step in the upward evolution. It has no independent reality, no distinct laws. It falls with all that depends upon it under the empire of force which rules all nature.[74]

If human apartness from the rest of nature was being questioned – an apartness which was fundamental to Christian belief – and the idea of the soul was faltering, then what lay outside and what remained within the human mind – and body – could no longer be certain. Tess, for example, is able to leave her body and float, as a free consciousness, untrammelled by the material world:

> our souls can be made to go outside our bodies when we are alive ... A very easy way to feel 'em go ... is to lie on the grass at night and look straight up at some big bright star; and, by fixing your mind upon it, you will soon find that you are hundreds and hundreds o' miles away from your body, which you don't seem to want at all. (p. 175)

Dairyman Crick remains sceptical.

Hardy's notebooks show an increasing fascination with mind. The human mind – or spirit – was, as Hardy elsewhere noted, habitually at odds with the material world – 'this great & eternal incongruity of man's existence – the conflict of a spiritual nature & such aspirations as man's with conditions entirely physical' – but mind over the course of the century is also increasingly seen to be at one with matter, constituted by the same stuff, and subject to the same laws. The close relations between mind and matter gave the environment a more effective role than had been hitherto imaginable, offering a way of countering the effects of heredity, for the idea that physical process infused the mental universe, underpinning all laws, displaced the controlling function of heredity, emphasising the external world, and thus nurture:

> Dr Weismann (*Studies in the theory of Descent*) goes so far as to say that the whole mechanism of the universe may well be conceived as having an interior & mental aspect corresponding to its external & self-complete framework. Unless you assume the ultimate atom to have some inner qualities analogous to those which we call mental – qualities such as the late Prof. Clifford used to speak of as those of mindstuff – there is no explaining how the mental universe developed out of the physical. ... *Another hypothesis* ... represents mind as never interfering in the course of physical events, but at best representing a mere inner aspect of the outward frame of things – a sort of backwater from the stream of physical forces.[75]

Hardy copied out George Lewes's assertion that:

> Physiology began to disclose that all the mental processes were (mathematically speaking) *functions* of physical processes, i.e. – varying with the variations of bodily states; & this was declared enough to banish for ever the conception of a Soul, except as a term simply expressing certain functions.[76]

In his preoccupation with mind Hardy becomes increasingly interested in the idea of the unconscious. A notebook extract foregrounds Kant's thinking about the unconscious in ways which show a remarkable affinity with Freud's later analysis: 'to have ideas, & yet not to be conscious of them', and '"the clear ideas" says Kant, 'are but an infinitely small fraction of these same <[total ideas]>, exposed to consciousness. That only a few spots on the great chart of our minds are illuminated may well fill us with amazement.'[77] The question of unconscious processes raised – and raises – questions about responsibility. In 1917 Freud remarked that the ego was not master in its own house,[78] an observation which had become increasingly clear in the preceding century. George Eliot seeks, in the absence of God, stability in the past: 'if the past is not to bind us, where can duty lie? We should have no law but the inclination of the moment.'[79] But if actions stem from unconscious processes, can the past – the collective accretion of past actions – provide reliable guidance?

A reviewer in *Blackwood's Magazine* remarked that nature, and rural custom, provided stability, and evidence of human permanence, in

Hardy's fiction: 'the immutable countryside, where three or four score years are included in the present, changes neither its picture nor its frame. The perfect blending of men with inanimate things is always before Mr. Hardy's eyes.'[80] Hardy himself declares early in *The Return of the Native* that 'to know that every thing around and underneath had been from prehistoric times as unaltered as the stars overhead, gave ballast to the mind adrift on change and harassed by the irrespressible new'. But his novels increasingly chronicle the dissolution of rural custom in the face of forced migration to the towns – a record of the *new*, of unrest and disruption which culminates in the rootlessness of *Jude the Obscure*. And, in his last novels he turns from the material world to the mind, as if there were more going on – more to explore – within than without. As the *Quarterly Review* noted in 1904:

> since writing *Tess of the d'Urbervilles* Mr Hardy has averted his eyes from the spectacle of the world, and devoted himself to the study of Schopenhauer and von Hartmann. In *The Well-Beloved* the elements of idealistic philosophy, and not the facts of life, are his theme ... *Jude the Obscure*, that much discussed work, is another of Hardy's essays in metaphysics.[81]

In fact, the material world, and issues of heredity, reproduction and biological instinct, also loom large in these works, with the language of *The Well-Beloved* increasingly racialised in later editions.[82] Nonetheless, it is true to say that the mind becomes more and more the focus of Hardy's work, culminating in *The Dynasts*, his study of history as the outcome of a purposeless, unconscious Immanent Will. The idea draws both on Schopenhauer's conception of the world as will and idea and von Hartmann's definition of the unconscious, which Hardy transcribed into his notebooks: 'I designate the united unconscious will & unconscious idea "the Unconscious."'[83] The unconscious offers Hardy a freedom – it even allows him to distance himself from his own work, observing, as he did in an interview in 1901 with his friend William Archer, 'the human mind is a sort of palimpsest, I suppose; and it's hard to say what records may not lurk in it'.[84] In his 1912 Preface to *Jude the Obscure* he remarked, 'no doubt there can be more in a book than the author consciously puts there'. However, if the unconscious is the determining force of individual and public action then it also offers a negative prospect for human progress and the assumption of responsibility. 'The Uncons. has, as Aristotle says, no memory: therefore it can learn nothing from its experience in the world', Hardy noted.[85] Where did that leave George Eliot's directive to look to the past for guidance? Ultimately, though, Hardy rejects von Hartmann's bleaker views that the world is governed by the unconscious in favour of the idea that consciousness is gradually increasing. The conclusion of his epic verse-drama offers hope that consciousness, and responsibility, will come to the process of – and the players in – history. In 1908, in a review of the final part of *The Dynasts*, Harold Child noted:

> he may jeer with the Spirit Ironic, with the Spirit of the Years he may be coldly impartial; but the Pities have the last word. Through them, all along, we have suffered with the sufferers; with them we are encouraged – or, at least, allowed – to hope.
>
> But – a stirring thrills the air
> Like the sounds of joyance there
>   That the rages
>   Of the ages
> Shall be cancelled, and deliverance offered from the darts that were,
>   Consciousness the Will informing, till It fashions all things fair!

'We are profoundly grateful to the dramatist who chooses that note,' Child continued, 'the only tolerable, the inevitable right note – on which to close his great work of art.'[86]

Hardy noted from Schopenhauer: 'Everything that is really fundamental in a man, & therefore genuine, works, as such, unconsciously, in this respect like the power of Nature',[37] and copied the following from the *Lancet*: 'viewed in the light of evolution, it is only those recently acquired functions that are perfectly conscious: repetition of functions leads to their unconscious performance'.[88] Likewise, he was struck by the definition of secondary personality by the philosopher and psychologist James Hervey Hyslop: '*Secondary Personality*:. – Subconscious mental processes – e.g. "hypnotize a man … suggest that he make a speech, & he may do so in a way that he could not in a normal state. He seems to be another person than himself."'[89] He was fascinated by the emergent psychoanalytical process of projection: 'Just in proportion as the reality is separated from the appearance does the knower become conscious of an activity of his own thought in determining things',[90] and, equally, by dreams, making notes on a report on automatic writing from the Society for Psychical Research: 'Automatisms. … The dramatizations of dream-characters – their seeming independence of our own personality, from which yet they are undoubtedly derived.' He noted their centrality to existence:

> dreams represent little more than that tumult of fragmentary images which I believe to be perpetually proceeding within us, beneath the level of anything which can be called an identity … The dreams which emerge into waking memory are for the most part a mere jumble of this kind … *disjecta membra* or raw material of self.[91]

Hardy's increasing interest in the unconscious sheds light on his emphasis on mental pathology in *Jude the Obscure*, a novel that was itself condemned as morbid, pathological and diseased by contemporary readers. Before his final phase of novel-writing he noted a meeting held by the Aristotelian Society to discuss the question 'whether mind is synonymous with consciousness':

> a decision was arrived at that it was not. Ribot, in his book on 'Heredity', said 'Mind has two parallel modes of activity, the one conscious, the other unconscious'; while Dr Henry Maudsley declared that 'It cannot be too distinctly born in mind that consciousness is not co-extensive with mind, that it is not mind, but an incident accompaniment of mind.' Mind, indeed, as Dr. Schofield points out, 'may be conscious, sub-conscious, or unconscious', and it is the sub-conscious or unconscious mind which is the great factor to be used in the curing of disease, as it is the great factor which produces disease.[92]

the rising sun

In *Tess of the d'Urbervilles*, in a chapter which opens with a strong sense of the economic laws that determine marriage patterns – 'a field man's wages being as high at twenty-one as at forty, marriage was early here' (p. 105) – Hardy remarks that the perspiring dancers, merging, quite literally, with their environment, form together 'a sort of vegeto-human pollen'. The term resonates with the integration of humans into the animal, indeed, the entire material world, compressing shifting socio-scientific paradigms into a new and single term. Moments later the dancers are lifted out of their vegetative state and expanded to mythical, visionary proportions, in another characteristically Hardyan shift of scale and register, becoming 'a multiplicity of Pans whirling a multiplicity of Syrinxes; Lotis attempting to elude Priapus, and always failing'. Hardy refuses to stay with the scientific, retreating here into the reassuring whirligig of Greek mythology; neither register holds sway.

'We with our modern ways of life are not aware how everything we think or speak or do is dependent on the sun', Hardy noted from Max Müller.[93] When Angel asks himself why he did not pay more attention to truth than fact (p. 456), we gain an insight into Hardy's attitude towards science. Knowledge must not be severed from truth, from the spirit. The knowledge that Tess has thrust upon her cannot touch her purity, and the knowledge that Angel has of the facts of Tess's life does not save him from his essential priggishness until it is too late (in a novel that was going to be called *Too Late, Beloved!*). In Brazil, he had come to ask himself 'why he had not judged Tess constructively rather than biographically, by the will rather than the deed' (p. 456). Even at the last moment, in response to her urgent question, 'do you think we shall meet again after we are dead? I want to know', he is silent, leaving her at a loss: 'What – not even you and I, Angel, who love each other so well?' He withholds a reassurance that they will meet again, a reassurance than neither science nor theology ultimately forbid: 'like a greater than himself to the critical question at the critical time he did not answer' (p. 486). The comparison with Jesus before his accusers is poignant, both genuine and ironic, for it is the truth about his divine nature that Jesus refuses to tell, and there is a sense in which, for all his rational thinking, it is a profound truth that Angel withholds, privileging the letter above the spirit.

Written in the heat of debates on the death of the sun, in the light of knowledge that much that had been created was already extinct, spent, wasted, or becoming so, *Tess of the d'Urbervilles* is nonetheless a hymn of praise to the life that goes on, to the imagination which worships the sun and makes life not only bearable, but an eventual joy, and to nature, pervaded by 'appetite for joy'; 'that tremendous force, which sways humanity to its purpose' (p. 255). On the day on which Tess is arrested, as she lies asleep on an oblong slab, sheltered by pillars at Stonehenge, altar to the sun, we are reminded of the narrator's earlier wisdom:

The sun, on account of the mist, had a curious sentient, personal look, demanding the masculine pronoun for its adequate expression. His present aspect, coupled with the lack of all human forms in the scene, explained the old-time heliolatries in a moment. One could feel that a saner religion had never prevailed under the sky. The luminary was a golden-haired, beaming, mild-eyed, God-like creature, gazing down in the vigour and intentness of youth upon an earth that was brimming with interest for him. (p. 137)

In this paragraph science jostles with theology, embracing the beliefs and imaginings which vie, and reach some sort of dynamic if precarious equilibrium in Hardy's writing. The sun takes on human qualities in the absence of the human form, and indeed in the absence or loss of God as man, highlighting and seeming to compensate for, or perhaps to gloat over, the century's gradual shift from anthropocentrism – the displacement of man from the centre of all things. But then religion is redeemed, or, more precisely, worship of the sun is reclaimed as profoundly rational, or 'sane', and the sun becomes a Greek god, youthful and fascinated, but simultaneously embodying Apollonian measure and reason. The novel itself, more than any other of Hardy's works, is infused with the rays of the sun; they are by turn iridescent, dazzling, effusive, glaring and relentless, and, in a deft transference, *scientific*, surrounding Tess and her hopes in 'an ideal photosphere which surrounded her as she bounded along against the soft south wind' (p. 157), or glorifying her so that she becomes 'like the angel whom St John saw in the sun' (p. 280).

Science, myth and the imagination are woven together in Hardy's fiction as he strives to represent life – mind and matter – without falling victim to a single scientific theory, a single way of seeing. Instead, he remains committed to *ways* of seeing. In his notebook he wrote: 'the geologist, the antiquarian, & the farmer, gazing at a landscape, will each see totally different things in it, & the poet & the artist different things also',[94] noting also that 'to look on our own time from the point <of view> of universal history, on history from the point of view of geologic periods, on geology from the point of view of astronomy – this is to enfranchise thought'.[95] At a time of shifting perspectives and clashing creeds, Hardy unsettles his reader, moving between, combining and inverting different ways of seeing. One of his notebook entries, taken from Darwin, perhaps forms the most fitting end to a consideration of Hardy and science, for no one was more alive than Hardy to the complicated but essential relation of science and the imagination, and to the importance of seeing things anew.

At last I fell asleep on the grass, & awoke with a chorus of birds singing around me, & squirrels running up the trees, & some woodpeckers laughing, & it was as pleasant & rural a scene as ever I saw, & I did not care one penny how any of the beasts & birds had been formed.[96]

notes

1. *Life*, p. 406. For further statements of the same principles see Harold Orel, ed., *Thomas Hardy's Personal Writings* (London, 1967), pp. 49, 53.
2. Thomas Kuhn, *The Structure of Scientific Revolutions* (Chicago, 1962).
3. 'Review of Man's Place', *The Athenaeum* (28 February 1863).
4. *Literary Notebooks*, II, p. 29, I, p. 104.
5. *Two on a Tower*, ed. Sally Shuttleworth (Harmondsworth, 1999), p. 289.
6. For a discussion of scale in Hardy's novels, see 'Finding a Scale for the Human: Plot and Writing in Hardy's Novels', in Gillian Beer, *Darwin's Plots: Evolutionary Narrative in Darwin, George Eliot and Nineteenth-Century Fiction* (1983; 2nd edn, Cambridge, 2000), pp. 220–41. On science in *Two on a Tower*, see Sally Shuttleworth's Introduction to the 1999 edition, pp. xvi–xxxi.
7. Grant Allen, *Charles Darwin* (London, 1885), p. 32.
8. Wordsworth, 'Lines Written in Early Spring'; *Tess of the d'Urbervilles* (Harmondsworth, 1986), p. 62. Subsequent references to this edition are cited parenthetically in the text.
9. *Literary Notebooks*, II, p. 99.
10. For further discussion of Hardy's treatment of the issue of chance, see Gillian Beer, 'The Reader's Wager: Lots, Sorts, and Futures', in Beer, *Open Fields: Science in Cultural Encounter* (Oxford, 1996), pp. 273–94, and Angelique Richardson, 'Hardy and Biology', in Phillip Mallett, ed., *Thomas Hardy: Texts and Contexts* (London, 2002), pp. 156–79.
11. Darwin, *The Descent of Man, and Selection in Relation to Sex*, 2 vols (1871; Chichester, 1981), I, p. 177.
12. Rudolf Clausius coined the term in 1859. In Clausius's sense 'the entropy of a system is the measure of the unavailability of its thermal energy for conversion into mechanical work' and 'the entropy of the universe tends to a maximum' (*OED*).
13. William Thomson, 'On the Age of the Sun's Heat', *Macmillan's Magazine* 5 (1862), p. 229.
14. Crosbie Smith, *The Science of Energy: A Cultural History of Energy Physics in Victorian Britain* (London, 1998), pp. 171–91; see also 'The Death of the Sun: Victorian Solar Physics and Solar Myth', in Beer, *Open Fields*. On solar myth in *Tess of the d'Urbervilles* see J. B. Bullen, *The Expressive Eye: Fiction and Perception in the Work of Thomas Hardy* (Oxford, 1986), pp. 204–22.
15. *Autobiographies of Charles Darwin and Thomas Henry Huxley*, ed. G. de Beer (London, 1974), pp. 153–4.
16. *Literary Notebooks*, I, p. 189.
17. *A Pair of Blue Eyes*, ed. Roger Ebbatson (Harmondsworth, 1986), pp. 271–2; see Beer, *Darwin's Plots*, pp. 253–4.
18. *Letters*, I. 110.
19. *The Woodlanders*, ed. Dale Kramer (Oxford, 1985), p. 41.
20. *Literary Notebooks*, II, p. 237.
21. See Ian Hacking, *The Taming of Chance* (Cambridge, 1990); see also Gerd Gigerenzer et al., *The Empire of Chance* (Cambridge, 1989).

22. Maxwell, 'Illustrations of the Dynamical Theory of Gases', *Philosophical Magazine*, 19 (1860), reprinted in E. Garber, S. G. Brush and C. W. F. Everitt, eds, *Maxwell on Molecules and Gases* (Cambridge, MA, 1986).

23. *A Laodicean*, ed. Jane Gatewood (Oxford, 1991), p. 127.

24. Abraham de Moivre, *The Doctrine of Chances: Or a Method of Calculating the Probabilities of Events in Play* (London, 1718). The book went through three editions in 1711, 1738 and 1756. As Hacking notes, De Moivre's fundamental chances were equipossible outcomes on some sort of physical set-up. Referring to De Moivre's 'unrelenting determinism', Lorraine Daston writes: 'by their own lights, the chief achievements of [Jacob] Bernoulli and De Moivre lay in scaling down Cardano's infinite number of throws to a finite, calculable number needed to guarantee that calculations and fact would very likely match. This is why determinism, far from stifling mechanical probability theory, actually promoted it' (Lorraine Daston, *Classica Probability in the Enlightenment* (Princeton, 1988), p. 37). While Cardano explained the discrepancy between calculation and actual outcome by 'luck', the new metaphysics in which Bernoulli and De Moivre participated banished luck.

25. Fifteen years after *A Laodicean*, Hardy recorded an incident which closely resembles the scene with Dare in the Casino: '*September 23 1896*. At dinner at the public table [of the hotel] met a man possessed of the veritable gambling fever. He had been playing many days at the Casino (Roulette and Trente-et-quarante). He believes thoroughly in his "system" and yet, inconsistently, believes in luck: *e.g.* 36 came into his head as he was walking down the street towards the Casino today; and it made him back it, and he won ... . His system appears to be that of watching for numbers which have not turned up for a long time; but I am not sure' (*Life*, p. 300).

26. *A Laodicean*, p. 286.

27. These ideas developed as game theory in the twentieth century; see for example John von Neumann and Oskar Morgenstern, *Theory of Games and Economic Behavior* (Princeton, 1944).

28. *National Inheritance* (London, 1889), p. 66, cited in Hacking, *The Taming of Chance*, p. 2.

29. Hacking, *The Taming of Chance*, p. 2.

30. From Matthew Arnold, 'Heine', in *Essays in Criticism*, 1st Series; *Literary Notebooks*, I, pp. 105–6, where the whole pasage is underlined. For further discussion of this passage, see David J. DeLaura, '"The Ache of Modernism" in Hardy's Later Novels', *English Literary History* 34 (1967), p 396; and Richard H. Taylor, *The Neglected Hardy: Thomas Hardy's Lesser Novels* (London, 1982), p. 44.

31. *The Return of the Native*, ed. Simon Gatrell (Oxford, 1990), p. 6.

32. For an excellent discussion of this, and nineteenth-century relations between science and the social more generally, see George Levine, 'Two Ways Not to Be a Solipsist: Art and Science, Pater and Pearson', *Victorian Studies* 43 (2000), pp. 7–42. See also Levine, *Dying to Know: Scientific Epistemology and Narrative in Victorian England* (Chicago, 2002).

33. *Literary Notebooks*, II, p. 242.

34. *Literary Notebooks*, II, p. 295.

35. *Jude the Obscure*, ed. Dennis Taylor (Harmondsworth, 1998), p. 225.

36. 'Books and Bookmen', *Manchester Guardian* (15 October 1904), reprinted in James Gibson, ed., *Thomas Hardy: Interviews and Recollections* (London, 1999).

37. *Literary Notebooks*, I, p. 227, from Alfred Fouillée, 'Les Transformations Futures de l'Idée Morale' (1888).

38. *Literary Notebooks*, I, p. 68.

39. *Literary Notebooks*, I, p. 201.

40. *Literary Notebooks*, II, p. 161; II, p. 357.

41. *Literary Notebooks*, II, p. 357.

42. *Letters*, IV, p. 63.

43. Carl J. Weber, *Hardy of Wessex: His Life and Literary Career* (New York, 1965), pp. 246–7.

44. *Literary Notebooks*, I, pp. 154–5.

45. See Harold Orel, 'Hardy and the Developing Science of Archaeology', *Thomas Hardy Annual* 4 (1986), pp. 19–44; Josephine Pentney, 'Archaeology and Thomas Hardy', *The Thomas Hardy Journal* 4 (1988), pp. 17–18.

46. *Literary Notebooks*, I, p. 104.

47. 'Christmas 1924', in *Winter Words*.

48. *Literary Notebooks*, II, p. 107.

49. *Literary Notebooks*, I, p. 66.

50. *Literary Notebooks*, I, p. 50.

51. *The Architectural Notebook of Thomas Hardy* (Dorchester, 1966), p. vii.

52. C. J. Beatty, Introduction, *Architectural Notebook*, p. 4. See also Beatty, 'Thomas Hardy's Career in Architecture (1856–1872)' (Dorchester, 1978).

53. *Critical Heritage*, p. 396.

54. *Literary Notebooks*, I, p. 174.

55. *Critical Heritage*, p. 446.

56. *Literary Notebooks*, II, pp. 16, 225; I, p. 65. 'T' is Tolstoy.

57. For recent studies of Hardy's treatment of place see Simon Trezise, *Thomas Hardy's Cornwall: The Story of the West of Wessex Muse* (Exeter, 2003) and Ralph Pite, *Hardy's Geography: Wessex and the Regional Novel* (London, 2002).

58. *Literary Notebooks*, I, p. 132.

59. *Literary Notebooks*, I, p. 90.

60. Comte, *Social Dynamics*, p. 15, *Literary Notebooks* I, p. 74. Abridged quotation with reversed word-order and Hardy's underlining.

61. *Literary Notebooks*, I, p. 168.

62. *Literary Notebooks*, I, p. 32. The note is a comment on and summary of a *Times* leader on putting the Artizans' Dwelling Act of 1875 into force.

63. *The Origin of Species, or the Preservation of Favoured Races in the Struggle for Life* (1859; Harmondsworth, 1985), p. 194.

64. *Literary Notebooks*, I, p. 50.

65. *Literary Notebooks*, II, pp. 187–8.

66. *Edinburgh Review* 207 (1918), in *Critical Heritage*, p. 460.

67. First published in *Pall Mall Gazette* (April 1894); the story was collected in *Wessex Tales* in 1896 before being transferred to the 1912 Wessex Edition of *Life's Little Ironies*.

68. Charles Whibley, 'Thomas Hardy', in *Critical Heritage*, p. 415.

69. *Literary Notebooks*, II, p. 110.

70. *Literary Notebooks*, I, p. 114, quoting from J. H. Bridges on 'Evolution and Positivism', *Fortnightly Review*, 1877.
71. Delivered before the British Association at Liverpool in 1370. Tyndall sent the proofs to Darwin for comment; for his response, see Darwin to Tyndall, 8 September 1870: Darwin Correspondence Online Database at <http://darwin.lib.cam.ac.uk>
72. Karl Pearson, *The Grammar of Science* (London, 1892), p. 35.
73. James D. Watson, *The Double Helix* (1968; Harmondsworth, 1997), p. 5.
74. Extract from [John Tulloch], 'Morality without Metaphysics', in *Literary Notebooks*, I, p. 88. Björk notes that Hardy's extract is from the hostile representation of the 'ethical school of experience' in comparison with traditional concepts of morality on a metaphysical basis (533n.).
75. *Literary Notebooks*, I, p. 148.
76. *Literary Notebooks*, I, p. 92.
77. *Literary Notebooks*, II, p. 109.
78. 'A Difficulty in the Path of Psychoanalysis' (1917), in James Strachey, trans. and ed., *Complete Psychological Works of Sigmund Freud*, 24 vols (London, 1953–74), 17, pp. 135–44.
79. *The Mill on the Floss* (1860; Harmondsworth, 1985), pp. 601–2.
80. Charles Whibley, 'Thomas Hardy', *Critical Heritage*, p. 414.
81. Edward Wright, 'The Novels of Thomas Hardy', *Critical Heritage*, p. 362.
82. On the treatment of race in *The Well-Beloved* see Angelique Richardson, '"Some Science underlies all Art": The Dramatization of Sexual Selection and Racial Biology in Thomas Hardy's *A Pair of Blue Eyes* and *The Well-Beloved*', *Journal of Victorian Culture* (3)2 (Autumn 1998), pp. 302–38.
83. *Literary Notebooks*, II, p. 109.
84. James Gibson, ed., *Thomas Hardy: Interviews and Recollections*, p. 66.
85. *Literary Notebooks*, II, p. 112.
86. Harold Child, 'The Dynasts, Part Third', *Critical Heritage*, p. 370.
87. Schopenhauer, *Studies in Pessimism*, in *Literary Notebooks*, I, p. 29.
88. *Literary Notebooks*, II, p. 78.
89. *Literary Notebooks*, II, p. 91.
90. *Literary Notebooks*, I, p. 172.
91. The report was by Frederic W. H. Myers, on 'Automatic Writing – III: Physiological and Pathological Analogies': *Literary Notebooks*, I, p. 193.
92. *Literary Notebooks*, II, p. 130.
93. Max Müller, 'Solar Myths', *Nineteenth Century*, 18 (1885): *Literary Notebooks*, I, p. 388.
94. *Literary Notebooks*, II, p. 198. Quotation unidentified.
95. From Blanche Leppington, 'Amiel's Journal', *Contemporary Review*, 157: *Literary Notebooks*, I, p. 162.
96. From a letter by Darwin to his wife: *Literary Notebooks*, I, p 204.

8

'the immortal puzzle': hardy and sexuality

phillip mallett

In the Preface to the 1896 edition of *The Woodlanders*, Hardy remarked that in this story, 'as in one or two others in this series which involve the question of matrimonial divergence, the immortal puzzle – given the man and the woman, how to find a basis for their sexual relation – is left where it stood'. Hardy liked to attach such disclaimers to his work, and all the more where it was bound to prove controversial, and his readers, then and since, have generally ignored them. But in exploring human sexual relations, one of the questions he left unresolved, if hardly where it stood, was how far the man and the woman – especially the woman – are indeed 'given'. Not very far, according to John Stuart Mill, who argued in *The Subjection of Women* that what was called 'the nature of women' was in truth 'an eminently artificial thing – the result of forced repression in some directions, unnatural stimulation in others', and so not to be made the basis for a theory of their political rights, nor of their sexual relation with men.[1] Begging his own question, Mill saw women's 'nature', so called, as 'artificial', 'unnatural': socially constructed, not given. Charles Darwin, among others, took the contrary position. Both *The Origin of Species* and *The Descent of Man* helped to underpin the biological determinism which shaped so many accounts of the nature of men and women in the years when Hardy was writing fiction. While almost every position in late Victorian science was contested, there developed a near consensus that women were inferior to men in the cultural realm, and that this inferiority was grounded in the physiological differences between them. Tentative elsewhere in his discussion of sexual difference, Darwin was unequivocal about this.[2]

Hardy considered himself 'one of the earliest acclaimers' of Darwin (*Life*, p. 158), but he also admired Mill – the chapter on 'Individualism', from the essay *On Liberty*, was one of his '[c]ures for despair' (*Life*, p. 59) – and much of his writing about sexual relationships tracks their differing views on 'the nature of women'. His love-plots typically situate the woman on the threshold of sexual awareness, poised in the space between the care of her father and that of the husband to whom he entrusts her: the space, then, in which she has to work out how to represent herself, before her name and identity are absorbed into that of the man she marries, after which, as Henry Knight tells Elfride in *A Pair of Blue Eyes*, we should hope 'to hear no more about her'.[3] With some modifications – in *Desperate Remedies* Cytherea's brother Owen takes the place of her dead father, in *Far from the Madding Crowd* Bathsheba has no immediate family – this plot forms the basis of Hardy's first four novels.[4] In each, current ideas about women's nature as given are both called into play and called into question. A few illustrations must suffice.

Recent critical attention has been drawn to *Desperate Remedies*, Hardy's first published novel, by precisely those generic and thematic disruptions which troubled earlier readers. The sensation novel thrives by suggesting that beneath the conventional lies the wild and aberrant: hence its fascination with secrets, doubles, and crimes of passion, and its questioning, with varying degrees of self-consciousness, of class and gender boundaries. This last echoes throughout *Desperate Remedies*. Miss Aldclyffe has 'a severity about the lower outlines of the face which gave a masculine cast to this portion of her countenance', while 'Womanly weakness was nowhere visible save in one part – the curve of her forehead and brows.' Aeneas Manston's features similarly divide into male and female aspects, though in a reverse fashion to his mother's – his forehead is 'square and broad, his brows straight and firm', and so suitably masculine, but his lips have 'a woman-like softness of curve' – while Edward Springrove exhibits 'sufficiently masculine regularity' in the upper part of his face, except that his eyebrows are 'somewhat too softly arched ... for one of his sex'.[5] The sexuality of Cytherea Graye's three would-be lovers is oddly ambiguous.

The instability of gender boundaries extends into the sexual relationships in the novel. Cytherea's father, brother and husband-to-be, the men who have her well-being in their care, are all lacking in sexual identity. Mr Graye's death, in a fall from a tower, briskly registers his inadequacy as a lover and as a father. Owen then assumes a paternal role towards his sister – somewhat uneasily, if we are to read his mysterious lameness in Oedipal terms – but for much of the novel he and Springrove, her future husband, seem interchangeable. Cytherea and Springrove first meet when

Owen leaves for a walk and Springrove returns in his place; her interest in him is aroused when Owen quotes his opinions verbatim and at length; twice, in their efforts to protect her, one initiates an action, and the other concludes it.[6] But if the patriarchal tradition falters here, Miss Aldclyffe inverts it further, as she plans for her son to marry the young woman with whom she shares not only a forename but, for one night, a bed. Here she frees herself from 'the last remnant of restraint', flings her arms around Cytherea and pleads for kisses, only to turn jealously away when she learns that the mouth she has been 'sipping at' has previously been 'sullied' by kisses from a man. Nothing follows from this episode, and the discursive invisibility of same-sex love between women in the nineteenth century has been adduced to show that Hardy's readers, and perhaps Hardy himself, would have interpreted it in terms of womanly affection rather than sexual desire. Yet at least one contemporary reader, John Morley, thought it 'highly extravagant', and advised against publication, while Hardy marks its subversiveness by having Miss Aldclyffe's father die in the room below while the two women are in bed together.[7]

A trick of the light causes Miss Aldclyffe to first appear to Cytherea 'like a tall black figure standing in the midst of fire'; a trick of perspective causes her son, Manston, to appear 'of towering height' and 'dark in outline' against the sky, which is soon to be lit up by lightning. Almost parodically phallic, both alarm Cytherea with their sexuality. Manston's organ-playing, while the storm rages, produces 'a gnawing thrill' which makes her look up at him 'with parted lips'; on the night before their wedding she has a sado-masochistic dream of being 'whipped with dry bones suspended on strings'. The return to heterosexual feeling, then, hardly restores the equilibrium threatened by the lesbian scene; nor does Cytherea's closing marriage to Springrove, when the couple emerge as a 'lithe young woman in an airy fairy dress' and 'a young man in black stereotype raiment'. The clerk's insistence on their typicality – 'rale liven specimens' of 'the married man and wife' – serves to remind the reader that whatever it was in Cytherea that drew Miss Aldclyffe to her bed, or made her thrill at Manston's approach, is left unexpressed, and unsatisfied, at the end of the novel.[8]

The narrative voice in *Desperate Remedies* frequently assumes an agreed stock of ideas about women's nature and behaviour – even the 'masculine' Miss Aldclyffe prompts the observation that 'Women make confidences and then regret them' – and similar remarks are scattered throughout the early novels.[9] So, after the abandoned elopement in *A Pair of Blue Eyes*, the narrator asserts, with apparent confidence, that 'Elfride had her sex's love of sheer force in a man, however ill-directed', and that Stephen could only have maintained his place in her life by 'dragging her by the wrist to the rails of some altar, and peremptorily marrying her'.[10] This accords with long-standing assumptions about courtship, that it was the right and duty of the man to initiate and of the woman to respond, which were currently being underwritten by the theorists of sexual difference. Thus Herbert Spencer argued that the woman's need, in a savage state of society, to choose a man strong enough to protect her and her children, had since evolved into a general 'admiration of power', while Havelock Ellis construed women's 'modesty' as an echo of their 'primordial urge' to be conquered, even to the point that they needed some element of pain to gain sexual pleasure.[11] Stripped of their evolutionary gloss, such arguments recapitulate the familiar claim that a woman's 'No' is merely an erotically charged 'Yes'; as so often, the scientific debate about women's nature only confirmed what had been described by earlier writers.[12] But what the narrative of Hardy's novel suggests is that however Stephen's docility may have disappointed her, Elfride's increasing subjection to Henry Knight's 'sheer force' leaves her deeply unhappy. In chapter 19, for example, with her mind 'impregnated with sentiments of her own smallness' (the only way Knight seems likely to impregnate her), 'her discomfort [is] visible in her face'; as the chapter continues, she has a 'forlorn sense' of Knight's 'unapproachableness', is 'a little frightened' in conversation with him, and speaks 'woefully', 'desperately', 'with a little breath of distress', 'regretfully', and 'with misgiving'. Knight overwhelms Elfride with the 'hard square decisiveness in the shape of his sentences', which seem to her 'not there and then constructed, but ... drawn forth from a large store ready-made'. The same can be said of the narrator's statements about women, or 'Woman'; and about both the reader might feel that they are more decisive and to hand than apt or relevant.[13]

The narrator's apparent willingness in these novels to collude with conservative ideologies of 'womanhood' or 'the womanly', expressed in dismissive aphorisms, or through the tolerance shown to the more censorious of the male characters (Knight, Oak), runs counter to the attempt to make the main female characters the subjects of their own experience.[14] Repeatedly, the texts open up on a discrepancy between the way the heroines perceive themselves and the way they are perceived by others. The responsibility for this conflict, however, is borne by its victims, as one after the other they internalise the criticism aimed at them. Bathsheba feels 'coerced' not only into the act of promising to marry Boldwood, 'but into the emotion of fancying that she ought to promise'; Cytherea, similarly coerced by her sense of 'duty' into marriage with Manston, condemns her misgivings as 'wicked frailty'. Both have a man on hand – Oak in the one case, Owen Graye in the other – to confirm them in taking a low estimate of their own right to happiness.[15] But in both novels, the narrative draws our attention to the difficulty of making the kinds of judgement made by Oak and Graye. 'Nobody can enter into another's nature truly, that's what is so grievous,' reflects Cytherea; while Bathsheba tells Boldwood that 'It is difficult for a woman to define her feelings in language which is chiefly made by men to express theirs.'[16] For a moment, at least, the (male) narrator suspends his claim to be able to describe, or prescribe, the nature of women, and makes room for the woman to voice her own experience.

What Hardy's conscious position might have been, this early in his career, is not easily determined. Rosemarie Morgan sees the narrative generalisations as a deliberate 'stratagem' to divert the wrath of the 'Grundyist' reader and allow Hardy to write as the champion of women's sexual independence; Patricia Ingham suggests that he 'struggles but fails to accept a patriarchal view'; Roger Ebbatson's reference to 'the creative uncertainties of Hardy's handling of gender issues' in the earlier novels is nicely neutral as to whether he is to be seen as diagnosing the contradictions in his society's attitudes, or merely symptomatic of them.[17] In the later novels, however, and especially in *Tess* and *Jude*, Hardy subjects contemporary views to an overt and increasingly fierce critique. The rest of this essay is concerned with these more openly challenging novels.

tess, virginity and the fallen woman

The elements of the 'fallen woman' narrative were well established by the time Hardy came to write *Tess of the d'Urbervilles*: seduction, abandonment and repentance, followed by redemption or punishment and, typically, by emigration or death. The topos was not confined to fiction – the popular and the serious press, stage melodrama, even the reports of the various rescue societies working with prostitutes, all used similar narrative means – and the elements could of course be reshuffled. In 'Saturday Night in Arcady', Hardy's reworked story of the events leading up to Tess's violation, Big Beauty, like numerous fictional heroines before her – Little Em'ly, Ruth, Hetty Sorrel, Fanny Robin – is deserted by her seducer.[18] In the novel, however, it is Tess who leaves Alec, signalling both her own individuality and Hardy's refusal to be bound by what most earlier writers had seen as the key narrative question: whether the seduced girl was wicked or foolish, and at least partly to blame for her fall, or 'innocent', a victim of the actions of others rather than an agent herself. Part of Hardy's strategy in *Tess* is to unpick this easy antithesis.

But while the novel takes its meaning in part from earlier fictional treatments of the fallen woman, another piece of writing, still more scandalous than *Tess*, provides an equally suggestive context. During the 1870s and 1880s, protests against the abuse of male power over women had begun to focus on juvenile prostitution. In 1875 the age of consent for girls had been raised from 12 to 13, but campaigners for sexual reform wanted to raise it further, to (at least) 16. Several earlier attempts to change the law had stalled in the House of Lords, where one less than noble Lord warned that 'few of their Lordships had not when young men ... been guilty of immorality. He hoped they would pause before passing a clause within the range of which their sons might come.'[19] In May 1885 the reformers persuaded William Stead, a campaigning journalist with a flair for the sensational, to join their cause. To verify what he had been told of the market for young virgins, he began to investigate the London vice trade, as the head of what he called a Secret Commission. The result was a week-long series of articles on 'The Maiden Tribute of Modern Babylon', published in the *Pall Mall Gazette* in July 1885. The first was the most significant. Six full pages long, it includes eye-catching subtitles more suggestive of pornography than moral reform: 'The Violation of Virgins', 'The Confessions of a Brothel-Keeper', 'How Girls are Bought and Ruined'. The key, final section was headed 'A Child of Thirteen Bought for £5'.[20]

Insisting that he could 'personally vouch for the absolute accuracy of every fact', Stead recounted the efforts of a procuress to buy a young virgin in a brothel. Learning of the negotiations, 'a drunken neighbour' offered her own daughter, 'Lily', aged 13, for sale. A price of £5 was agreed. The girl was examined by a midwife to confirm her virginity, and then taken to a brothel where she was undressed and chloroformed:

All was quiet and still. A few moments later the door opened and the purchaser appeared in the bedroom. He closed and locked the door. There was a brief silence. And then there arose a wild and piteous cry ... and the child's voice was heard crying, in accents of terror, 'There's a man in the room! Take me home; Oh, take me home!'

Stead left a row of asterisks before the next sentence: 'And then all once more was still.'[21]

The articles raised a storm. Extra copies of the paper were printed, but even so it was soon selling on the black market at ten times its usual price of one penny. W. H. Smith, the biggest newsagent in the country, refused to handle it; some of the newsboys who did were arrested on charges of vending indecent material. Within days the government had agreed to push forward legislation to raise the age of consent to 16, under what became the Criminal Law Amendment Act of 1885. Even this did not stop an enormous demonstration, when on 22 August an estimated 250,000 people marched into Hyde Park in nine separate processions, accompanied by 34 brass bands, to demand that the new Act be vigorously enforced.

This was not the end of the story. The procuress, described by Stead as 'an old hand at the game', was in fact a former prostitute, Rebecca Jarrett, working for one of the groups who rescued fallen women, and the male purchaser Stead himself; the girl was not violated – or at least not in the narrow sense Stead gave the word: that she was drugged and medically examined seems violation enough – but taken to a refuge on the Continent. Suspecting something amiss, Stead's newspaper rivals soon discovered that the original of 'Lily' was Eliza Armstrong, whose mother tearfully insisted that she had been duped into letting her daughter go. In October, Stead, Bramwell Booth of the Salvation Army, Rebecca Jarrett and the midwife, were charged with having taken a girl under 16 years of age from her parents without their permission. Booth was acquitted, but the two women were jailed for six months and Stead for three, a sentence he regarded as a badge of honour; every 10 November, until his death in 1912, he marked the anniversary of his conviction by wearing his prison uniform to work.[22]

Even with the evidence produced in court it is impossible to be certain what had happened: in particular whether, as Mrs Armstrong claimed, she believed her daughter was going to a place as a servant, or whether, as Stead insisted, she had knowingly sold her into the sex trade. Jarrett had taken Eliza away in a new purple dress, new boots, and a straw hat with a yellow feather: evidence, perhaps, that she was being prepared for something other than domestic service, but hardly conclusive. It is, however, one of the points at which Stead's story touches that of Tess, since Mrs Durbeyfield also dresses her daughter up before she leaves to work at Trantridge. When Tess protests that she is only going to work, her mother thinks, privately, that 'at first there mid be a little pretence o't', but she fully expects that her daughter will be seduced. Stead used the conventions of melodrama to represent the Armstrong family as stock types: a wicked mother, a drunken and brutal father, an innocent daughter sacrificed. Hardy resists such simplicities, not least because he knew more about the sexual mores of rural Dorset, and the economic pressures of village life, than Stead did of the London poor. The Durbeyfields drink, but their evenings at Rolliver's inn shed 'a sort of halo' over their lives, making them hopeful rather than violent, and it is in a spirit of optimism, not cynicism, that Joan Durbeyfield plans for Tess to claim kin. She is a feckless but not an unloving mother, guided by the same pragmatism as the fieldwomen who react to Tess's misfortunes: 'Lord, 'tis wonderful what a body can get used to o' that sort in time.'[23]

The episode of Tess's move to Trantridge suggests a more complex link between the two narratives. 'Lily' is 13, and Tess 16: in each case, the age of consent, under the legislation operative at the time. But as the 'Maiden Tribute' controversy had demonstrated, what 13 'means', or 16, is as much a cultural as a biological matter, linked to the age of entry into the workplace, or to legal majority, as well as to puberty. Hardy ensures that Tess's age is an issue in the novel. The strawberries Alec pushes into her mouth are greenhouse fruits, forced to ripen early; he is responding to what the narrator calls 'a luxuriance of aspect, a fulness of growth, which made her appear more of a woman than she really was' (p. 56). At Chaseborough, she is described as being 'on the momentary threshold of womanhood' (p. 84); on her return home, she tells her mother 'I was a child when I left this house' (p. 117). Most strikingly, at the club-walking, we learn that '[p]hases of her childhood' are visible in her aspect: 'you could sometimes see her twelfth year in her cheeks, or her ninth sparkling from her eyes; and even her fifth would sometimes flit over the curves of her cheek now and then' (p. 23). Hardy is visibly treading along the line that separates child from woman, the one protected by the law, the other unprotected. One might wonder whether, had the novel been written a decade earlier, Tess, like 'Lily', would have been 13.

It is central to Stead's narrative that 'Lily' is a victim, rather than an agent in her own fate; even her cry is not loud, but 'a helpless, startled scream like the bleat of a frightened lamb'. Since the rape never took place, Stead had tactical reasons to conceal the crisis of his story behind a row of asterisks. But Hardy too conceals, or at least blurs, the story of what happens to Tess in The Chase (itself associated with a hunted animal).[24] There is more at issue here than the novelist's need to be circumspect in writing of sexual matters. In the serial version of the novel, in the

Graphic, Alec tricks Tess into a bogus marriage; she is cruelly deceived, but the sexual relationship is otherwise a consensual one. In the first volume edition, he carries 'a druggist's bottle', from which he makes her drink. Here there is no question of consent, and Tess is clearly raped. In both versions, Alec's behaviour is not only immoral, but under the 1885 Criminal Law Amendment Act illegal, which may be in part why Hardy revised the narrative again.[25] In the 1892 and subsequent editions, there is no evidence that what happens in The Chase was premeditated. When Alec leaves to find the way, he covers Tess 'tenderly' with his coat (p. 101), and when he returns it is her 'gentle regular breathing' which draws him towards her: 'He knelt, and bent lower, till her breath warmed his face, and in a moment his cheek was in contact with hers.' There is no suggestion that the 'hopping rabbits and hares', or the 'gentle roosting birds' asleep in the yews and oaks of The Chase, are startled by an act of violence. The last paragraphs of the chapter are more a lament that so often things go wrong, that the wrong man takes the woman or the wrong woman the man, than an attack on male depravity. The 'pity of it' is that an 'immeasurable social chasm' divides Tess's later personality from her younger self. The emphasis is on the injustice of society, and on Tess's internalisation of it, rather than on Alec's individual unjust act (pp. 102–3).[26]

Tess's responses too become more difficult to interpret. The ambiguity of her reaction when she discovers that Alec has allowed them to get lost, 'between archness and real dismay', recalls her mingled response when he feeds her with strawberries, which in the 1892 edition she accepts in 'a half-pleased, half-reluctant state'. While she mistrusts him in all the versions, in 1892 Hardy adds that she is 'flattered' by his attentions. When she leaves Trantridge, a full six weeks after the night in The Chase, she answers Alec 'listlessly': 'if I had ever sincerely loved you, if I loved you still, I should not so loathe and hate myself' (p. 109). To say one has not sincerely loved, or no longer loves, only makes sense if one has earlier loved in some way *not* sincere. Tess makes a distinction between real love and some lesser kind, not between love and no love at all. She says herself that she was 'dazed' by Alec; the narrator describes her as 'temporarily blinded by his ardent manners', and 'stirred to confused surrender awhile' (p. 117). The phrase is carefully poised between response and submission. To adopt the terms Angel Clare learns to use in Brazil, Tess's encounter with Alec is more than the thing done, but less than the thing willed (p. 462).

Hardy's text, then, from 1892 onwards, both invites and frustrates a quasi-legal analysis of the differences between rape-seduction and seduction-rape.[27] The point is underlined by the refusal to reveal what Tess tells Angel in her confession. In answer to his admission of 'eight-and-forty hours' dissipation with a stranger' she tells him that her offence is 'just the same' (p. 318); later she insists 'I was a child – a child when it happened!' (p. 329). But whether she represents herself as Alec's willing mistress, or as a violated girl, is finally unimportant: who Tess is does not depend on the events of one night. To invest so heavily in examining the precise moment of her defloration is to make a fetish of virginity, as both Alec and Angel do when they tell her that Alec, as the first comer, is her 'husband in Nature' (p. 342).[28] That the two men should agree on this is essential to the novel's critique. They are more alike than they care to imagine. For a time Alec abandons his role as a rake and becomes a preacher; Angel Clare, in the aftermath of his marriage to Tess, is briefly tempted to play the cad with Izzy Huett. No less than Alec, Angel is baffled by his desire for Tess, which runs up against his sense of cultural distance from her, his belief in restraint as a virtue, and his assumption that any woman he could love must of necessity be a virgin, an 'Artemis' or 'Demeter', not an unmarried mother: in the terms of the narrator's mocking commentary, 'entire', not 'defective' (p. 369). Tess's combination of moral strength with the capacity to desire, and to be desired, reveals the same sexual insecurity in the cad and the gentleman.

The tendency to make a fetish of virginity is evident throughout the 'Maiden Tribute' articles. Virgins fetched a higher price in the sex market; they also sold more copies for the *Pall Mall Gazette*, and gave more status to the rescue agencies. Perhaps the most unpleasant part of Stead's campaign was his insistence that Eliza Armstrong should be examined by a midwife, to prove, as he put it, 'that a little harlot had not been palmed off on us'.[29] The remark reflects what he was told by the Matron of a Lock Hospital, that the initial violation produced 'a lasting blight of the moral sense': 'the foul passion of the man seem[s] to enter into the helpless victim of his lust'.[30] A 'little harlot' could not expect Stead's concern, just as, under the 1885 Act, women of 'known immoral character' – that is, unmarried non-virgins – were not protected against 'false representations' by their seducers. The rescue societies offered a counter-narrative to this story of inevitable and continuing decline, in which the reformed prostitute figured as a type of Mary Magdalene, and an agent in the redemption of others.[31] This was the role that Rebecca Jarrett was invited to play, and which she seems to have taken to heart. Both narrative lines are suggested in the novel. When Tess baptises Sorrow, the 'ecstasy of [her] faith' has 'a transfiguring effect', so that her face shows 'as a thing of immaculate beauty' (pp. 133–4); much later, after the murder, Angel wonders if her love for him has 'extinguished her moral sense altogether' (p. 524). Significantly, however, Hardy disconnects both scenes from the fall itself: in the first it is love for her child, in the second the differing pressures brought to bear upon her by Alec and Angel, that cause Tess to act as she does, and not her identity as a fallen woman.[32]

Stead's position in the 'Maiden Tribute' articles was intended to be simple, a defence of the innocent poor against the predatory rich, but in fact it was riven with contradictions. Some of these emerged more clearly at the trial, where his claim to be protecting the vulnerable was compromised by his bullying of both Rebecca Jarrett and Mrs Armstrong, whose feelings of family and community loyalty he wholly ignored. Others were evident in the text itself. While there is no reason to doubt his genuine concern for moral decency, he was all too obviously caught up in his adopted role of roué; it is hard to imagine why else he insisted that Eliza should be examined a second time, to prove that he had not taken the opportunity to violate her. Crucially, while attacking the market in juvenile prostitution, he came close to colluding with it in the exaggerated value placed on virginity. But as Hardy is at pains to show, it is not the supposed 'blight' of her lost virginity which causes Tess to suffer, so much as the 'social chasm' between the virgin and the fallen: precisely the gulf opened up by men like Stead, or like Angel Clare. Angel's sense of the 'grotesque – prestidigitation' by which his imagined Tess is changed to the flesh and blood woman in front of him (p. 325) is less coarsely phrased than Stead's concern that he might be 'palmed off' with a 'little harlot', but it is essentially the same. For both men, only the woman without a history, the blank page that has yet to be written on, is of real value.[33]

the body and soul of sue[34]

Sue Bridehead, wrote Kate Millett in 1969, is by turns 'an enigma, a pathetic creature, a nut, and an iceberg'.[35] Much of the critical discussion of *Jude the Obscure* has been an attempt to decide which of these she is, and why. If Tess is gazed at, Sue has been interrogated, within the novel by Jude, Phillotson and the narrator, and outside it by the critics and reviewers, typically in the same terms: so, for example, Jude finds her 'perverse' and 'unpredictable', while Robert Langbaum argues that her decisions are 'never prepared for', and often 'unfathomable'.[36] Yet the emphasis on Sue's psychology, or pathology, creates its own problems. As Terry Wright observes, she is 'portrayed mainly through men's eyes, as seen by the narrator, by Phillotson, and, most of all, by Jude'; but she is mainly mis-seen, and again most of all by Jude.[37] Even before they meet he is half in love with her, kissing her photograph and preparing to install her as 'a kindly star, an elevating power' in his life.[38] He has already constructed Christminster as a heavenly Jerusalem, in opposition to ugly, utilitarian Marygreen; now he constructs Sue in opposition to Arabella, as a female saint to answer the female animal.[39] His imagining of her is conspicuously at odds with what follows, when Sue buys her pagan statuettes, and having 'unrobed' them, and undressed herself, is too excited to sleep (p. 95). The narrator's comment on Jude's entry into Christminster, that when he passed 'objects out of harmony' with his vision 'he allowed his eyes to slip over them as if he did not see them', applies equally to his view of Sue (p. 79). If she is a puzzle to Jude, much of the reason lies within him.

Sue attracts Jude in part because she represents for him the culture to which he aspires. Like Christminster, which he hopes will satisfy 'the yearning of his heart to find something to anchor on' (p. 25), Sue seems to offer 'an anchorage for his thoughts' (p. 92). In his eyes, she is aligned by nature and experience with the world of learning: widely read, intellectually confident, and steeped in Christminster life.[40] Sue is sympathetic to Jude's project of self-improvement – she tells him that she has always wanted to 'ennoble some man to high aims' (p. 153) – but her position is as usual more complex than he allows. Many Victorian feminists, including many New Women of the 1890s, implicitly valorised the male world by framing their demands for access to education and the professions in terms of the privileges already offered to men.[41] Sue is more ambivalent. For her Christminster is 'full of fetichists and ghost-seers' (p. 151). With good reason, she opposes as well as stands for 'culture': like the voices which greet Jude on his entrance to the city, the books she has read represent a male tradition which has no room for her. Nor is this a merely theoretical exclusion. Her father refuses to have her in his house after she shares a flat with the Christminster graduate; and while 'experience and unbiassed nature' tell Jude to sympathise with her unhappiness as a wife, and 'instinct' persuades Phillotson to allow her her freedom, both know that as 'order-loving' men, pledged to uphold the 'dogmas' and 'principles' of church and state, they ought to condemn her (pp. 210, 230).[42] As Arabella reminds Phillotson, men have the laws on their side: 'Moses knew' (p. 318).[43]

In a Postscript added in 1912, Hardy offered Sue as a type of 'the woman of the feminist movement – the slight, pale "bachelor" girl – the intellectualized, emancipated bundle of nerves that modern conditions were producing' (p. 468),[44] and she herself occasionally argues that other women think and feel as she does, as when she insists to Jude that her reluctance to marry is 'not so exceptional ... as you think' (p. 260). But the context here is her need to defend herself against the charge of abnormality, and more often she insists on her differentness. Unlike Jude, who joins an Artizans' Mutual Improvement Society, she makes no friends of her own sex, even among the students who support her at the Training College. This separateness may reflect Hardy's wish to rebut any suggestion that her nature is 'perverted or depraved': as he explained to Edmund Gosse, whose review in *Cosmopolis* described Sue as 'degenerate', her 'abnormalism consists in disproportion: not in inversion, her sexual nature being healthy so far as it goes, but unusually weak and fastidious'.[45] The term 'inversion' was about to acquire wider currency through the work of Havelock Ellis, who used it to describe a congenital predisposition which might or might not lead to overtly sexual relations between persons of the same sex.[46] Hardy seems to have used it in the same way. Female inversion, as Ellis construed it, was defined by self-presentation as much as by the desire for sexual contact. It could be inferred from the presence of such 'masculine' characteristics as straightforwardness in speech, the absence of shyness towards men, brusque or energetic movements, and the ability to whistle. These are not Sue's traits – despite her tomboy behaviour as a child, her 'bounding manner' (p. 132) and impulsive speech, her figure, dress and demeanour are conventionally feminine – but as an adult she does enter the space traditionally reserved for men, most obviously in her relationship with the Christminster graduate, 'like two men almost' (p. 148). When she tells Jude about this part of her life, she is dressed in his great-coat and looks 'boyish as a Ganymedes' (p. 154).[47] The allusion is suggestive. The abduction of Ganymedes, a beautiful youth snatched into heaven to serve as cup-bearer to Zeus, was a favourite subject of Renaissance artists, usually, as Hardy must have been aware, as a symbol of male homosexual love. In her happier moments, Sue lays claim to 'Greek joyousness', as opposed to the 'sickness and sorrow' learned from Judaeo-Christian teaching about sexual love (p. 297). But Greek ideas about love had become part of the culture of male homosexuality: especially in Oxford/Christminster, under the influence of Walter Pater and John Addington Symonds, and especially in 1895, the year both of *Jude the Obscure* and of Oscar Wilde's trial and imprisonment.[48] Sue's dream of comradeship, like her wish to 'ennoble some man to high aims', recalls the male–male friendships celebrated by Oxford Hellenism, in which an older man sought to guide a younger one on the path of wisdom and virtue. Sue is not an invert in Havelock Ellis's sense, but what she seeks with Jude has an affinity with the Platonic doctrine of Eros propounded by male inverts like Wilde.[49]

One of the peculiarities to which Sue admits is that she has 'no fear of men, as such', since 'no man short of a sensual savage' will molest a woman: 'Until she says by a look "Come on" he is always afraid to, and if you never say it, or look it, he never comes' (pp. 147–8).[50] What Jude interprets as her 'curious unconsciousness of gender' (p. 149) has seemed to many readers deliberately tantalising, but it is better understood in terms of her desire for sexual self-determination. This is clearly the basis of her resistance to marriage, where in both substance and tone – 'the sordid conditions of a business contract' (p. 286), a licence to be 'loved on the premises' (p. 259) – her views closely follow those of Mona Caird, whose attack on 'common respectable marriage' as merely 'the worst, because the most hypocritical, form of woman-purchase' launched a long-running public debate on the 'Marriage Question'.[51] Sue's further anxiety, which Jude shares, that a marriage contract must be inimical to 'a passion whose essence is its gratuitousness' (p. 272), is also voiced by Caird ('obligation enters into the very citadel of the heart. All spontaneity must and does evidently depart').[52] For Jude and Sue, as for the feminists of a later generation, the personal is the political. Thin-skinned though they are, they were not alone in the fear that private feeling was vulnerable to the power of public institutions.

But Sue's misgivings about her sexual life go beyond the question of marriage. Here too the divisions within her reflect wider uncertainties in society. When Jude doubts the warmth of her feelings, she insists he is mistaken: 'I should shock you by letting you know how I give way to my impulses, and how much I feel I shouldn't have been provided with attractiveness unless it were meant to be exercised!' (p. 204). Hardy originally made her speak of her 'heart'; the substitution of 'attractiveness' shifts the emphasis to her desirability rather than her role as wife and future mother.[53] She seems, briefly, to envisage sexual pleasure as a good in itself, even as a pleasure she is 'meant' to seek.[54] But sexual liberationism played only a small part in Victorian feminism, and she turns instantly to the fear that her 'love of being loved', and her 'love of loving', might prove to be 'insatiable'.[55] Love and desire might even be incompatible: 'My liking for you is ... of a supremely delicate kind, and I don't want to go further and risk it by – an attempt to intensify it!' (p. 240). Later she tells Jude that his 'wickedness' was 'only the natural man's desire to possess the woman' (p. 352). The equation of the wicked and the natural – closer to Christian dualism than Greek joyousness – was by no means an extreme position in the 1890s. The evolutionary feminist Ellis Ethelmer explained the inordinate level of male sexual desire as a vestige of men's abuse of women in the past. More than that, excessive male demands had caused a parallel 'abnormality' in women, the development of menstruation, which would disappear once men and women had learned together to reach a higher level of 'psychic love'. For Ethelmer, the task for the future was to make sex not freer and more joyous, but less important.[56] This is the position Sue is taking when she insists that it is possible to be 'passionately erotic' in feeling but 'self-contained' in deed (p. 149). She looks for support to the poets, but she might equally have turned to contemporary feminist writing: in the pages of the *Freewoman*, for example, where the suffragist Kathlyn Oliver praised the virtue of self-restraint. In the event Oliver found herself accused by her co-feminists, as Sue is by Jude, of a deficiency either of courage or of passion, but the arguments deployed against her were precisely those Sue herself uses in her more confident moments: that women have a right, and even a duty, to exercise their sexuality.[57] Sue's attempt at self-determination ends in her collapse, but the contradictions which destroy her belong to her time as well as to her own personal history.

The novel reveals Sue as less the autonomous individual she aspires to be when she quotes John Stuart Mill on the right to choose one's own 'plan of life' (p. 223) than the site, or in Hardy's phrase the 'nodal point', where the pressures of the age are made visible.[58] This helps to explain the way her character is rendered through a series of gaps and hesitations. Often the narrator is silent where we might have expected commentary. Early in Part Fourth, for example, Jude watches from outside the house as Sue presses a photograph to her bosom, and wonders if it his; the narrator is either unwilling or unable to tell.[59] After her wedding with Phillotson, Sue returns briefly to Jude's lodgings and seems about to speak: 'But she went on; and whatever she had meant to say remained unspoken' (p. 175). There the chapter ends, and neither Jude nor the reader learns what she might have said. Elsewhere alternative accounts of her feelings are allowed to lie side by side. She herself attributes her reluctance to sleep with Phillotson to 'a reason I cannot disclose' (p. 212); at various points the reader is invited to feel that many women are similarly reluctant, that it is a sign of her exceptional fastidiousness, and that it is the consequence of a peculiarity in Phillotson rather than in her.[60] The narrator's seemingly authoritative comment, that she is 'quite unfitted by temperament and instinct to fulfil the conditions of the matrimonial relation with Phillotson', is instantly modified: 'possibly with any man' (p. 218).[61] The caution here is characteristic: 'Perhaps she knew that [Phillotson] was thinking of her thus' (p. 105); 'That was just the one thing that [Jude] would not be able to bear, as she probably knew' (p. 134). The narrator makes no claim to 'understand' Sue as she struggles to come to terms with her identity as a woman – to learn how she is seen, what is demanded of her, the ways in which she is to represent and articulate herself. To make such a claim would imply that there was some standing ground, accessible to the reader and narrator but not to Sue, from which the conflicting sexual ideologies of the age could be reconciled.[62] And this Hardy is unwilling to suggest.

Jude provides a useful analogy for Sue's position: like someone caught in a crowd, she is 'the helpless transmitter of the pressure put upon [her]' (p. 287). For Arabella, who in the course of the novel marries two men twice each, one of these marriages being bigamous, sexual life is unproblematic; it means the satisfaction of her physical desires, or the exchange of her favours in return for economic security. This is sex without mystery. For Sue, however, in part because of the pressure from Jude, sex is made not one experience, but the defining experience: the ultimate personal act. Jude accuses her of frigidity and a lack of 'animal passion' (p. 260); yet from the outset his love for her is based on the belief that she is a 'refined creature' (p. 343), whose 'freedom from everything that's gross' has 'elevated' him (p. 266). She is required to be sexually responsive, at the same time as she is asked to be 'above' sexual desire. On the one hand, as she realises with mounting distress, sexual love has been secularised, made subject to the law, to written contracts, and the involvement of courts, forms and registrars; on the other, it has been sacralised, made a mystery. It has become simultaneously the defining private act, and a matter for public legislation. Sexual love is nothing, and everything; it is gross, and the mark of a personal commitment; it belongs to a world that is refined and elevated, and it is licensed by a contract between two 'parties' of stated age, rank and occupation. It is no surprise that she finds her position intolerable.

The narrator of *Jude* insists that 'a chronicler of moods and deeds' has no obligation to express 'his personal views' on the Marriage Question (p. 288). The novel offers no answers to the problems that face Sue and Jude; nor did Hardy, in his non-fictional writings, claim to have solved them. Like other writers of the time, he offered suggestions: that 'a marriage should be dissolvable as soon as it becomes a cruelty to either of the parties'; that young women should be given 'a plain handbook on natural processes', so that they, unlike Sue, would know what matrimony would entail; that children should be told as much as they could understand about conception and birth, rather than left puzzled, as is Father Time, by half-truths.[63] But more important than these nostrums is Hardy's ability to reconstruct what was written in the law, or argued in contemporary polemic, as part of the lived experience of his characters: and most especially of Sue, as moment by moment she endures, seeks to evade, or to exploit, the ways in which she is made to inhabit her gender. The male novelist, speaking through a male narrator, claims no access to what might be her 'nature'; what he can do, and what Hardy offers in *Jude* as a step towards a better understanding of the immortal puzzle of human sexual relations, is trace the processes, the 'forced repression in some directions, unnatural stimulation in others', by which she is fitted into her role as a 'woman'.

notes

1. *John Stuart Mill: Three Essays*, ed. Richard Wollheim (London and Oxford, 1975), p. 451.
2. Darwin grounds his claim that 'man has ultimately become superior to woman' on the effects both of sexual selection, or the contest of rival males, and of natural selection, or the struggle for the resources necessary to life, from which, at least in the Victorian middle class, women were supposedly exempt: 'Difference in the Mental Powers of the Two Sexes', in *The Descent of Man and Selection in Relation to Sex* (London, 2003), pp. 563–6. For a critique, see Cynthia Eagle Russett, *Sexual Science: The Victorian Construction of Womanhood* (Cambridge, MA, 1989), pp. 80–9.
3. *A Pair of Blue Eyes*, ed. Pamela Dalziel (Harmondsworth, 1998), p. 158.
4. The heroines of *The Hand of Ethelberta* and *The Return of the Native* enter the novels as sexually experienced women. Hardy returned to the courtship plot in the 1880s, with *The Trumpet-Major*, *A Laodicean* and *The Woodlanders*.
5. *Desperate Remedies*, ed. Mary Rimmer (Harmondsworth, 1998), pp. 448 (Preface to 1889 edition), 57, 135, 32.
6. In Volume II, 'The Events of One Day', and Volume III, 'The Events of Three Hours'. Fittingly, Owen's job is to trace drawings in the office where Springrove is head draughtsman.

7. *Desperate Remedies*, pp. 82–6. Fathers are notably ineffectual in this novel (and in most of Hardy's fiction). Mr Graye falls to his death; Springrove senior is left helpless by the loss of his home in the fire; Manston's father is absent. Miss Aldclyffe inherits her property through her mother.

8. *Desperate Remedies*, pp. 56, 133, 242, 406. So too whatever drew Bathsheba to Troy will not be satisfied by Gabriel Oak, despite his request that for their wedding she wear her hair 'as she had worn it years ago on Norcombe Hill', so that she seems 'in his eyes remarkably like the girl of that fascinating dream': in his eyes, perhaps, but not in those of the reader (*Far from the Madding Crowd*, eds Rosemarie Morgan and Shannon Russell (Harmondsworth, 2000), p. 351). Cytherea similarly engineers, on the last page of the novel, a repetition of an earlier outing with Springrove.

9. *Desperate Remedies*, p. 75. Such observations are less in evidence in *Under the Greenwood Tree*, but even here Fancy Day makes a general rule of her own failings: 'It is my nature – perhaps all women's – to love refinement of mind and manners' (*Under the Greenwood Tree*, ed. Simon Gatrell (Oxford, 1985), p. 176).

10. *A Pair of Blue Eyes*, p. 126.

11. Herbert Spencer, *The Study of Sociology* (London, 1873), p. 377; Havelock Ellis, *Studies in the Psychology of Sex, Volume 3: Analysis of the Sex Impulse, Love and Pain* (Philadelphia, 1903), p. 33. Spencer's comments on the 'earlier arrest of individual evolution in women than in men' are also relevant here: Stephen, as a man, can aspire to become Knight's equal; Elfride, as a woman, is destined always to lag behind him.

12. Cytherea's 'whispered No' to Springrove comes 'from so near the positive frontier as to be affected with the Yes accent': *Desperate Remedies*, p. 50.

13. This 'hard' narrative voice might owe something to Hardy's wish to compensate for his 'lateness of development in virility' (*Life*, p. 37).

14. As several critics have noticed. Penny Boumelha comments on Hardy's 'narrative ambivalence' in *Thomas Hardy and Women: Sexual Ideology and Narrative Form* (Brighton, 1982), p. 32; Patricia Ingham, in *Thomas Hardy* (Hemel Hempstead, 1989), writes of a 'fault-line' running through the early novels (p. 12).

15. *Far from the Madding Crowd*, p. 310; *Desperate Remedies*, p. 253. So too Elfride agrees to marry Lord Luxellian 'for the benefit of my family', and to turn her 'useless life to some practical account' (*A Pair of Blue Eyes*, p. 377). Ethelberta's decision to marry for the good of her family is taken more dispassionately, but she also has male advice, from Mill's essay on *Utilitarianism*: *The Hand of Ethelberta*, ed. Tim Dolin (Harmondsworth, 1996), pp. 287–9.

16. *Desperate Remedies*, p. 254; *Far from the Madding Crowd*, p. 308.

17. Rosemarie Morgan, *Women and Sexuality in the Novels of Thomas Hardy* (London, 1988), p. 13; Ingham, *Thomas Hardy*, p. 14; Roger Ebbatson, *Hardy: The Margin of the Unexpressed* (Sheffield, 1993), p. 18.

18. *National Observer*, Special Literary Supplement, 14 November 1891. Called away to visit a sick relative, Big Beauty implores her lover not to desert her; he promises to visit, but never does.

19. *Hansard Parliamentary Debates* (Lords), 3rd. ser., 289 (24 June 1884), col. 1219; quoted from Deborah Gorham, '"The Maiden Tribute of Modern Babylon"

Re-Examined: Child Prostitution and the Idea of Childhood in Late-Victorian England', *Victorian Studies*, 21 (1977–78), p. 366.

20. A similar point might be made about Hardy's 'phases': 'The Maiden', 'Maiden No More', 'The Woman Pays'.

21. *Pall Mall Gazette*, 6 July 1885. For discussion, see Michael Pearson, *The Age of Consent: Victorian Prostitution and Its Enemies* (Newton Abbott, 1972), Deborah Gorham, 'The Maiden Tribute', and, especially, Judith R. Walkowitz, *City of Dreadful Delight: Narratives of Sexual Danger in Late-Victorian London* (Chicago, 1992).

22. Two other people were brought to trial. Samuel Jacques, who had acted as Stead's agent, was sentenced to one month's imprisonment; Elizabeth Combe, the Salvation Army officer who had taken care of Eliza after her abduction, was acquitted.

23. *Tess of the d'Urbervilles*, eds Juliet Grindle and Simon Gatrell (Oxford, 1986), pp. 64, 31, 127. Subsequent references to this (variorum) edition are cited parenthetically in the text.

24. The Chase recalls the Forest of White Hart, in Tess's own Vale of Blackmoor, as J. Hillis Miller notes in *Fiction and Repetition: Seven English Novels* (Harvard, 1982), p. 129.

25. *Tess*, p. 100. The Act made it a misdemeanour, punishable by up to two years' imprisonment, to use 'false pretences or false representations', or to administer a stupefying drug, in order to procure 'unlawful carnal connexion' with 'any woman or girl, not being a common prostitute or of known immoral character'.

26. In 1892 Hardy removed a reference to the 'sons of the forest' who might have come to Tess's rescue had they known that she was 'in the hands of the spoiler' (pp. 102–3). The role of the honest rescuer, familiar in stage melodrama, is played by Angel Clare when he strikes the man who insults her (p. 295), but this is before she has made her confession. The 'sobbing' in The Chase, added in 1892, might suggest '[a] little more than persuading' (p. 127); but perhaps this is the sound Tess makes when 'stirred'.

27. Patricia Ingham, *Thomas Hardy*, p. 73, makes this distinction.

28. Alec tells Tess, 'If you are any man's wife you are mine!' (p. 453). In his own copy of the 1912 edition, Hardy added two sentences in which Tess tells Angel that the step back to Alec 'was not so great as it seems. He had been as a husband to me: you never had!' (p. 514).

29. W. T. Stead, *The Armstrong Case: Mr Stead's Defense Told in Full* (London, 1885), p. 12; quoted from Walkowitz, *City of Dreadful Delight*, p. 112.

30. *Pall Mall Gazette*, 8 July 1885, p. 3 col 2.

31. See Michael Mason, *The Making of Victorian Sexual Attitudes* (Oxford and New York, 1994), pp. 82–115.

32. Cf. Gillian Beer, *Darwin's Plots: Evolutionary Narrative in Darwin, George Eliot, and Nineteenth-Century Fiction*, 2nd edn (Cambridge, 2000), p. 200: 'The social emphasis on virginity, Hardy suggests, cannot be naturalised.'

33. It has often been argued that in attempting to demolish the 'doll of English fiction' (*Letters*, I, p. 250) by creating fully sexual heroines, Hardy risked making them seem all sex, and that Tess's body in particular is made the object of an insistently male gaze. Lynn Pykett, for example, draws attention

to two passages in the novel, Tess's dawn rising at the dairy (pp. 242–3), and the closing scene, 'in which her body is viewed by the "riveted" eyes of the spectators of her execution'. However, the passage leading to the description of the sleepy Tess is an ironic account of Angel Clare's 'sense of luxury' at his 'power of viewing life' in the countryside. The last words before Tess appears are 'in his eyes'; the narrator is consciously distanced from Clare, as is Hardy. In the closing scene, the eyes of the spectators (Angel and Liza-Lu) are in fact riveted to the flag signalling Tess's execution: to the public statement about her body, not the body itself. Hardy lays the blame for Tess's difficulties not on her body, but on those who seek to appropriate it, or trace their own patterns upon it. See Lynn Pykett, 'Ruinous Bodies: Women and Sexuality in Hardy's Late Fiction', *Critical Survey*, 5(2) (1993), pp. 157–66.

34. This was at one stage Hardy's title for *Tess*.

35. Kate Millett, *Sexual Politics* (1969; London, 1973), p. 133.

36. Robert Langbaum, *Thomas Hardy in Our Time* (London, 1995), p. 16.

37. T. R. Wright, *Hardy and the Erotic* (London, 1989), p. 120.

38. *Jude the Obscure*, ed. Dennis Taylor (Harmondsworth, 1998) p. 91. Subsequent references to this edition, based on the 1895 text, are cited parenthetically. Part of what follows draws on an earlier essay, 'Sexual Ideology and Narrative Form in *Jude the Obscure*', *English*, XXXVIII (Autumn 1989), pp. 211–24.

39. In January 1894 Hardy copied out a sentence from George Egerton's story 'A Cross Line': 'She laughs softly to herself because of the derseness of man; his chivalrous conservative devotion to the female idea he has created blinds him, perhaps happily, to the problems of her complex nature' (*Literary Notebooks*, I, p. 60, where however 'blinds' is wrongly given as 'binds'. The *un*happiness caused by such blindness is part of the subject of *Jude*.

40. In an early version of the story, Sue was to have been adopted by the Provost of an Oxford college.

41. See Gail Cunningham, '"He-Notes": Reconstructing Masculinity', in Angelique Richardson and Chris Willis, eds, *The New Woman in Fiction and Fact: Fin-de-Siècle Feminisms* (London, 2001), pp. 96–7.

42. Phillotson appeals to a notion of 'manliness' linked to 'chivalry' to defend his generosity. When he goes further – 'I don't see any reason why the woman and the children should not be the unit without the man' – his friend Gillingham exclaims 'Matriarchy!' (p. 231). That this was Hardy's own position, at any rate by 1906, is clear from a letter to Millicent Fawcett on the probable results of female suffrage: *Letters*, III, pp. 238–9.

43. Not just the Old Testament law, but until 1891 the law of the land, which allowed a husband to imprison his wife in pursuit of his conjugal rights. The case which changed the law, *R* v. *Jackson*, was certainly known to Hardy; see Phillip Mallett, '"Smacked, and Brought to Her Senses": Hardy and the Clitheroe Abduction Case', *Thomas Hardy Journal*, VIII, May 1992, pp. 70–3.

44. This is offered as the opinion of a female German reviewer, but she remains unidentified, and may be Hardy's invention.

45. *Letters*, II, p. 99. Hardy had presumably seen an advance copy of Gosse's review, which appeared in January 1896, after this letter was written. The idea of 'disproportion' implies a proper level of female desire; even in *Jude*

Hardy's radicalism about sexuality was not enough to allow him to escape notions of normality and deviancy.

46. Ellis's *Sexual Inversion*, co-written with John Addington Symonds, was first published in a German translation in 1896, and in English a year later. Almost at once it ran into difficulties in the courts; later editions, with Symonds's name removed, were published in America. For its history and arguments, see Phyllis Grosskurth, *Havelock Ellis: a Biography* (London, 1980), pp. 173–204.

47. 'Cupid' in the manuscript. The erotic element of the story was developed by the Roman poets; 'catamite' derives from 'catamitus', the Latin version of Ganymedes. The abduction was painted by Michelangelo, Correggio and Rubens, among others.

48. See Linda Dowling, *Hellenism and Homosexuality in Victorian Oxford* (Ithaca, 1994).

49. Jude himself is eager for such a relationship: hence his hero-worship of Phillotson, and his visit to the composer of the hymn which so moves him. Jude's character resembles that of what Edward Carpenter calls 'the normal type of the Uranian man', which combines 'masculine powers of mind and body with the tenderer and more emotional soul-culture of the woman'. Such men, according to Carpenter, are tender towards children and animals, moved by intuition rather than reason, and often dreamers, with the sensibilities of the artist. See Edward Carpenter, *Love's Coming of Age* (1914), in Ann Heilman, ed., *The Late Victorian Marriage Question: A Collection of Key New Woman Texts* (London, 1998), 5 vols, II, pp. 129–30. The story of Jude and Sue shows Hardy testing the boundaries set by conventional accounts of male and female sexual identity.

50. Her confidence is sadly misplaced. Phillotson is hardly a sensual savage, but at the end of the novel he takes her into his bed. What the sensual savage had to take by force, the Victorian husband could claim as a right.

51. The debate was triggered by Caird's 1888 articles on 'Marriage' and 'Ideal Marriage' in the *Westminster Review*, CXXX, pp. 186–201 and 617–36. The *Daily Telegraph* received 27,000 letters on the topic; a selection of these, edited by Harry Quilter, was published under the title *Is Marriage a Failure?* Hardy knew and admired Caird; in 1890 he tried, unsuccessfully, to place her article on 'Evolution in Marriage' in the *Contemporary Review* (*Letters*, I, p. 208).

52. Mona Caird, *The Morality of Marriage and Other Essays on the Status and Destiny of Women* (London, 1897), p. 106. Caird, like Sue Bridehead, and like Hardy, shared, and often cited, Mill's commitment to individual development.

53. The change was made on the proofs.

54. Sue's words echo one of the age's more notorious books about sexuality, George Drysdale's *The Elements of Social Science* (1855, but frequently reprinted). Arguing the necessity of sexual intercourse to the health and virtue of both men and women, Drysdale proposed a 'law of exercise': that the sexual organs, like any others, needed to be used if they were not to atrophy. For Drysdale's work and influence, see Michael Mason, *The Making of Victorian Sexual Attitudes* (Oxford, 1994), pp. 188–213.

55. It was more important among socialist and Owenite thinkers such as William Thompson and Robert Dale Owen. Later in the century the necessity of sexual

pleasure is implicit, if generally unvoiced, in attacks on spinsterhood as a more or less pathological condition.

56. Ellis Ethelmer was the pseudonym of Ben Elmy, the husband of Elizabeth Wolstenholme, though it is likely that work published over the name reflects the thinking of them both: see Lucy Bland, *Banishing the Beast*, (Harmondsworth, 1995), pp. 141–2, and Sheila Jeffreys. *The Spinster and Her Enemies: Feminism and Sexuality 1880–1930* (London, 1985), chapter 2, 'Continence and Psychic Love'.

57. The debate took place in the spring of 1912, while Hardy was writing the Postscript to the Wessex edition of *Jude*; see Bland, *Banishing the Beast*, pp. 281–6.

58. The phrase is used of Father Time: 'He was their nodal point, their focus, their expression in a single term' (p. 337).

59. So far as the reader can guess, it will not be Jude's; the two photographs she has with her at the Training College are of Phillotson and the Christminster graduate.

60. As Widow Edlin suspects: 'there be certain men here and there that no woman of any niceness can stomach. I should have said that [Phillotson] was one' (p. 198).

61. In the 1912 edition, 'possibly with scarce any man' The confident generalisation about the young women at the Training College – 'every face bearing the legend "The Weaker", as the penalty of the sex wherein they were moulded' – is made when Sue is absent (p. 141).

62. Sally Ledger argues that Hardy tries but is unable to 'pin down' Sue as a realist character. Her argument comes closer to my own when she says that Sue's 'incomprehensibility' is 'rooted in the crisis of gender relations' in the 1890s: see *The New Woman: Fiction and Feminism at the Fin-de-Siècle* (Manchester and New York, 1997), pp. 182, 184.

63. Postscript to *Jude*, p. 467; contribution to the *New Review* symposium (June 1894) headed 'The Tree of Knowledge', quoted from Michael Millgate, ed., *Thomas Hardy's Personal Voice: The Essays, Speeches, and Miscellaneous Prose* (Oxford, 2001), p. 132; for Hardy's advice to Agnes Grove on her article on 'What should children be told?', see *Letters*, II, pp. 101, 114–24.

9
hardy and englishness

james s. whitehead

'All Englishmen they', said the old man.
(*The Trumpet-Major*, chapter I)

The opening chapter of *The Trumpet-Major* touches upon the subject of national identity. An old man, Simon Burden, is drawn from the local pub to observe the manoeuvres of troops upon the downs. The pub is named 'The Duke of York'; there is a curious sense of continuity in this environment, as soldiers are marched up and down hills before military action. Simon was a soldier 'many years ago' and he carries the 'burden' of history as he struggles to explain military practice to the novel's female protagonist, Anne Garland. He recognises the regiment they are watching:

> ''Tis the York Hussars,' said Simon Burden, brightening like a dying ember fanned. 'Foreigners to a man, and enrolled long since my time. But as good hearty comrades, they say, as you'll find in the King's service.'

Observing the arrival of a Dragoons regiment, Burden makes the comment quoted at the beginning of this chapter, drawing a distinction, therefore, between 'Englishmen' and 'Foreigners' serving in the British Army (irrespective of the laudable 'hearty'-ness of the latter). The Duke of York's folkloric world reflects a type of continuity and yet the world has changed irrevocably. The battles of the Napoleonic era are the last in a long sequence of conflicts that helped form a sense of national identity, but a new era is dawning in which understanding of complex international political affiliations is necessary. This is the key shift in national consciousness depicted in Hardy's writing. It becomes too much for Simon Burden, representative of the 'dying ember' of old-fashioned Englishness.

It is only in recent years that critical strategies have been developed to investigate the complex political challenges presented in Hardy's work. In exploring his treatment of ideas of national identity, in particular, we need to remain sensitive to the cultural context(s) in which he wrote. Several recent studies have examined these, including *The Idea of Englishness 1880–1920*, edited by Robert Colls and Philip Dodd, which surveys cultural manifestations of Englishness across a range of types of expression, political, linguistic, literary and musical.[1] Passing reference is made to Hardy in this work, and this is helpful, especially when supplemented by reference to David Gervais's more recent *Literary Englands: Versions of Englishness in Modern Writing*, which concentrates primarily on the way in which a sense of national nostalgia permeates the work of Hardy's twentieth-century literary successors.[2]

More focused on Hardy is Peter Widdowson's *Hardy in History: A Study in Literary Sociology*, which analyses the way his obvious involvement with Englishness functions both in terms of his role as author-creator and as a subsequent 'cultural construct', as ideas of Hardy's work, of 'Wessex' and of the author himself, are developed for different ideological projects. The history of 'Hardy and Englishness', in this sense, will continue to develop, as new editorial projects, biography, critical reinterpretation, school and university syllabi, and other cultural adaptations and appropriations, appear. A bipartite process for readers should be the result: a process of return to texts, criticism and biography for reinterpretation within specific social and cultural contexts, combined with ongoing analysis of new Hardyan cultural products. The problem that has faced Hardy studies in this connection to date is that 'Hardy's work is variously dehistoricized and simultaneously rehistoricized in the ideological discourses of the present.' Widdowson summarises one tendency of Hardy studies, at least until the late 1980s, as 'the crucial displacement of history by pastoral – a crux in the ideology of any national culture'.[3] Often Hardy's work has been treated selectively and in a ideologically conservative fashion; it has been filed away under headings such as 'Victorian Pastoral', partly as a result of Hardy's own classification in 1912 of his most popular Wessex fiction under the label of 'Novels of Character and Environment'. Widdowson's suggestion is that Hardy's radical approach to questions of form in the fiction (improbablism versus literary realism) and content (social cohesion versus social change and injustice), has been underestimated or misunderstood.[4]

Widdowson's study limits its gaze to the fiction, focusing in particular on *The Hand of Ethelberta*, as a much under-rated, anti-realist work that deserves critical attention. Subsequently, in *On Thomas Hardy: Late Essays and Earlier* (1998) and in his selection of poetry and prose, *Thomas Hardy* (1996), Widdowson has argued the need for consideration of other Hardy texts, such as the lyric poems. Although his work is controversially dismissive of criticism based upon supposedly apolitical, but in fact broadly conservative, liberal-humanist assumptions, Widdowson's contribution to Hardy studies, along with critics such as George Wotton, John Goode and Roger Ebbatson, has been to pioneer more ideologically aware critical methodologies.[5] However, Hardy's engagement with ideas of Englishness requires further elucidation through extended comparison with the cultural engagement of his literary (especially poetic) contemporaries, before the full pattern of literary influence becomes clear, and this forms part of the aim of this chapter. The concluding section will examine, albeit within a narrow compass, the political confusion that has attended discussion of Hardy's poetry in relation to concepts of national identity. This chapter attempts, then, to combine an awareness of the cultural contexts in which Hardy wrote, with analysis of those in which he has been read.

Hardy's long-term engagement with ideas of national identity has not received extensive critical treatment, but a clear line of thematic development can be traced through his writing. The early fiction, after *Desperate Remedies*, concentrates primarily on the rural environment Hardy knew so well and which he depicted with sympathy, appreciation and humour, as well as with his characteristic sense of tragic potentiality. *Under the Greenwood Tree*, in particular, depicts a scene that seems designed to be quintessentially English, portrayed by means of the quasi-realist aesthetic indicated by the subtitle, 'A Rural Painting of the Dutch School'. The carefully invented world of the church musicians is not far from that of Shakespeare's England in some of the comedies and history plays, although the rural idyll of literary convention is threatened by modernity in various guises, represented by the replacement of the church band by the organ: as Simon Gatrell has pointed out,

The church musicians and their fate would become profoundly emblematic of the greater social and cultural upheaval, and their unease in church after the loss of their occupation would be the beginning of a narrative of displacement and confusion that could only end bleakly.[6]

England was changing, although Hardy's great early success *Far from the Madding Crowd* seemed to present readers with a character who became a defiant justification of a peculiarly English hybrid in the character of Gabriel Oak, who combines the hireling shepherd with the farmer's bailiff and man of property, in a solid human form whose name alone suggests the annunciation of Englishness. Twentieth-century pastoral nostalgia, evident in media adaptations of Hardy's work, inevitably harks back to this text, as in John Schlesinger's 1967 film, and the recent television adaptation in 1999. The Wessex that Hardy created here remains a mythic world of great power for the public imagination. As Jonathan Bate points out in his eco-critical treatise, *The Song of the Earth*: 'Hardy ... represents nostalgia for a simple, honest, rustic way of life among hedgerows, haystacks and sturdy English oak trees.'[7] Gervais has noted a debt to Wordsworth here:

> Adam Bede, Gabriel Oak, even Sturt's real-life Bettesworth, are all offspring of Michael, grounded in reality on one side and shading into myth on the other. At a time when English workmen were leaving the land in droves to become railwaymen and industrial 'hands', such figures were offered as exemplary in their 'Englishness'.[8]

The psychological power and poetic resonance of the 'tragic' novels, from *The Return of the Native* to *Jude the Obscure*, all of which use mythic Wessex as their field of action, have focused critical attention upon the way local identity becomes fractured in the later fiction, as the seemingly rooted, historical Englishness of the Wessex village scene is affected by changes in local trade and industry, and by the advent of the railways. An interest in historical England provides the means of contrast with modernity; ancient Stonehenge in *Tess of the d'Urbervilles* becomes the locale for the final vision of a modern sacrificial victim, affected by Victorian social mores. The popularity of these novels should not prevent readers from paying attention, however, to other, less well-known novels. Characters in *The Hand of Ethelberta*, *A Laodicean*, *Two on a Tower* and *The Well-Beloved* depart in different ways from the Wessex scene, to voyage to South Africa in *Two on a Tower*, or simply to London, in *The Hand of Ethelberta*. Englishness does travel in Hardy's fiction, in the form of representative protagonists (rural workmen in *The Hand of Ethelberta*, the socially alienated scholar-astronomer in *Two on a Tower*). Moreover, as Gervais has pointed out,

> The world of *Jude the Obscure* is in the grip of accelerated change and fragmentation; it allows no nostalgic backward glances to rural Wessex. If Hardy has not had all the credit he deserves for chronicling this for us it is because so many of us want to look back on him with nostalgia.[9]

Hardy represents a shift of consciousness from the memorialising of quasi-traditional Englishness to a harsh late-Victorian social realism in relation to class and gender, but in addition to this, he demonstrates full cognisance of the wider reach of Englishness, from the material success gained by architect Stephen Smith in Bombay in *A Pair of Blue Eyes*, to the sufferings of farmer Angel Clare in Brazil in *Tess*. In the later fiction, Englishness is becoming world-wide in its dimensions, as imperial expansion and mercantile adventurism take characters into unfamiliar territory; the nemesis of 'Hodge', so ably defended by Hardy in 'The Dorsetshire Labourer' (*Longman's Magazine*, 1883), is finally found in the famous lyric poem on the South African War, 'Drummer Hodge'. Emigration represents an ultimate type of fracture for a community, in whatever form it appears.[10] Hardy's complex fascination with both rural and traditional 'patriotic' Englishness, revealed clearly in *The Trumpet-Major*, modulated into an absorption with the various socio-economic, metropolitan and imperial dimensions of Englishness. The investigation can be taken further: Hardy's lyric poetry and epic-drama tell another story in relation to Englishness, especially in relation to Englishness abroad. Their depiction of an emphatically *imperial* Englishness is crucial in terms of understanding Hardy's engagement with concepts of national identity.

Hardy's career as a published poet from 1898 onwards provided him with an opportunity to tackle challenging, even controversial, subject matter that he felt might suffer unreasonable censure if depicted in fiction. A diary entry of 1896 states:

> Poetry. Perhaps I can express more fully in verse ideas and emotions which run counter to the inert crystallized opinion – hard as a rock – which the vast body of men have vested interests in supporting. (*Life*, p. 302)

This sentiment is echoed in his poem 'Mute Opinion', where he expresses distrust of the contemporary understanding of history promulgated by 'pulpit, press and song'. Certain sections of the poetic corpus, including the epic-drama, *The Dynasts*, present readers with a series of challenges to social and political revaluation, as they focus on the several discourses (for example, historicist, gender-focused and religious) that together constitute the 'meta-discourse' of imperialism. While Hardy's first collection, *Wessex Poems*, concentrates primarily on personal and occasional subject matter, the 'War Poems' section of *Poems of the Past and the Present* (1901) begins a process of political engagement, addressing key questions of imperialism and national identity.

This poetry should be read in context. In the early years of the twentieth century, the British nation that effectively appropriated Hardy's 'Wessex' in cultural terms also relied upon particular ideas of 'Englishness' in order to project itself. Poets such as Alfred Austin and Henry Newbolt wrote specifically in relation to a popular imperial ideology in which 'Englishness' was paramount. As Kenneth Millard has noticed,

> there is scarcely a poem of Newbolt's in which the word 'England' does not appear ... The turn of the century period is characterized by celebrations of national identity; W. E. Henley published *For England's Sake* in 1900. William Watson's *For England* appeared in 1904, and Laurence Binyon's *England and Other Poems* in 1909. Even Edward Thomas wrote of 'This England', which once 'was called Merry'.[11]

As Alfred Austin points out in the 'Explanatory' note to his collection *Songs of England* (1898):

> by 'England', for which no other appellation equally comprehensive and convenient has yet been discovered, it is intended to indicate not only Great Britain and Ireland, but Canada, Australia, South Africa, India, and every spot on earth where men feel an instantaneous thrill of imperial kinship at the very sound of the name [Victoria] that lends its title to the opening poem in the present volume.[12]

For England, read 'Empire'. The perspective that Austin and others were busily projecting in their writing was that triumphantly (and militaristically) evoked in Kipling's 'The Song of the English', the initial poem of *The Seven Seas* (1896), in which messages of loyalty to England are sent from imperial locations around the world, and an ethic of blood sacrifice is promoted for 'Men in a world of men!' Englishness, in this context, is an emphatically masculine, global affair. Hardy's failure to participate in imperial enthusiasm led to the exclusion of his political poetry from popular consideration, at least until a general process of cultural re-evaluation during the First World War. Just as his poetry could not easily be equated with 1890s aestheticism, so too it could not be associated with the poetry of the 'New Imperialism'.[13] Eventually loosely associated with the work of the 'Georgian' poets, Hardy's poetry required a new political era to bring it to cultural prominence.

Why was this the case? The national mood during the years 1898–1916 dictated that attention was devoted only to outspoken literary-political comment on both sides of the political spectrum; if Kipling became the laureate of empire, inheriting the mantle from Tennyson, then W. S. Blunt, William Watson and Robert Buchanan became the outspoken critics of imperialistic Englishness.[14] Hardy took a more or less critical standpoint on 'New Imperialism', but poems such as 'Departure' (*Poems of the Past and the Present*) were more complex than those produced by fellow internationalists, and he was less easy to place. Nationalism and imperialism affected the production of poetry during this era in a number of ways, and Hardy's literary response was equally various. The 'Poems of Pilgrimage' section of *Poems of the Past and the Present* develops an implicit criticism of the imperial project through an extended comparison with Imperial Rome. These poems were originally written on visits to the Continent in 1887 and 1897, during years marked in England by Jubilee junketings. They were eventually published as a companion section to the initial 'War Poems', the latter offering a commentary on the war in South Africa. The sonnet 'Embarcation' focuses on imperial historicism in a style similar to Joseph Conrad in the opening chapter of *The Heart of Darkness*, and on the 'tragical To-Be' involved in the repetition of national militarism, while 'Departure', also a sonnet, is outspokenly internationalist and anti-imperial:[15]

When shall the saner, softer polities
Whereof we dream, have sway in each proud land,
And patriotism, grown Godlike, scorn to stand
Bondslave to realms, but circle earth and seas?

Similarly, there are poems that reply to masculinist discourse by highlighting a female perspective upon conflict ('The Going of the Battery', 'A Wife in London'), poems that focus on the fate of dead soldiers ('The Souls of the Slain', 'Drummer Hodge'), and poems such as 'The Sick Battle-God', which attempt a philosophical perspective, though the outbreak of the First World War led Hardy to question the tentative political optimism it expressed. 'At the War Office, London', which refers to 'scheduled slaughter' and locates death at the heart of the imperial metropolis, indicates that Hardy was seeing the conflict in emphatically global terms: before the South African War, 'Peace smiled unshent / From Ind to Occident'; the supposedly civilised English capital becomes defamiliarised linguistically as the 'Occident'. Hardy writes here against the 'orientalist' assumptions current in late Victorian Britain, defined by Edward Said as 'a Western style for dominating, restructuring and having authority over the Orient'.[16] Similarly, a critical, morally haunting perspective on Christian Englishness is seen in the war poem 'A Christmas Ghost-Story', which can be read as a reply to the quasi-religious literary discourse employed by writers like Kipling and Swinburne.[17]

The revaluation of imperial Englishness becomes a key concern at this point in Hardy's work. In this regard, the war poetry deserves reappraisal in the light of Hardy's singular divergence from contemporary poetic practice. *Poems of the Past and the Present* was published, for example, in the same year as Newbolt's unself-consciously patriotic *The Sailing of the Long Ships*. As Elleke Boehmer has noted, 'Hardy met with social disapproval for his criticism of British aggression in the South African War.'[18] In 1903 he copied out part of a review of Gilbert Murray's translation of Euripides. The passage encapsulates the sense of risk with which writers opposed the New Imperial movement:

> *Euripides – Imperialism.* 'Half a century elapsed between "Hippolytus", & "The Bacchae." In the interval the tragedy of Athens had been played. All the high hopes had faded. Hegemony had degenerated into empire. And then came the war, with its pitiful relaxation of moral and intellectual fibre. Athens, once "farther removed from primitive savagery" than any other people had learnt from Cleon not to be "misled by the three most deadly enemies of empire, Pity & Eloquent Sentiments, & the Generosity of Strength". Euripides himself had incurred the dislike of his fellow countrymen, & had to leave Athens.'[19]

It is only in retrospect that we can see Hardy in a tradition of poets and novelists before him, fulfilling the role of the radical writer in the awkward drama of the late nineteenth and early twentieth century, risking the kind of social alienation afforded certain predecessors and, indeed, contemporaries. William Watson, ostracised for his opposition to the South African War, appropriately entitled his collection, *For England: Poems Written During Estrangement* (1904).

After the publication of *Poems of the Past and the Present*, Hardy devoted himself to the literary project that culminated in the epic-drama, *The Dynasts* (1904, 1906, 1908). He had long been interested in the Napoleonic Wars; now he set himself to explore national and international consciousness in a dramatic scheme that would both attend to, and attempt to transcend, the limitations of time and place. Before the composition of the first draft, he embarked on a period of scholarly investigation. As Harold Orel and R. J. White have pointed out, *The Dynasts* required familiarity with a significant amount of British and Continental academic literature.[20] It was to be an emphatically English literary project that nevertheless made use of a wide range of historical material.

One key literary work Hardy consulted was Tolstoy's *War and Peace* (1869); certain passages in the novel, marked in pencil in Hardy's text, correspond clearly to key episodes within *The Dynasts*.[21] While critics have explored Tolstoy's influence in relation to the structure and supernatural machinery of the epic-drama, the impact of *War and Peace* on *The Dynasts* has yet to be explored in detail in relation to shared literary objectives, biographical connections between the two authors, and the contemporary political significance of Hardy's work. But as the Preface points out, Hardy felt the investigations of 'Continental Writers' required a response:

the slight regard paid to English influence and action throughout the struggle by so many Continental writers who had dealt with Napoleon's career, seemed always to leave room for a new handling of the theme which should re-embody the features of this influence in their true proportion.[22]

An English literary version of the Napoleonic story was essential partly because of the developing popularity of Tolstoy's work throughout Western Europe. E. J. Simmons, for example, has noted the large number of translations commissioned during the 1880s.[23] Hardy bought the first edition of *War and Peace* to be made widely available in the United Kingdom, the translation by N. H. Dole which appeared in the late 1880s. His interest in Tolstoy's stance on war is confirmed not only by his reading and annotation of this edition, but also by the section of the

Life which recounts support for Tolstoy's anti-war letter to *The Times* of 27 June 1904.

Tolstoy's controversial letter on the subject of the Russo-Japanese War had a peculiarly challenging title, 'Bethink Yourselves!', and carried an equally provocative epigraph: 'This is your hour and the power of darkness' (Luke, xxii. 53). The title was transposed from a passage in *War and Peace* describing the slaughter at the Battle of Borodino. In Tolstoy's literary schema, penitence for the folly of war becomes a national imperative if the central assumptions of imperial culture are to be addressed. A genuinely felt Christianity is seen to function in direct opposition to the blood-letting of international warfare:

> Again war. Again suffering, necessary to nobody, utterly uncalled for; again fraud, again the universal stupefaction and brutalization of men.

> ... Is it a dream or a reality? Something is taking place which should not, cannot be; one longs to believe that it is a dream and to awake from it.
> But no, it is not a dream, it is a dreadful reality![24]

The senselessness of imperial conflict is stated straightforwardly, while the nightmarish opposition of 'dream' and 'reality' is additionally significant in relation to the various dream-like, almost surreal, descriptive sequences of *The Dynasts*.[25]

Hardy became the only major literary figure to support what in a letter to *The Times* of 28 June 1904 he described as Tolstoy's 'masterly general indictment of war as a modern principle, with all its senseless and illogical crimes' (*Life*, p. 346). The publication of Tolstoy's letter formed a rallying call to those writers working from an anti-war perspective. Resisting the journalistic dismissal of the 'Bethink Yourselves!' protest, Hardy became the English representative of a long-term, internationalist response to Tolstoy's anti-war writing; Romain Rolland in France, Herman Hesse and Rainer Maria Rilke in Germany, and Mohandas K. Gandhi in South Africa, would go on to echo support for Tolstoy's stance.[26] In March 1908 Hardy became a member of a committee set up by C. T. Hagberg Wright of the British Library, which had as its object the delivery of a letter of congratulation to Tolstoy on his eightieth birthday, despite the fact that in Russia public celebration of the event was banned. Hardy's name was on a list of signatories that included, among others, George

Bernard Shaw and Edmund Gosse. Significantly, Hardy records having dinner with fellow internationalists, including Conrad, Wells, Shaw and Gorky in May 1908, during the period when the congratulatory letter and address were being organised: 'an informal but most interesting dinner at the house of his friend Dr Hagberg Wright ... it was a late hour when the party broke up' (Life, p. 360).

Hardy's appreciation of Tolstoy's outburst is indicated not only by the account in the Life, but also by the fact that in The Dynasts he borrows from the passage in War and Peace that Tolstoy had drawn upon. The translation that Hardy used describes the battlefield of Borodino as 'a rack of damp and smoke ... the air was foul with a strange reek of nitrous fumes and blood'. In The Dynasts we read the speech by the 'Shade of the Earth' after the battle:

The fumes of nitre and the reek of gore
Make my airs foul and fulsome unto me!

To which the 'Spirit Ironic' replies pithily:

The natural nausea of a nurse, dear Dame.[27]

The additional comment contributes an element of modernist irony to the description of war, heightening the alienation felt by the reader.

Tolstoy's biblical prophetic appeal ('Bethink Yourselves!') is equivalent to Hardy's reiteration of the idea of psalmic 'lovingkindness', an idea that Tolstoy also utilises in Anna Karenina.[28] Both writers reclaimed religious language and rhetoric from the established authors of nationalistic imperial destiny, as for example in Kipling's appropriation of 'the Lord our God most High' for New Imperial politics in 'The Song of the English'. Hardy took satisfaction in noting a similarity (albeit not exact) in religious perspective between his epic-drama and Tolstoy's protest. In a letter to Violet Hunt, excusing himself from a social engagement, he states: 'I suppose I should say the Immanent Will arranged it for me ... (By the way Tolstoy calls it in to-day's Times the "Higher Will").'[29] As the South African War progressed, Hardy distanced himself politically from many of his literary contemporaries. While he resisted the expansionist imperialism recommended by poets such as Kipling and Swinburne (the latter's position was illustrated in his virulent sonnet, 'The Transvaal'), he simultaneously sought out alternative literary allies. Despite his reservations about some parts of Tolstoy's non-fictional prose, the main thrust of the latter's work seemed to provide an indicaton of a political way forward.[30]

In their respective national epics, Tolstoy and Hardy attempted to rewrite the historical record, analysing the evidence of one historical period in order to illustrate the futility of international conflict. In this, they drew attention to the ideological distortions that affect popular, political assumptions within imperial societies. Tolstoy's historicist method is of significance, in that it clearly resembles that employed in *The Dynasts*. Hardy insists on the 'intrinsical' interrelatedness of all human actions (as seen in the majority of his initial scene descriptions and 'Dumb Shows') while at the same time attacking, through character depiction and choric commentary, the Carlylean 'great man' theory of history. These standpoints reflect the positions taken by Tolstoy throughout his work (for example, the discursive opening section of Book Three of *War and Peace*). Contemporary assumptions are revised in favour of a more complex understanding of history; in deconstructing ideological assumptions in relation to the role of great men (key assumptions that underpinned the political functioning of imperial culture) both Tolstoy and Hardy wrote against the grain of contemporary literature, and against the dominant ideological structures of the societies whose audiences they sought.

As Hardy states in the Preface to Part First, his object in *The Dynasts* was 'the modern expression of a modern outlook'. It was important that his writing chimed with the political sentiment of internationalist Continental literature. Active engagement in contemporary European cultural debate is reflected in an article on European realist literature by E. M. de Vogüé, copied into the *Literary Notebooks*:

Un esprit Européen:–
Owing to the frequency & the rapidity of every kind of interchange, owing to the growing solidarity which unifies the world, there is created in our days, above any preferences of coterie and nationality, an European mind ([un] esprit européen), a groundwork of culture, of ideas, & of inclinations, common to all intelligent societies.[31]

Hardy was conscious that his work was being published in a pan-European cultural milieu in which social politics informed literary subject matter. *The Dynasts*, while reflecting Englishness in action, is geared towards engagement with contemporary, radical European thought.

Tolstoy's influence is the key to appreciating the cultural politics of 'the Napoleonic' during the late nineteenth and early twentieth centuries. While the treatment of the figure of Napoleon as hero, villain and cultural icon in Romantic literature has been investigated by Simon Bainbridge, there remains a critical gap at present in relation to discussion of Victorian and twentieth-century appropriation of Napoleonic subject matter, for projects concerned with national identity.[32] The Napoleonic conflict of 1803–15 had a long-term socio-political and cultural resonance in British society at the beginning of the twentieth century similar to the ongoing cultural impact of the First World War now, at the beginning of the twenty-first century. There are differences, however, between Tolstoy and Hardy's treatment of their Napoleonic subject matter. Rather than attempting to speak like Tolstoy on behalf of the individual reader and so instruct them in what might be loosely described as the 'path to righteousness', Hardy uses Spirit and Choric voices in *The Dynasts* to represent different perspectives on the Napoleonic drama, in order to build up, in polyphonic fashion, a general picture, a representative perspective; whereas Tolstoy employs a monologic narrative voice within passages of philosophic commentary, the dialogic commentary provided by Hardy is delivered by several choric voices, in the speeches of the 'phantasmal Intelligences', even though some Spirits (for example, the 'Spirit of the Years') seem more reliable than others (for example, the 'Spirit Sinister'). In a sense, therefore, Hardy's schema develops a more open, as well as a more ingenious method of historical depiction. Despite being warranted by the choric strategies of ancient Greek drama, Hardy's dramatic method has met with only mixed appreciation and the supernatural machinery still seems as strange and off-putting to the casual reader as it did to early reviewers. The choric and spirit voices of *The Dynasts* are, in Hardy's words, 'contrivances of the fancy merely', designed to fulfil a particular function; the 'supplementary scenes' further the argument of the epic-drama and provide multiple perspective on the action.[33] *The Dynasts* can be read as an attempt to reflect problematic group identity and the processes that lie behind the formation of national consciousness.

Hardy wrote his epic-drama in order to engage with historical notions of 'Englishness', at a time when certainties established during the Napoleonic period were due for reappraisal. If Linda Colley's central thesis in *Britons: Forging the Nation 1707–1837* holds true, and a specifically 'British' consciousness was formed during the long period of the Anglo-French wars, Hardy was, in effect, responding to a key historical phase in the (re)definition of imperial consciousness. He was writing in an historically informed fashion about an era during which ideas of 'Englishness' and 'Britishness' had been redefined in relation to that which was 'Other': 'This was how it was with the British after 1707. They came to define themselves as a single people not because of any political or cultural consensus at home, but rather in reaction to the Other beyond their shores.'[34] In broad terms, one effect of the Napoleonic wars was to stabilise British national identity to an unprecedented degree, and in a manner which lasted until the First World War; this aspect of the redevelopment of core 'British' national identity operated in conjunction with that confrontation with the 'Other' in wider imperial experience which simultaneously delivered both a sense of self and a sense of purpose.

One of the benefits of Hardy's technique of multiple perspective in *The Dynasts* is that while national consciousness is effectively reappraised in relation to the Napoleonic era, it is never redefined in narrow, self-regarding terms. 'English-ness' is resident as much in the ignorant, the superstitious and the cowardly, as it is in the generally redeemable, but often flawed, heroic characters of the main protagonists; Britishness seems indelibly linked to jingoism. If a quintessentially English national consciousness is his main focus, Hardy nevertheless avoids both stereotyping and eulogy. Here is the primary English protagonist in Part First commenting on the general problem facing Europe:

> PITT
> … Realms, laws, peoples, dynasties,
> Are churning to a pulp within the maw
> Of empire-making Lust and personal Gain![35]

Critical perspective on political behaviour is available throughout the epic-drama; the speech and behaviour of the characters are chronicled dispassionately by the 'Spirit' and 'Chorus' of the 'Years', while 'Spirits Ironic' deflate patriotic self-delusion. The characters, similarly, comment ironically on the behaviour of the grandiose and the misguidedly patriotic. An example of this is found in the commentary provided on the jingo enthusiasm of the Prince Regent, who spouts heroic couplets to a momentarily receptive audience. A conversation follows:

> A NOBLE LORD (aside to Sheridan)
> Prinny's outpourings taste suspiciously like your brew Sheridan. I'll be damned if it is his own concoction. How d'ye sell it a gallon?

SHERIDAN
I don't deal that way nowadays. I give the recipe, and charge a duty
on the gauging. It is more artistic, and saves trouble.[36]

This cynicism about 'Prinny's outpourings' forms part of a pattern of
ironic comment within the text which focuses the reader's attention
on ideological distortion. Ironic perspective provides a key strategy in
Hardy's treatment of popular jingoism. When the Prince of Wales forecasts
success for the ill-fated expedition to Walcheren by attempting to evoke
'British' fervour, we are prepared for what can be described as the dialogue
of deflation. The Prince's positive reference to 'every twang of British
dialect, / Clamorous to loosen fettered Europe's chain!', is immediately
followed by the dialogue quoted above, where the literary representative
(Sheridan) illustrates opposition to the establishment rhetoric of the
'little England[er]'.[37] In no sense, therefore, does Hardy's epic-drama draw
from, or feed into, the sense of cultural superiority that characterised
imperial 'Britishness' in the first decade of the twentieth century. His
investigation of 'Englishness' in *The Dynasts* eschews reliance on the
inclusivity of 'British-ness' and avoids emphasis upon the 'foreignness'
of the French (among other nations); wherever jingoist rhetoric appears,
it is treated with significant irony. To use the terminology of Gayatri
Spivak, Hardy manages to avoid both a 'self-consolidating Other' and an
'absolute Other' by rejecting national cultural stereotypes; his Frenchmen
are not caricatures (see the complex depiction of Admiral Villeneuve in
Part First). His Englishmen, and the group perspective evoked by the
Spirit machinery, similarly avoid type.[38]

One of the main points of the epic-drama is to deliver a paradigm
of opposites for the reader to consider in terms of human behaviour, a
paradigm that has ideological implications. One half of the paradigm
has Napoleon at its centre, as we are invited in the initial 'Fore Scene'
to consider the meaning of 'this strange man's career' and of the
'large potencies / Instilled into his idiosyncrasy'.[39] The psychological
development within the epic-drama is forecast in the judgement that such
potencies, the personal qualities that constitute Napoleon's personality,
are 'taking taint':

SPIRIT OF THE PITIES
... 'twere better far
Such deeds were nulled, and this strange man's career
Wound up, as making inharmonious jars

In her creation whose meek wraith we know.
... For the large potencies
Instilled into his idiosyncrasy –
To throne fair Liberty in Privilege's room –
Are taking taint, and sink to common plots
For his own gain.[40]

The 'Spirit of the Pities' wishes that Napoleon's career cou:d be '[an]nulled', in order that the 'inharmonious' jarring effect of his career should not disturb an hypothetical equilibrium in Nature. In this, 'Pities' represents a discourse of suffering detectable throughout Hardy s writing. In the presentation of the essential meaning of Napoleon's career at the outset (talent tainted by vainglorious self-interest), we are shown one half of a paradigm designed to reflect humanity in genera:. The discussion continues:

SHADE OF THE EARTH
   ... And who, then, Cordial One,
Wouldst substitute for this Intractable?

CHORUS OF THE PITIES
We would establish those of kindlier build,
   In fair compassions skilled,
Men of deep art in life-development;
Watchers and warders of thy varied lands,
Men surfeited of laying heavy hands
   Upon the innocent,
The mild, the fragile, the obscure content
Among the myriads of thy family.
Those, too, who love the true, the excellent,
And make their daily moves a melody.[41]

The central opposition of *The Dynasts*, therefore, is between 'vaingloriousness' and 'lovingkindness', the former represented by Napoleon and the latter by 'Men of deep art in life-development', of whom we have various (notably imperfect) examples within the epic-drama (Pitt, Nelson, Sir John Moore). The term 'vaingloriousness' is relevant here in the specific Hardyan sense revealed in the poem 'The Convergence of the Twain', where it is used to describe the overweening imperial pride that was associated with the destruction of the *Titanic*. S.milarly, in the poem

'A.H., 1855–1912', written in memory of Florence Henniker's husband, Major-General Arthur Henniker, a lack of 'vaingloriousness' is seen as the key to the character of an ideal soldier: 'who could find / In camp or court a less vainglorious mind?' The argument of the 'Pities' goes to the heart of Hardy's value-system, as an alternative model of human behaviour is presented in contrast with those (like Napoleon) who attract the attention of writers and historians. Napoleon's personality is depicted in a negative light at the outset and the reader is instructed to value those who care for 'the *obscure* content', who, like Jude in Hardy's novel, suffer as a result of the behaviour of people in positions of power. This passage presents a condensation of the positive ingredients in Hardy's understanding of human character. His life-long appreciation of music is indicated by the emphasis on the melodiousness of the lives of those who remain kind and compassionate in behaviour ('their daily lives a melody'). A well-constructed life, tuned to avoid the misuse of power, creates an internal harmony that resounds beyond the immediate.

The general problem presented to the reader in the paradigm of human character depicted in the 'Fore Scene' is both structural and ideological in the nature of its function in, and effect on, society. The reason 'vainglorious' characters have a major impact in terms of human suffering is related both to the way in which they are represented in ideological terms, and to the way basic political structures assist the abuse of power. Shortly after the 'Chorus of the Pities' has delineated its model human behaviour, the 'Spirit of the Years', time's recorder, notes the ongoing operation of familiar patterns in history:

> ... old laws operate yet; and phase and phase
> Of men's dynastic and imperial moils
> Shape on accustomed lines. Though as for me,
> I care not how they shape, or what they be.[42]

In mentioning 'dynastic and imperial moils', the 'Spirit of the Years' states the facts; the troubling of nature caused by Napoleon is one of many phases repeated as a result of the historical patterns created by 'imperial[ism]'. The literary investigation in *The Dynasts* is defined, in part, by a preoccupation with 'old Laws' that govern the 'phases' of human history. Inextricably linked with political forces that shape history, these 'Laws' are to be subjected to analysis, in order that the fundamental character paradigm is illuminated and power structures made transparent. At the time Hardy was writing, 'dynastic and imperial moils' had culminated in the deliberate but unreflective expansionist Englishness of the present. Hardy, in effect, presents a test-case for his readers' appreciation. *The Dynasts* functions as a moral fable for imperial culture.

To suggest that Hardy opposed the mis-appropriations effected by imperial ideology is not to claim that he stood opposed to genuine patriotic example. Shortly after the discussion of the political after-effects of Trafalgar, Pitt, the reluctant hero of Part First, rises to speak at the Guildhall. His nobility of example rests upon humility, far-sightedness in public policy, and appropriate, understated political rhetoric:

> My Lords and gentlemen: You have toasted me
> As one who has saved England and her cause.
> I thank you gentlemen, unfeignedly.
> But – no man has saved England, let me say:
> England has saved herself, by her exertions:
> She will, I trust, save Europe by her example!
> > Loud applause, during which he sits down, rises,
> > and sits down again. ...
>
> SPIRIT OF THE YEARS
> Those words of this man Pitt – his last large words,
> As I may prophesy – that ring tonight
> In their first mintage to the feasters here,
> Will spread with ageing, lodge, and crystallize,
> And stand embedded in the English tongue
> Till it grow thin, outworn, and cease to be ...
> For words were never winged with apter grace,
> Or blent with happier choice of time and place,
> To hold the imagination of this strenuous race.[45]

Pitt's suggestion that the good fortune of the nation cannot be attributed to the behaviour of any one man ('no man has saved England') counters the argument for hero-worship, while at the same time, in his emphasis on the positive nature of enlightened group endeavour ('Save Europe by her example!'), he confirms his own validation within the moral scheme of the epic-drama. His language assists the deflation of pseudo-heroic status, and his words engage profoundly with a sense of what the 'Spirit of the Years' calls the 'imagination of this strenuous race'. Understatement and modesty, it is implied, are more fundamental to Hardyan Englishness than the adulatory rhetoric of a 'dynastic' society.

Pitt believes in saving Europe, however, and apart from providing a sensitive analysis of Englishness, the epic-drama moves beyond this into new territory. The text itself constitutes a crucial point in the history of literary-political representation; the point where a purposively fractured and reformed sense of 'Englishness' happens to 'cease to be', dissolving into internationalism. The text itself is both a battle-ground and a literary-political journey. To quote the closing scene of Wells's contemporary novel, *Tono-Bungay* (1909):

> Light after light goes down. England and the Kingdom, Britain and the Empire, the old prides and the old devotions glide abeam, astern, sink down upon the horizon, pass – pass. ... London passes. England passes.

During the First World War, *The Dynasts* was adapted by Granville Barker and performed at the Kingsway Theatre, London, achieving a degree of popular success. The war years, however, were not simply a time during which Hardy sat back, content in his diagnosis of the perils of nationalism. During this period he developed his interest in multiple perspective within the vehicle of lyric poetry, thereby providing poetry of 'polyphonic' insight. Recent critics have focused on the doom-laden elements within Hardy's poetry at this time. For example, Dennis Taylor's *Hardy's Poetry 1860–1928* discusses the war poetry in terms of apocalyptic language and imagery. This inevitably ties in, however, with the largely negative understanding of Hardy's personality, the pessimistic 'Hardy' promulgated by Robert Gittings, and recently deconstructed by Widdowson. Taylor's study of the poetry offers a great deal, but there is more to say about the way Hardy balances individual and group perspective on military conflict in a body of writing which does justice to the complexity of war experience on the home front.

By claiming 'patriotism' as an internationalist entity, Hardy removed it from the realm of imperialist rhetoric. The basic idea is expressed in a letter to Percy Ames:

> That nothing effectual will be done in the cause of peace till the sentiment of *Patriotism* be freed from the narrow meaning attaching to it in the past (and still upheld by Junkers and Jingoists) – and be extended to the whole globe.

On the other hand, that the sentiment of *Foreignness* – if the sense of contrast be necessary – attach only to other planets and the inhabitants if any.

I may add that I have written in advocacy of these views for the last twenty years.[44]

The influence of Wells's *War of the Worlds* is perhaps discernible in the reference to 'inhabitants' of 'other planets'; Hardy had attended a meeting with Wells, called by C. F. G. Masterman in September 19_4 to discuss the role eminent authors might play in formulating and publicising British principles and war aims.[45] Hardy assumed an even-handed literary role, criticising both German and British imperialists ('Junkers and Jingoists'). Pre-war poems such as 'The Convergence of the Twain' and 'Channel Firing' sounded warning notes about the dangers of a 'vainglorious' imperial culture; they also provide useful points of comparison with the nautical verse published by Kipling in *The Seven Seas* (1896) and by Newbolt in *Admirals All and Other Verses* (1897) and *The Sailing of the Long Ships* (1901). During the war, however, Hardy wrote a series of poems, eventually published in the 'Poems of War and Patriotism' section of *Moments of Vision*, which tackle the issue of national identity. Perhaps the most interesting are the public poem 'Men Who March Away (Song of the Soldiers)' and its companion piece, the more intimate 'Before Marching and After', together with 'His Country , a curious poem which adopts the form of Coleridge's 'The Ancient Mariner', providing multiple perspective by means of a side-commentary. 'In Time of "the Breaking of Nations"' is the most anthologised of these poems, perhaps because it fits neatly into the pastoral drawer in public consciousness marked 'Hardy', but many of the war poems deserve reappraisal. 'Men Who March Away' and 'Before Marching and After' display the tensions between individual and group perspectives, embodying both the fervour of group participation, the scepticism of the observer and the self-sacrifice of the knowing victim.[46] 'His Country' presents an argument not for Englishness abroad but for an internationalist perspective. As the side-commentary notes, the protagonist 'cannot discover the boundary of his country; or where his duties to his fellow creatures end; nor who are his enemies': 'My country seems to have kept in sight / On my way everywhere.' Almost unwittingly, he becomes internationalist in political understanding.

While Hardy condemns German militarism in poems such as 'England to Germany in 1914' and focuses on the plight of individual countries in poems such as 'On the Belgian Expatriation' and 'Cry of the Homeless', his main impetus is to encourage a wider-than-national perspective. 'The Pity of It' locates political guilt in the activity of those who encourage conflict, the 'gangs whose glory threats and slaughter are', whatever their nationality. Hardy's interest in England and Englishness remains subservient to a broader sense of international political responsibility. In this, his is a positive poetic record, one acknowledged by a generation of combatant poets if not by subsequent critics.[47] The net result was a profound influence upon younger poets and writers of the war generation, including Siegfried Sassoon, Edmund Blunden and T. E. Lawrence. Sassoon carried a copy of Hardy's *Selected Poems* (1916) with him in the trenches. His quasi-fictional autobiography, *The Complete Memoirs of George Sherston* (incorporating *Memoirs of Fox-Hunting Man*, *Memoirs of an Infantry Officer* and *Sherston's Progress*) includes many references to Hardy, despite the fact that Sherston supposedly represents Sassoon's non-literary alter ego, the man of action, hunter and soldier. In 'Part Four: Battle' of *Memoirs of an Infantry Officer*, Sherston goes into battle with *Tess* in his pocket:

> … my personal impression was that we were setting out for the other end of nowhere. I had slipped a book into my haversack and it was a comfort to be carrying it, for Thomas Hardy's England was between its covers.[48]

Sassoon, as Sherston, is fighting for 'Thomas Hardy's England', a place representative of affirmative truth-telling, while he moves literally and metaphorically into the 'nowhere' place, the waste land region of the front-line. In some senses, it is a representative journey from the Victorian to the Modern. Hardy's novel is carried by the alienated individual into the 'nowhere' place of the imagination, that place evoked in a passage from *The Dynasts* quoted by Sassoon in his *Diaries*, characterised by a sense of 'deep wells of nothingness'.[49] Hardy's influence, not only on Sassoon but on many other war poets and writers was crucial, as they produced poetry that, for generations after the war, has come to be seen as quintessentially 'English', in a broad sense that includes the poetry of Wilfred Owen, Edward Thomas and Edmund Blunden, if not that of the Anglo-Welsh modernist, David Jones.

In his later years, Hardy wrote poetry of different types, lyric and narrative, on a range of subjects, anecdotal, philosophically speculative, pastoral, political, published in the collections *Late Lyrics and Earlier*, *Human Shows*, and the posthumously published *Winter Words*; given the range and breadth of his literary output, easy generalisations about his work's engagement with, or portrayal of Englishness, need to be avoided. Certainly the overtly political poetry constitutes a relatively small proportion of the overall output. What is curious, however, is the way in which the political poetry has been treated in the critical history, remaining largely ignored or misinterpreted. Indeed, the appropriation of Hardy's physical remains for the nation, in a Westminster ceremony (separate from the heart burial in Dorset) parallels the ideological appropriation to which the literary remains became subject. The heart burial in Wessex symbolises, as it was meant to, the fact that Hardy's affections lay close to home. It can also, however, be seen to represent the marginalisation of the political heart of Hardy's message by the need to incorporate his work within conventional boundaries.

John Betjeman, the paragon of self-deprecatory Englishness, showed a degree of cultural condescension toward Hardy in his disturbing poem, 'The Heart of Thomas Hardy', published in 1937 in the collection *Continual Dew*, which marked one stage in Betjeman's progress towards the position of Poet Laureate.[50] In the poem, Hardy's heart is seen attempting to escape the confines of the rural Stinsford churchyard. It becomes a 'little thumping fig' determined to relay ideological messages (stories of 'Tess and Jude and His Worship, various unmarried mothers, / Woodman, cutters of turf, adulterers, church restorers'), becoming in its verbosity 'the twittering heart of Hardy'. Hardy's characters and social standpoint are, within the perspective of the poem, of as fleeting importance as a flower, and so die 'away in the night as frost will blacken a dahlia'. The poem is as macabre as its subject matter, the whole aesthetic product being part of a familiar process of appropriation, limitation, and exclusion: Hardy's characters supposedly die away in the 'night' of cultural history, as a result of their triviality and bogus morality (being momentarily 'weighted down with a conscience'). Despite the humour and humane sensitivity evident elsewhere in his work, Betjeman joins the cultural establishment where the issue of 'Hardy' is at stake. He proves his own credentials by degrading Hardy's achievement; the bizarre arrangements for Hardy's burial provide a perfect opportunity for this approach. This condescension finds its critical equivalent in the work of F. R. Leavis, who famously dismissed Hardy from *The Great Tradition*: 'Hardy, decent as he is, [appears] as a provincial manufacturer of gauche and heavy fictions that sometimes have corresponding virtues.'[51] In Betjeman's poem, of course, Hardy's characters are significantly 'weighted down' and therefore, as in Leavis's judgement, 'heavy'; incapable of effortless imaginative flight. Hardy becomes a mere industrial 'manufacturer' of 'gauche' literature, or, in Betjeman's terms, a 'twittering' literary failure. Betjeman's poem suggests the redundancy of Hardy's moral and political seriousness, while the narrative voice embodies a characteristic treatment of Hardy's political relevance in literary history. The tradition of Hardy criticism typified by Robert Gittings's attribution to him of political cowardice, sexual incompetence and physical impropriety, is represented in paradigmatic form in Betjeman's poem. Hardy becomes the parochial, insignificant rural Englishman; the 'anxiety of influence' affects the poetry of Betjeman, someone who feels compelled to claim the English 'heart'-land.[52]

Donald Davie's later patronising reference to Hardy's '*decent* liberalism' probably reflects the influence of F. R. Leavis ('*decent* as he is'), thus providing an example of the way in which a chain of negative influence can affect a literary reputation. In his influential study, *Thomas Hardy and British Poetry*, Davie defined the politics of Hardy's poetry in terms of the 'decent liberalism' of a literary 'technician':

> Hardy in his poetry is this sort of cop-out, a modest (though proudly expert) workman in a corporate enterprise which from time to time publishes a balance sheet called *The Golden Treasury* or *The Oxford Book of English Verse*.[53]

While a degree of irony is evident in Davie's balance sheet analogy, his diagnosis of Hardy as a 'cop-out' conforms with a general pattern in the critical history of Hardy's poetry, including the acknowledgement of its quintessential Englishness. A supposedly reticent 'liberalism' is found irremediably insufficient: 'For surely the poet, if any one, has a duty to be radical, to go to the roots.'[54] Hardy's verse is seen as both technically adept and also inveterately unambitious, and a negative influence on successors such as Auden and Larkin. Davie, however, fails to pursue the logic of his own analysis. While dismissing certain of Hardy's war poems as 'sabre-rattlings or morale builders or worse', he nevertheless attacks Hardy for avoiding comment on contemporary events:

> Major issues of national policy were among the matters that Hardy was too modest to concern himself with, and his modesty was that of the expert technician, imperious within his own enterprizes, diffident or indifferent outside it.[55]

Davie's judgement that Hardy's work reflects a 'crucial selling short of the poetic vocation' is echoed in much later critical opinion.[56] The long-term process of minimising Hardy's political contribution in his poetry, seen in the work of critics such as Davie, requires a detailed and carefully managed critical response. The real state of affairs in discussion of the politics of Hardy's poetry is that confusion reigns, something illustrated by juxtaposition of Leavis's diagnosis of 'conservatism' and Davie's 'liberalism'. In investigation of the politics of Hardy's poetry and his national literary role, nowhere has Philip Larkin's advertisement 'Wanted: Good Hardy Critic' been more relevant.[57] A liberal at heart, politically engaged in a literary sense and yet avoiding active participation in politics, Hardy provides an extended analysis of Englishness that deserves wider critical notice.

notes

1. Robert Colls and Philip Dodd, eds, *The Idea of Englishness 1880–1920* (Beckenham, 1985).
2. David Gervais, *Literary Englands: Versions of Engishness in Modern Writing* (Cambridge, 1993).
3. Peter Widdowson, *Hardy in History: A Study in Literary Sociology* (London and New York, 1989), p. 125.
4. Widdowson, *Hardy in History*, p. 226.
5. George Wotton, *Thomas Hardy: Towards a Materialist Criticism* (Dublin, 1985); John Goode, *Thomas Hardy: The Offensive Truth* (Oxford, 1988); Roger Ebbatson, *Hardy: The Margin of the Unexpressed* (Sheffield, 1993).
6. Simon Gatrell, in Norman Page, ed. *The Oxford Reader's Companion to Hardy* (Oxford, 2000), p. 455.
7. Jonathan Bate, *The Song of the Earth* (London, 2000), p. 1
8. Gervais, *Literary Englands*, p. 4.
9. Gervais, *Literary Englands*, p. 16.
10. See Roger Robinson's entry on emigration in *The Oxford Reader's Companion to Hardy* (Oxford, 2000) and Simon Gatrell's article 'England, Europe and Empire: Hardy, Meredith and Gissing' in Simon Gatrell, ed., *English Literature and the Wider World*, Vol. 4, *The Ends of the Earth 1876–1914* (London, 1992).
11. Kenneth Millard, *Edwardian Poetry* (Oxford, 1991), pp. 26–7.
12. Alfred Austin, *Songs of England* (1898), quoted in Millard, *Edwardian Poetry*, p. 28.
13. See R. Koebner and H. D. Schmidt, *Imperialism: The Story and Significance of a Political Word 1840–1960* (Cambridge, 1964), pp. 212–14.
14. See Watson's collection, *For England: Poems Written During Estrangement* (London, 1904) and Robert Buchanan's *The New Rome: Poems and Ballads of Our Empire* (1899) in *The Complete Poetical Works of Robert Buchanan*, 2 vols, (London, 1901). My choice of dates here corresponds to the dates of *Wessex Poems* (1898) and the Battle of the Somme in 1916, which heralded widespread

revaluation of the country's attitude to patriotic endeavour and to poetry that dealt with the subject.

15. See my article, 'Thomas Hardy and The South African War', in Rosemarie Morgan, ed., *The Hardy Review* Vol. 1, No. 1 (New Haven, 1998), pp. 144–7.
16. Edward Said, *Orientalism: Western Conceptions of the Orient* (1979; London, 1995), p. 3.
17. See my article 'Puzzled Phantoms – Thomas Hardy's "A Christmas Ghost Story"', *Times Literary Supplement*, 24 December 1999, No. 5047, p. 12.
18. Elleke Boehmer, *Colonial and Postcolonial Literature* (Oxford, 1995), p. 43.
19. *Literary Notebooks*, II, p. 136.
20. See Harold Orel, 'Introduction' to his New Wessex Edition of *The Dynasts* (London, 1978), pp. ix–xxiii, and R. J. White, *Thomas Hardy and History* (London, 1974), pp. 79–89.
21. Including Emma Clifford, '*War and Peace* and *The Dynasts*', *Modern Philology*, LIV, No. 1 (Chicago, 1956), Martin Seymour-Smith, *Hardy* (London, 1994), pp. 660–3, R. J. White in his chapter 'Hardy and Tolstoy' in *Hardy and History*, and Walter F. Wright, *The Shaping of The Dynasts* (Lincoln, Nebraska, 1967), pp. 222–7.
22. *The Dynasts*, p. 4.
23. E. J. Simmons, *Tolstoy* (London, 1973), pp. 223–4.
24. *The Times*, 27 June 1904, p. 4.
25. See Susan Dean, *Hardy's Poetic Vision in 'The Dynasts': The Diorama of a Dream* (Princeton, 1977).
26. Herman Hesse, *If the War Goes On: Reflections on War and Politics* (London, 1985), pp. 155–6; Louis Fischer, *The Life of Mahatma Gandhi* (London, 1951), pp. 111–17.
27. *The Dynasts*, p. 468.
28. *Anna Karenina*, trans. Rosemary Edmonds (London, 1978), p. 52.
29. *Letters*, III, p. 127.
30. In July 1899 Hardy wrote to Florence Henniker: 'I have just read Tolstoi's "What is Art?" – a suggestive book, in which there are a good many true things, & many more that hover round the truth but just miss it' (*Letters*, II, p. 225).
31. *Literary Notebooks*, I, p. 223.
32. See his *Napoleon and English Romanticism* (Cambridge, 1995). Iain Pears's essay 'The Gentleman and the Hero' in Roy Porter, ed., *The Myths of the English* (Cambridge, 1992) is the exception that proves the rule.
33. *The Dynasts*, p. 4.
34. Linda Colley, *Britons: Forging the Nation 1707–1837* (1992; London, 1994) p. 6.
35. *The Dynasts*, p. 184.
36. *The Dynasts*, p. 343.
37. *The Dynasts*, p. 339.
38. Gayatri Spivak, 'Overdeterminations of Imperialism: David Ochterlony and the Ranee of Sirmoor' in Frances Barker, Peter Hulme, Margaret Iversen and Diane Loxley, eds, *Europe and Its Others*, Vol. 1, Proceedings of the Essex Sociology of Literature Conference (Colchester, 1985), pp. 128–51.
39. *The Dynasts*, p. 23.

40. *The Dynasts*, p. 23.
41. *The Dynasts*, pp. 23–4.
42. *The Dynasts*, pp. 23–4.
43. *The Dynasts*, p. 153.
44. *Letters*, V, p. 202.
45. Michael Millgate, *Thomas Hardy: a Biography* (London and New York, 1982), p. 502.
46. See my article on these poems in *The Thomas Hardy Journal*, Vol. XV (October 1999), pp. 85–98.
47. 'Thomas Hardy and the First World War: Case Studies in Literary Influence', in Rosemarie Morgan and Richard Nemesvari, eds, *Human Shows: Essays in Honour of Michael Millgate* (New Haven, 2000).
48. Siegfried Sassoon, *The Complete Memoirs of George Sherston* (London, 1940), p. 325.
49. Rupert Hart-Davis, ed., *Siegfried Sassoon: Diaries 1915–1918* (London, 1983), pp. 80–1, from *The Dynasts*, 'After Scene', p. 702.
50. John Betjeman, *Collected Poems* (London, 1988), p. 36.
51. F. R. Leavis, *The Great Tradition* (1948; London, 1962) p. 248; Donald Davie, *Thomas Hardy and British Poetry* (London, 1973), p. 40.
52. Harold Bloom, *The Anxiety of Influence: A Theory of Poetry* (New York, 1973).
53. Davie, *Thomas Hardy*, p. 40.
54. Davie, *Thomas Hardy*, p. 40.
55. Davie, *Thomas Hardy*, p. 39.
56. See for example Kathryn R. King and William W. Morgan's otherwise stimulating article on 'Hardy and the Boer War: The Public Poet *in Spite of Himself*' (my italics) in *Victorian Poetry*, (Spring 1979) 17, No. 1.
57. Philip Larkin, *Required Writing: Miscellaneous Pieces 1955–1982* (London, 1983), pp. 168–74.

10
visual inspiration in hardy's fiction
john hughes

Many acquaintances of Hardy commented on the vigilant qualities of his eyes, clearly evident still in portraits, sketches and photographs. Virginia Woolf remarked, after meeting him at Max Gate in July 1926, on his 'quizzical bright eyes, for in talk they grow bright',[1] and Ford Madox Ford wrote eloquently of how Hardy's gaze betrayed a similar kindling of mind. At one of Edward Clodd's house parties, Ford observed the 'amazing powers of perception in his keen, limpid, liquid, poet-peasant's eyes', and went on to associate this visual alertness with an impulse for exuberant truancy. Hardy, he continued, was 'as instinct with the feeling of escape as a schoolboy who had run out from his school ranks on some down and was determined on naughtiness'.[2] Certainly, Hardy himself conveyed a mild guilt about his inability to stop himself from stealing glances at the faces of others. He once confided to Rosamund Tomson as to this 'literary habit', 'rather a terrible thing', whereby 'whenever I travel by train or omnibus, I find myself instinctively observing my fellow-passengers and constructing the story of their lives from what I see in their faces'.[3]

Most of what follows in this chapter is implied in these rather scattered comments. Above all, my focus is on the complex centrality of observation – of looking and being looked at – in Hardy's fiction and imagination. Crucially, for Hardy himself, observation is a gift not simply for physical description, but for spiritual divination. People's faces contain histories, novels and tales, though it takes a rare and peculiar susceptibility like his to discern in these 'the story of their lives'. For example, in June 1879, Hardy saw two girls on a train, and the fastidious exactitude of his note suggests how meticulously he scoured their features for narrative cues and clues:

From Tooting to Town again. In railway carriage a too statuesque girl; but her features were absolutely perfect. She sat quite still, and her smiles did not extend further than a finger-nail's breadth from the edge of her mouth. The repose of her face was such that when the train shook her it seemed painful. Her mouth was very small, and her face not unlike that of a nymph. In the train coming home there was a contrasting girl of sly humour – the pupil of her eye being mostly half under the eyelid. (*Life*, pp. 130–1)

Such everyday encounters offer an irresistible provocation to the erotic and romantic day-dreaming to which Hardy was prone. However, there is more to it than this, and one needs to emphasise how such accidental meetings also stimulate his distinctive kind of curiosity, and engage his sympathies in subtle, surprising and mysterious ways. Here he appears to search among the stray details of each girl's face for the key that will unlock the secret principles of her personality. In this way, a peremptory male desire enters into circulation with a more patient and watchful impulse, a wish to establish an empathetic inwardness by which the unique inner life of the woman will constitute itself in his mind. In the process, Hardy's artistic capacities and imperatives are drawn out by this spell-bound study of the outward, singular, and enigmatic traits of the face.

In what follows, my aim is to explore this compound type of erotic, intuitive and visual inspiration in Hardy's fiction, as a way of examining the sensory and affective bases of his art and imagination. Close attention to his texts reveals the primary ways in which the initial promptings of Hardy's narrative sense, and the individuality of his characters, are decisively conjured into being through what Tony Tanner called 'the incomparable clarity of his eyes'.[4] J. B. Bullen has recorded Hardy's own admission as to the way in which

images, in the form of mental 'pictures', actually preceded the formulation of ideas in language. He confessed to at least two of his biographers that ideas which were later clothed in verse or prose frequently presented themselves to him at first as pictures ...[5]

Accordingly, the first part of the chapter centres on examining how much Hardy seems to follow his eyes as he develops his material. Often the specific dramas, and even the different formal and thematic configurations, of particular novels can be seen as latent, condensed, within the visual dynamics of key scenes. To provide a thread in what is necessarily a selective discussion, I have predominantly concentrated on important early scenes in various novels. These are scenes in which Hardy first observes the central figure whose personality and talent for entanglement will provide the motor for the drama of the text. 'Character is fate' for Tess or Eustacia, as for Jude or Henchard, but one could as easily say 'character is face' or even 'face is fate', insofar as it is often the face and eyes of the characters that provide Hardy's imagination with a privileged access to both their individuality and the story that unfolds from it.

In the second half of the chapter, I shall extend the discussion, beyond the narrator's viewing of his characters, to focus on the dramatically crucial moments where the characters view each other: where they steal or exchange glances, feel themselves observed, and so on. There is something fateful, as instantaneous as a chemical reaction, when eyes fasten or meet in a Hardy scene, and Hardy's writing is peculiarly adjusted to tracing not merely what goes on at such moments, but also the consequences that unfold from them. In *A Pair of Blue Eyes* we read of Elfride's piano playing for Stephen:

> Then comes a rapid look into Stephen's face, and a still more rapid look back again to her business, her face having dropped its sadness, and acquired a certain expression of mysterious archness the while.[6]

Out of the ping-pong of glances between Elfride and Stephen, her new look of 'mysterious archness' emerges, an expression that is both facial and spiritual, and that indicates how she will relate to Stephen. Hardy's eye as a writer is inimitably attuned to such modulations and revelations of personality. My argument is that this is because his writing turns on physically produced moments of becoming, on irruptive and unpredictable passages where altered aspects and qualities of the self emerge, as new relationships are precipitated out of the emotional turmoil of the characters. In this context, events of looking, and of eye contact, take on a real centrality and importance. Finally, my ultimate contention is that Hardy's novels in such fashion enact as well as dramatise Comte's dictum, transcribed by Hardy into his notebook in 1873, that 'Thought depends upon sensation'. To put it another way, observation, and particularly the observation of another person, is a privileged form of self-revelation, for Hardy himself as much as for Elfride and Stephen, since such looking entails response, and response entails an answering expression of oneself. When one looks, it seems, it is always also oneself that one comes to discover.[7] It was an idea he was to reiterate many times in his notes, as in his celebrated comment about the Impressionists in December 1886:

> ... what you carry away from a scene is a true feature to grasp; or in other words, *what appeals to your own individual eye and heart in particular* amid much that does not so appeal, and which you therefore omit to record. (*Life*, p. 184)

I

In 1888, Richard Bowker, an American publisher, wrote an article entitled 'Thomas Hardy: The Dorset Novelist' for *Harper's New Monthly Magazine*. The piece focuses on Hardy's creative processes and working habits, and draws on information, as James Gibson has pointed out, that was largely supplied by Hardy's own notes. Of particular interest here are the moments in which we read about the apparently separate and prior existence of Hardy's characters in his mind:

> His characters, in fact, do become entirely real to him, though for a long time he finds difficulty in making acquaintance with them, and particularly in calling them by name, so that Mrs Hardy, always his first reader and kind critic, sometimes has to suggest that this John Jones is really Daniel Smith.

It is almost as if Hardy is waiting for the character to make the first move, or for Mrs Hardy to introduce him to them properly. In this respect, his stance suggests that of the male figures in novels like *Far from the Madding Crowd* or *A Laodicean*, who find themselves mesmerised as they observe an unnamed woman's inadvertent display – Bathsheba's riding overlooked by Oak; or Paula's baptismal caprices observed by Somerset, or her gymnastic undulations spied on by de Stancy. Certainly, for Oak, Somerset or de Stancy, an unsought surrender to what is before one's eyes is where it all begins. As observation provokes an imagined connection that subjugates these men, so Bowker goes on to relate how Hardy too would become enthralled by his characters and allow them to dictate the direction and outcome of the story:

But soon the characters take possession of him and of the story, he comes to know what each will think and will do in given circumstances, and for this reason he never plots the final development, the latter half, of a novel, but lets the *dramatis personae* finish it for themselves, and literally work out their own salvation or the contrary.[8]

In an obviously related way, Hardy's texts often begin with a narrator who refuses information and omniscience. Characteristically, he will withhold the names of his characters, while mindfully inhabiting the scene he describes, alert to the intimations of atmosphere, gesture, mien. His watchfulness is an index of what Tanner also refers to as the 'illusion that the tale exists independently of Hardy's rendering of it', and that gives the world of the fiction its special quality of 'anonymity' and 'impersonality'.[9] One of the further effects is that the characters are granted a kind of autonomy and space to shape the action and imbue the writing with their own individuality. In the opening scenes of *Two on a Tower*, for instance, Lady Constantine's ennui is staged through a desultory succession of largely inconsequential scenes whereby Hardy follows her still unnamed figure getting nearer to visiting the tower before she finally does so:

> … The trap-door leading on to the roof was open, and on looking through it an interesting spectacle met her eye.
> A youth was sitting on a stool in the centre of the lead flat which formed the summit of the column, his eye being applied to the end of a large telescope that stood before him on a tripod. This sort of presence was unexpected, and the lady started back into the shade of the opening. The only effect produced upon him by her footfall was an impatient wave of the hand, which he did without removing his eye from the instrument, as if to forbid her to interrupt him.
> Pausing where she stood the lady examined the aspect of the individual who thus made himself so completely at home on a building which she deemed her unquestioned property.

Hardy's imagination is liberated, like those of his characters, in this anonymous setting where names, and distinctions of class and age appear temporarily suspended. Constantine is surprised and engaged by Swithin's presence and his obliviousness to earthly surroundings and her identity and status, and the scene begins to become more overtly charged with her unconscious need for romance. In these ways, the scene acts as a kind of lodestone that attracts and conducts the personal and dramatic forces of the text (as well as Hardy's own creative capacities), and that arguably announces – through the divergent gazes and responses of the characters, and the secret setting – the nature of the tragedy to come.

Of course, it is can be said that *Two on a Tower* as a novel, like *A Laodicean*, *Desperate Remedies*, or *A Pair of Blue Eyes* or *The Hand of Ethelberta*, is excessively dependent on this type of physical and affective inspiration, so that the second half of each of these novels – everything tending to sketchy, even bizarre, throwaway, contrivance – suffers by its departure. We know too that Hardy was conscious of this, and he would have been sensitive to Henry James's patronising denunciation of *Far from the Madding Crowd*, lamenting what he saw as the lack of an acceptable sense of 'composition' and 'proportion' on the part of this farmyard writer.[10] Again, Hardy was badly shaken by early reviews of *Desperate Remedies* that latched on to its plot weaknesses, and in particular, what was seen as its over-reliance on visual elements. Thus, an anonymous reviewer deplored how the plot was resolved 'by the very dull expedient of a detective *seeing* the murderer remove the body', while another complained of how events were made to turn upon the colour of a woman's eyes.[11] Certainly, Hardy's first published novel suffers because he does not know when it is time to stop looking and turn back to the official business of narrative. Hardy does not keep his contract with us, any more than Manston wishes to keep his contract with his wife; his best designs are always sabotaged by more immediate temptations, like Bob's in *The Trumpet-Major*:

> When he was thrown under the influence of Anne's eyes again, which were more tantalizingly beautiful than ever just now (so it seemed to him), his intention of offering his services to the Government would wax weaker, and he would put off his decision till the next day.[12]

In this context, it is possible to read Hardy's career as a novelist as a series of ever more conscious attempts to head off the criticism that perception overrides structure, that detail wags the dog, as it were. In the later novels, this took the form, as John Bayley has argued, of fictions that were much more artistically wrought and thematically directed in accordance with Hardy's conception of the characters' social predicaments, with the effect that Hardy self-censors his 'natural gifts of inconsistency and separation'.[13] The world of Hardy's fiction becomes dependent on his personal preconceptions, rather than being the independent source of his 'impersonal' perceptions (as in Michael Irwin and Ian Gregor's formulation).[14] Bayley writes:

> ... the fact that it is Hardy's own exclusive view of things reminds us how little the world of his earlier novels appears to belong to him in this way, but he is the sole proprietor of the somberness of *Jude* as he was of the romance of *Tess*.[15]

Bayley's point is a telling one, though one has to offset the losses of the quotidian and comic against the obvious gains in intensity, formal innovation and political power that have been emphasised by many recent critics as a feature of the greater focus of these later books.[16]

Nonetheless, the question of how we evaluate the difference between different phases of Hardy's career as a novelist is less important than emphasising the continuity, throughout every phase, of his dependence upon the visual principles that I have outlined. And if we turn to the opening pages of *The Woodlanders*, or *Tess* or *Jude*, we find that the characters' identities are still initially deferred, as always, while our attention is directed to their physicality:

> A young member of the band turned her head at the exclamation. She was a fine and handsome girl – not handsomer than some others, possibly, – but her mobile peony mouth and large innocent eyes added eloquence to colour and shape.[17]

Hardy is transfixed by Tess, as is conveyed by the evocative exactitude of her 'mobile peony mouth and large innocent eyes'. As Bayley suggests, however, there is evident even here a type of conscious presentiment alien to the more exploratory modes of the earlier fiction. Tess's features also function as symbolic motifs, consciously deployed by the narrator to convey her innocence, grace, susceptibility and refinement at odds with the world of the novel. From the start, Hardy's conception of Tess and her fate is in this way a *given* in the text, and epitomised in the spiritual qualities with which her face is irradiated. In the *Two on a Tower* extract, the scene was also full of a sense of an accidental but possibly fateful meeting, like that between Tess and Angel, but Hardy himself appeared largely curious, within the provisional and contingent dimension of the narrative, as to where the scene might lead (if anywhere) for all concerned. It is a moment where things appear to hang in the balance. Contrastingly, it is an important aspect of the *Tess* scene, and of its amenability to the critic, that Hardy's thumb appears, in Lawrence's phrase, to be in the balance.

So, Tess's future (in this novel of omens) seems definitively foreshadowed in the layer of connotation that accompanies our initial image of her. Similarly our first glimpse of Jude, 'A little boy of eleven', directs us to his face, but here (as throughout the novel), Hardy uncharacteristically bypasses the actual detail of his hero's face, in pursuit of its meaning: defeated aspiration. Jude confronts life without Phillotson, his hitherto inspiring alter ego, in the first of the novel's intensifying series of like disappointments, and we read of how

> Tears rose into the boy's eyes, for he was not among the regular day scholars, who came unromantically close to the schoolmaster's life, but one who had attended the night school only during the present teacher's term of office.[18]

The passage intently suggests how Jude's dreams, associated with Phillotson, are created out of both deprivation and distance: his romance of the schoolteacher is both a function of need, and an illusion in inverse ratio to knowledge. Thus we are introduced into the world of *Jude*, and its typical combination of sympathy and irony, the tender pity and excoriating anger that drives the novel as it strips off society's mask and confronts it with its hidden inhumanity. In these ways, the social critique of the text dominates it from the start, and has the effect here of obscuring the visual specificities of Jude's features. Hardy's 'vision', in Bayley's phrase, thus has the ironic effect of attenuating the merely visual, even as this novel too uses the face of the unnamed central character as its focal and departure point.

The Woodlanders contrasts with *Jude* in that it is a much more visual, descriptive, novel. At the same time, though, it is directly comparable in the way in which it focuses on a socio-economic tragedy, this time the tragedy of a community rather than an individual. As always, the novel begins by staging its particular drama and world through scenes where a character's face and eyes are observed. In chapter 2 we follow the man we come to know as Barber Percomb before he, unobserved, spies the unnamed Marty through the window. Percomb's predatory designs on Marty's hair, and her isolation, vulnerability and lack of any protective sophistication are given in the scene:

Her face had the usual fullness of expression which is developed by a life of solitude. Where the eyes of a multitude continuously beat like waves upon a countenance they seem to wear away its mobile power: but in the still water of privacy every feeling and sentiment unfolds in visual luxuriance, to be interpreted as readily as a printed word by an intruder.[19]

Hardy is the intimate witness in this book to a vanishing way of life, and it is his solicitous feeling for the loss of the rural community that informs this depiction of Marty, as it moves from her face to discuss the different expressions of those who live in solitude as opposed to those who are used to 'the eyes of a multitude'. So, too, the internal visual configuration of the scene anticipates the drama of the novel: time and again in *The Woodlanders* the rending conflicts of the old and the new worlds are played out through scenes where one character spies upon another without eye contact, communication or reciprocity. So, at the end of chapter 8, Giles spies Fitzpiers, 'who was looking over the hedge to the opposite side of the way upon the figure of the unconscious Grace'. Always a character is painfully encountering, or violently intruding into, another's world, these scenic features providing formal equivalents of the way in which modernity, in the text as a whole, as the next invasive stage of human development, preys on, breaks into and breaks up the world of the woodlands. At the end, Little Hintock – that 'one-eyed spot' in Barber Percomb's phrase – is left to Marty, that 'solitary and silent girl' who is a kind of emanation both of place and of the anachronous logic of the novel itself, caught at the crossroads between the remembered past and the incursive future (p. 393).

Phillip Mallett has suggested that the unsparing depiction of historical strife and transition in *The Woodlanders* was a conscious corrective to the static and relatively idyllic representation of the society of *Under the Greenwood Tree*, and it is a conclusion that can be approached through contrasting the visual aspects and values of the texts.[20] Certainly, the visual dynamics of *Under the Greenwood Tree* belong to a different novelistic world from those of the later book. The band who come together in the wood, before journeying to view Fancy Day at her window, offer a typical tableau of time-honoured unity totally at odds with the spatial and historical alienation of the characters in the later novel. At the same time, though, the scene also manifests Fancy's ever-intriguing resistance to stable and totalising representation. Throughout the book she creates the dramatic and romantic discords of the text by eluding the interpretive desire she inspires. Fancy's face, unlike Marty's, is no open book. So, we hear of her face several times before we see her, 'framed as a picture by the window architrave', as 'the blind went upward'. At this moment, 'thirty concentrated eyes' find '[h]er bright eyes were looking into the grey world outside with an uncertain expression, oscillating between courage and shyness'.[21]

In this way, Fancy at the open window instils what can be seen as a saving indeterminacy into the text, her disruptive effect on the rustic community a means by which Hardy can keep the text itself open, and avoid a merely sentimental retrospection in his handling of the narrative. J. B. Bullen has reached a similar conclusion in his study of the pictorialising techniques in the text, particularly in relation to Fancy. He shows how we are constantly confronted by partial, framing views of her, as in the scene just discussed, or when we read later of how 'a slice of her left-hand side' was 'cut off by the edge of the door' (*Under the Greenwood Tree*, p. 84). Bullen's argument is a complex one, since he wants to suggest the novel's indebtedness, in its rustic portraits, domestic interiors, and group vignettes, to the themes and compositional techniques of Dutch and English genre painting, while also suggesting that the text's comically 'self-conscious stylizing of images' introduces a reflexive, proto-modernist, crease into the representation. By baring the frame, Bullen suggests, Hardy preserves a knowing distance from what could otherwise appear a merely picturesque rendition of a rural world from which 'all the harshness of agrarian life is excluded'.[22] So Hardy wriggles off various generic hooks, and the text finds a saving principle of provisionality and instability throughout its scenic and dramatic focus on Fancy. A creature of 'uncertain expression', she persistently eludes assimilation beneath the protective branches of the novel's rustic world and pastoral mode, while eliciting desire and anticipating new artistic and narrative departures.

I want to revisit some of these points through a slightly more sustained discussion of this type of visual inspiration as it runs through *The Return of the Native*. In the opening chapters, the narrator postpones not only naming his characters but even their entrance, before he comes to observe several anonymous figures: an old man, a reddleman and a mysterious woman, the hitherto 'queen of the solitude' who is in turn displaced by the arrival of the 'bonfire-makers'.[23] In the gathering shadows of the evening scene, the narrator's impressions and rumination intensify our imagination and curiosity, and at the beginning of chapter VI we come closer to visualising Eustacia, the 'Figure Against the Sky' of the chapter's title:

> When the whole Egdon concourse had left the site of the bonfire to its accustomed loneliness, a closely wrapped female figure approached the barrow ... That she was tall and straight in build, that she was ladylike in her movements, was all that could be learned of her just now ... Her reason for standing so dead still as the pivot of this circle of heath-country was just as obscure ... It might reasonably have been supposed that she was listening to the wind, which rose somewhat as the night advanced, and laid hold of the attention. (p. 80)

Hardy, as he notes and quizzes the detail of the lonely and 'obscure' scene, and the call of the wind, manifests the need for human significance which immemorial Egdon provokes. For Eustacia, this desire for meaning is an intense and consuming eagerness, and it leads her here to convert the physical environment – the pond, the fire – into a private domain of signs and signals, for herself and for Wildeve who soon answers her call. And so the two meet with Wildeve emerging from the darkness. At this point we have the first view of her eyes: 'She let her joyous eyes rest upon him without speaking, as upon some wondrous thing she had created out of chaos' (p. 88). This moment of actual illumination and observation is, once again, not merely descriptive but prefigurative. It gives us access into Eustacia's individuality as it will be played out as drama. The hint of irony ('as upon some wondrous thing') intimates her appetite for illusion, at the same time as other details ('She let her joyous eyes rest upon him without speaking') suggest her overriding desire for a transporting amorous connection by which she can translate her own inchoate and solitary emotional life into meaning.

At this significant moment, then, our sense of Eustacia crystallises, and she is revealed to us from the nocturnal obscurities that have shrouded our previous sense of her. She is still an enigma, but crucially her eyes suggest the yearning for ecstatic and sympathetic relatedness that propels her throughout the novel. Importantly, this desire for pleasure and expression mirrors and realises our own fascinations at this moment, artfully provoked as these have been by the narrator's reticence. Further, Hardy's own creativity, as well as our own readerly pleasures, is mirrored by the aesthetic element in Eustacia's longing ('some wondrous thing she had created out of chaos'). Beneath any mere moral reservations, then, the emotional and physical texture of the writing introduces us into a much closer rapport with her, one that binds together her wish for escape and expression with the primary aesthetic effects of 'pleasure' and 'renovation' that Hardy associates with the innate sorcery of literature in 'The Profitable Reading of Fiction'. Literature can create wondrous things from chaos and nothingness, and its spells can move us to other places, as where, in an image reminiscent of Eustacia herself, Hardy writes of reading that '[i]n such a case the shifting of scene should manifestly be as complete as if the reader had taken the hind seat on a witch's broomstick'.[24] For these reasons, we watch Eustacia as closely and absorbedly as Hardy watched the girls on the train, and share her abiding wish that soon her individuality will fully disclose itself.

However, if the reader and narrator establish in these ways a secret intimacy with Eustacia, it is noticeable that she does not establish any real face to face with Wildeve himself. He does not look back at her, and her needs are too excessive to require or allow dialogue ('without speaking'). Her desire is too impatient, and in the ensuing discussion she imperiously steamrolls Wildeve's half-hearted desire to have done with the relationship, and to marry Thomasin after all. Of course, Eustacia's imaginative desire for recreation (in every sense) is tragically her undoing. She is unable to see what is in front of her, because the obdurate world of the heath is obscured by the compensatory fantasies that it provokes in her. Nevertheless, her longing for transcendence makes her the presiding spirit of this novel where every character has to struggle to achieve meaningful expression and relationships amid the resistant materiality of Egdon. She is, like us, a creature of an overweening projective desire – often crucially expressed in terms of vision, as when she looks towards Wildeve's home:

> There was no doubt that her mind was inclined thitherward; indefinitely, fancifully – twining and untwining about him as the single object within her horizon on which dreams might crystallize. (p. 120)

or when, a little later, we read of her outside Clym's house, before she has yet seen him but when he has just become the focus of her longings:

> Eustacia stood just within the heath, straining her eyes in the direction of Mrs Yeobright's house and premises. (p. 140)

II

When Virginia Woolf wrote in 'The Novels of Thomas Hardy' that we remember Hardy's characters for their 'passions', and for the 'sudden' and 'overwhelming' catastrophes that overtake them, or when D. H. Lawrence expressed the opinion that '[n]owhere, except perhaps in Jude, is there the slightest development of personal action in the characters: it is all explosive', they both suggested a view of his writing similar to that which underpins this chapter: the sense that, for Hardy, the spiritual life is conducted through the body and the emotions, with the consequence that, as Barbara Hardy memorably puts it, a Hardy character is 'a variable, not a constant'.[25] While this affective and interpersonal logic applies to the large and memorable events in Hardy's fiction, as Woolf and Lawrence suggest, it is true too of small, inconsequential moments, like the following from *Desperate Remedies*. Cytherea and Miss Hinton argue animatedly over Edward Springrove, until the moment when '[t]he two rivals had now lost their personality quite', and

> There was the same keen brightness of eye, the same movement of the mouth, as they looked doubtingly and excitedly at each other.[26]

The loss of socialised 'personality' is coterminous with the comically automatic, bristling, disclosure of individuality conveyed by Cytherea and Adelaide's excited and distrustful eyes. Each is surprised by jealousy and indignation, and introduced into a discomfiting intimacy.

To hazard a quasi-philosophical description of this, one can say that Hardy's writing entails a *cogito* of a non-rationalist kind. The mind for Hardy is not an inviolable core of logically indubitable identity, but a changeable capacity of individuation, dependent on affective affinities and contingencies, and expressed through the body. Broadly, it is not a case of the logical certainty of 'I think, therefore I am', but of the empirical surprise of 'We are here, therefore I am becoming different ...'. Self-consciousness is on this model not the unifying condition of perception and material experience, but an incidental and transitory effect of it. For these reasons moments of eye contact, of all sensory moments, take on a paradigmatic status in Hardy. They provide key instances of where the mind reveals itself to itself and to others by way of the body's sentient and expressive powers. In *The Well-Beloved*, for instance, Pierston falls for the second Avice as she looks back at him, a moment of change for both:

> When she glanced up, her lineaments seemed to have all the soul and heart that had characterized her mother's, and had been with her a true index of the spirit within.[27]

The self or 'soul' (in his terminology) is, as I have argued elsewhere, for Hardy a matter not of self-certitude, or rational will, or motive, or social morality, but of affective responsiveness and involuntary relatedness. Individual expression is dependent on physical modes of association. Accordingly, the various serial manifestations of the 'soul and heart' or 'spirit within' in Hardy's fiction are dependent on chance encounters, those face-to-face meetings that put social identity into a flat spin, and that anticipate the complications and possibilities of the future.[28]

So, this section will explore how in Hardy's fiction we recurrently get this sense of unconscious engagement, as in the erotic, comic, or perilous pinball of glances out of which emerge new versions of the self, as it forges its erotic and affective connections. Indeed, one can imagine that Lawrence had such scenes in mind when he wrote about the explosive individuality of Hardy's characters. However, Lawrence's own characters tend to appear only individualistic in comparison, since they lack the radical and generative instability, the *futurity*, of Hardy's characters. Time and change are of the essence of Hardy's characters because, as we have seen, they are so embodied and independent in his imagination. For this reason, the characters' eyes often betray provisional, new, versions of the self that precede and exceed their own self-knowledge, and which similarly lead on the narrator himself. So, for instance, a scene like the following from *Under the Greenwood Tree* holds in itself, *in potentia*, the dramatic possibilities of the text. Dick and Fancy are jogging along behind the farmer's cart, before they are overtaken by Shiner and friend in a dazzling 'brand-new gig', whose

> panels glared like mirrors in Dick and Fancy's eyes. The driver, and owner as it appeared, was really a handsome man; his companion was Shiner. Both turned round as they passed Dick and Fancy and stared with bold admiration in her face till they were obliged to attend to the operation of passing the farmer. Dick glanced for an instant at Fancy while she was undergoing their scrutiny; then returned to his driving with rather a sad countenance. (p. 136)

Typically, the plot here turns on this weave of glances, as Dick looks at Fancy being looked at by Shiner. Dick's gloom is prophetic, for later she will have to confess how she has come to let Shiner fall in love with her: 'He looked at me, and I looked at him' (p. 144). In the first version of these events to Dick, she is all evasion, but then Dick looks into her eyes to find:

Misery of miseries! – guilt was written there still.

'Now, Fancy, you've not told me all!' said Dick ...

'Well, when I put my hand on the bridge, he touched it ... And then he looked at me, and he said, "Are you in love with Dick Dewy?" And I said, "Perhaps I am!"' (p. 145)

Dick ignores her words, and pursues in her eyes the truth of this earlier moment on the bridge when Shiner too had looked into them. Eye contact offers a more direct and viable access to her personality than words, because Fancy Day is a creature of passion and the moment, and as such, it is her eyes that offer the best testimony to the thoughts and feelings that will be played out in subsequent pages. In a comparable moment in *Desperate Remedies*, Cytherea confesses to her brother, and as it were to herself, looking defiantly and 'stonily into his face', that her feelings for Edward have resurfaced:

'Owen,' she said, and paused. Her lip trembled; her eye told of sensations too deep for tears. 'No, Owen, it has not left me; and I will be honest. I own now to you, without any disguise of words, what last night I did not own to myself, because I hardly knew of it. I love Edward Springrove with all my strength, and heart and soul.' (p. 277)

Similarly, in *A Pair of Blue Eyes*, Stephen, in his campaign to wring an avowal of love from Elfride, seeks to influence her by looking into her eyes:

'Eyes in eyes,' he murmured playfully; and she blushingly obeyed, looking back into his.

'And why not lips on lips?' continued Stephen daringly.

'No, certainly not. Anybody might look; and it would be the death of me. You may kiss my hand if you like.'

He exclaimed by a look that to kiss a hand through a glove, and that a riding-glove, was not a great treat in the circumstances.

'There, then; I'll take my glove off. Isn't it a pretty white hand? Ah, you don't want to kiss it, and you shall not now!'

Elfride's innate delight in the open-ended pleasures of courtship comes up against Stephen's counter-wish to tie her down. In the rest of the chapter Stephen does accomplish his desire, moving from exchanging looks to exchanging kisses, avowals, and ultimately promises of fidelity.

Yet the reciprocity conceals real conflicts. For all his mildness, Stephen is coercive and insistent, while for all her apparent willingness, Elfride is resistant:

> 'Love is new, and fresh to us as the dew; and we are together. As the lover's world goes, this is a great deal. Stephen, I fancy I see the difference between me and you – between men and women generally, perhaps. I am content to build happiness on any accidental basis that may lie near at hand; you are for making the world to suit your happiness.' (p. 93)

Elfride sees here a fundamental difference between her and Stephen, and between the sexes. At its crudest, it is the difference between enjoying love and enjoining it, between making contact, and the contract of marriage itself. The woman, it seems, has a different conception or temporal experience of love: she wishes to prolong the ecstatic immediacy of the time when 'love is new, and fresh to us as the dew, and we are together', whereas Stephen, as a man, needs to pin it down within a system of obligation. In this respect, Elfride voices the tension that she feels in this chapter, and throughout the novel, between past and present lovers. Arguably, indeed, this is an abiding predicament, not only for her, but for Fancy, Eustacia, Lucetta, Anne Garland, Grace Melbury, and so on – in fact, for nearly all of Hardy's heroines where new love, or romantic opportunism, or a tendency to vacillation, threaten to override fidelity.

Whether or not this generalisation about the genders is suggestive, though, is secondary to the fact that the distinction that underlies it – between self-consciousness and unconscious response – has from another viewpoint nothing to do with gender. After all, the division of socialised identity and spontaneity is one that distinguishes all of Hardy's characters, male or female. It also applies to Hardy himself, for whom the subversive values of immanence and self-differentiation, of 'change and chancefulness', are intrinsic to his work.[29] Hardy's women may seem to embody this principle more extremely, but one must equally say that their readiness for new associations depends on the other person being equally ready to forget himself. As in the face to face of eye contact, there can be no destabilising exchange of signals without the assumption or actuality of correspondences – of sensibility, sexuality or sympathy. Further, insofar as Hardy's own creativity is dependent on perception, it is possible to describe individual novels as successively various experiments in vision, where 'The poetry of a scene lies in the minds of the perceivers'

(*Life*, p. 52). So, for instance, *Desperate Remedies* could be described as an exhilaratingly experimental novel, so heedlessly and instinctively committed is it to seeking (in Elfride's phrase) to 'build happiness on any accidental basis that may lie near at hand'.

Contrastingly, *The Mayor of Casterbridge* is an experiment of a different kind, one that employs a succession of powerful tableaux to find memorable, theatrical, equivalents for Henchard's titanic character and passionate volatility. How much, for instance, of his volcanic and perverse personality, and the large canvas technique of the novel, is already signalled in the opening scene, or in chapter 38, where his murderous hatred for Farfrae is illustrated by the fight in the loft of the corn store. In this huge set-piece Henchard's violent antipathy is instantaneously and bewilderingly transmuted to its opposite as his eyes meet those of the younger man:

> 'Now,' said Henchard between his gasps, 'this is the end of what you began this morning. Your life is in my hands.'
> 'Then take it, take it!' said Farfrae. 'Ye've wished to long enough!'
> Henchard looked down upon him in silence, and their eyes met. 'O Farfrae! – that's not true!' he said bitterly. 'God is my witness that no man ever loved another as I did thee at one time ... And now – though I came here to kill 'ee, I cannot hurt thee!'[30]

In contrast to these Old Testament climaxes in *The Mayor of Casterbridge*, we can consider the very different world of *A Laodicean*, a book that could be loosely described as anti-climactic – a novel of interrupted or deferred desire, as in the many early scenes where George strives to gain a clear view and sense of Paula, only to be frustrated. Where Henchard cannot contain himself, the opening chapters of *A Laodicean* are a protracted teasing of George's longing, as he attempts unavailingly to see Paula, and the same logic applies to those later scenes where he expects to see her, only for William Dare, Mrs Goodman or sundry de Stancys to get in the way. Ultimately, of course, he has to negotiate the intrusions of Captain de Stancy and William Dare, and the destruction of her imposing castle, before she will marry him. Undoubtedly, Hardy's illness during the writing of the novel is largely responsible for the collapse in quality in the later part. However, flawed as the book is, and different as it is from *The Mayor of Casterbridge*, it also pursues visual principles, and dramatises, however differently, the confusions of identity and the fluctuations of passion.

It might be that it is Paula's social position, and the power and constraints that it brings with it, that make her so elusive, and define the peculiar affective world of *A Laodicean*. This social inaccessibility makes her superficially similar to Ethelberta in *The Hand of Ethelberta*, though there the social divisions are located intractably within the heroine herself. Unlike Paula, Ethelberta's social position means that she becomes sadly love-proof, and the ending of the book is informed by the pathos of her self-denial. This makes the lapse in chapter 4, when she spontaneously exchanges glances with Christopher at the dance, all the more affecting. Initially, he plays the keyboard, giving 'himself up with a curious, and far from unalloyed pleasure to the occupation of watching Ethelberta, now and again crossing the field of his vision like a returned comet whose characteristics were becoming purely historical'. Then, though, their eyes meet:

> It was only a look, and yet what a look it was! One may say of a look that it is capable of division into as many species, genera, orders and classes, as the animal world itself. Christopher saw Ethelberta Petherwin's performance in this kind – the well-known spark of light upon the well-known depths of mystery – and felt something going out of him which had gone out of him once before.[31]

Ethelberta reveals more than she means, and perhaps more than she herself knows, about her latent or buried feelings for Christopher. However, the drawbridge of her self-control clangs down, leaving Christopher and the reader on the outside. At the same time, we are left in no doubt that her reticence is primarily a function of her contorted social position and divided loyalties. Ethelberta as a character, like Hardy himself, is torn between the class she is coming from and the class she is going towards, and the price of her ambition and loyalty to her family is a repressive secrecy.

In *Far from the Madding Crowd*, there is an unusual, if hard-won degree and kind of reciprocity and mutual knowledge between the central female character and Oak, notwithstanding the warning note with which the novel ends. In the process, Bathsheba perhaps becomes more satisfactorily assimilated by plot and society than almost any other female character in Hardy. Nonetheless, she has to travel through much consternation and uncertainty before her surprised recognition that she loves Oak. She is oddly constrained when she calls on him to try and prevail on him against going away:

It was very odd to these two persons, who knew each other passing well, that the mere circumstance of their meeting in a new place and in a new way should make them so awkward and constrained. In the fields, or at her house, there had never been any embarrassment; but now that Oak had become the entertainer their lives seemed to be moved back to the days when they were strangers.

The mutual estrangement that take place here is again prompted and conveyed by looking:

> Gabriel looked her long in the face, but the firelight being faint there was not much to be seen.[32]

The moving ironies at the end of *Far from the Madding Crowd*, as this suggests, are that Bathsheba can only recognise Oak by losing her customary image of him, and can only recover her own self-image and autonomy by recognising her unacknowledged dependence upon him.

As the pair move towards the shared identity and understanding of their marriage, then, there is a complex comic renegotiation of identity involved. This breaks up that previous pattern by which Bathsheba had benefited from a clear asymmetry of need, power and desire, a pattern likewise expressed in scenes where the characters look at each other. So, in the opening pages, Oak spies Bathsheba in various situations – smiling at her mirrored reflection, talking to her aunt, riding her horse, and carrying her milk pail, before she sees 'Gabriel's face rising like a moon behind the hedge' (p. 54). As Bathsheba returns his gaze, both are discomfited: Oak feels as if has been caught reading over her shoulder, and she wonders what it is that he has been reading there:

> That the girl's thoughts hovered about her face and form as soon as she caught Oak's eyes conning the same page was natural, and almost certain.

Their eye contact carries the nuance of a privacy invaded, and in the ensuing confusion it is a question of who will regain their composure first. Ultimately, of course, it is Oak who is more rattled by the situation:

> The self-consciousness shown would have been vanity if a little more pronounced, dignity if a little less. Rays of male vision seemed to have a tickling effect upon virgin faces in rural districts; she brushed hers

with her hand, as if Gabriel had been irritating its pink surface by actual touch, and the free air of her previous movements was reduced at the same time to a chastened phase of itself. Yet it was the man who blushed, the maid not at all. (p. 55)

This exchange of glances sets the terms for Oak and Bathsheba's relationship for most of the book. His embarrassment cedes to her the upper hand, because his blushing offers incontrovertible evidence of his prior emotional investment. This is repeated a page or two later where Bathsheba is momentarily thrown by Oak's confession that he had descried her when she lost her hat earlier. However, Oak is again finally the one at a disadvantage. He feels sympathy, and shame at having spied on her, and then comically redoubles this by his embarrassed feeling that he is now re-enacting the shameful act as he observes her 'nettled palpitation' and blushes:

A perception caused him to withdraw his own eyes from hers as suddenly as if he had been caught in a theft. Recollection of the strange antics she had indulged in when passing through the trees was succeeded in the girl by a nettled palpitation, and that by a hot face ...
    The sympathetic man still looked the other way, and wondered when she would recover coolness sufficient to justify him in facing her again. (p. 56)

Oak's prostration before Bathsheba is given in graphic terms when she rescues him from suffocation in his hut. Where his intrusion into her unconscious world had resulted in his loss of face, her intrusion into his confirms her power over him. At the close, she exploits this freedom and gives poor, lost Gabriel the run-around. She supposes that he is thinking that he would like to kiss her mouth:

'I wasn't thinking of any such thing,' said Gabriel simply, 'but I will—'
'That you won't!' She snatched back her hand.
Gabriel felt himself guilty of another want of tact.
'Now find out my name,' she said teasingly, and withdrew. (p. 60)

Further, outside of this relationship, one can see more generally how productive are these connections between visibility, individuality and narrative in the novel, and how far scenes of gazing or eye contact take on a generative power and significance in Hardy's mind. Boldwood begins by looking at Bathsheba surreptitiously, as did Oak, but then his emotion comes to give him away. As he looks at her in the meadows, we read that his face 'showed that he was now living outside his defences for the first time, and with a fearful sense of exposure' (p. 154). Contrarily, Troy is as expert and direct with eye contact as he is with his sword, and we read of how with Bathsheba in the fir plantation:

> He looked hard into her eyes when she raised them for a moment; Bathsheba looked down again, for his gaze was too strong to be received point-blank with her own. (p. 193)

At their next meeting, when he comes for pleasure to make hay, she tries to avoid eye contact:

> As soon as she had entered the field Troy saw her, and sticking his pitchfork into the ground and picking up his crop or cane, he came forward. Bathsheba blushed with half-angry embarrassment, and adjusted her eyes as well as her feet to the direct line of her path. (p. 200)

Troy's presence is typically impertinent and intrusive, but the scene again expresses Bathsheba's affective confusion. She tries to fix her mind and gaze on the straight and narrow path ahead, but is inconveniently divided between anger at Troy's incursions into her privacy, and her involuntary attraction to him and all that he represents, with his pitchfork and his 'crop or cane'.

In contrast to the coming together of Oak and Bathsheba, the failure of genuine eye contact in the tragic world of *Jude* can be said to encode the novel's drama of misrecognition and disappointment. When Jude and Arabella meet, his reverie about higher forms of fulfillment is graphically punctuated by the pig's pizzle, and by Arabella's eyes which convey 'a momentary flash of intelligence, a dumb announcement of affinity in posse' (an instinctual message sardonically noted by the narrator as 'conjunctive orders from headquarters' (p. 59)). Eye contact here is debased to an animalistic summons that prevents authentic individual expression in the most graphic and explicit ways. Similarly, throughout the novel, Jude's 'dark harmonizing eyes' convey his persistent openness for meaningful connection, but his looking is a function of inner selections and projections that have no correspondence with the world.

Desire and fact are persistently mismatched, a state of affairs often troped through images of eye contact. So, the world that will not return his gaze in the same manner. After his 'first ecstasy or vision of Christminster' (p. 49), when the city was described as 'either directly seen or miraged in the peculiar atmosphere' (p. 41), we read of the demeaning reality, as with the city lights that 'winked their yellow eyes at him dubiously' (p. 97). Again, Jude feels that the road to Alfredston 'stared him cynically in the face' (p. 86), or that 'the colleges had treacherously changed their sympathetic countenances' (p. 103). Reciprocity in *Jude* is a delusion, and in human terms, this means that the face of the other person is only readable retrospectively, as an ironic commentary on gullibility, as when Jude finds in the broker's shop the photograph of himself he had inscribed for Arabella on their wedding day.

Sue's eyes offer an equally fateful lure. That 'pretty, liquid-eyed, light-footed young woman' (p. 113), Sue is less someone who won't disclose her feelings, than someone whose feelings remain virtual and mobile, ever on the edge of articulation, and Jude reads her lack of availability as an inspiring token of affective and spiritual possibility, as if her fluid diffuseness were a counterpart for his own idealising nature. If Jude never really sees or looks at Sue, it is not merely because she is not easily seeable, but also because he is not fully capable of seeing her. Sue is as much a 'target' as a 'cause' of Jude's excessive emotion,[35] as it 'insensibly began to precipitate itself on this half-visionary form' (p. 109). Hardy unremittingly indicates this phenomenology of affective illusion on Jude's part through his failure to establish meaningful eye contact with the neurotically fearful and masochistic Sue:

Sue stood like a vision before him – her look bodeful and anxious as in a dream. (p. 206)

This lack of mutual recognition is announced in their ominous first meeting in the darkness, at the Martyr's memorial, where there is, tellingly, no description of eye contact, though Jude confesses to having stolen glances at her 'now and then'. Sue defers the moment of meeting slightly, by telling Jude to walk on because of the 'gloomy and inauspicious' associations of the scene. Jude's overeagerness, and Sue's pained withdrawal from emotional openness are evident here, a prefiguring that is itself ironically prefigured in the earlier scene, where Sue, unknowing, had gazed through Jude in the street, as she looked right into his face with liquid, untranslatable eyes, that combined, or seemed to him to combine, keenness with tenderness, and mystery with both ... She no more observed his presence than that of the dust-motes which his manipulations raised into the sunbeams. (p. 109)

There are many such passages where looking as mutual revelation has been replaced by an enigmatic kind of tantalisation, as when we read later that 'She looked into his eyes with her own tearful ones, and her lips suddenly parted as if she were going to avow something. But she went on; and whatever she had meant to say remained unspoken' (p. 195).

In *Jude*, then, the failures of self-expression and relatedness can be tracked through these failures of eye contact. In *Tess*, too, the broken correspondence between the central character and the world of the novel is expressed at times through a fraught drama of the gaze. In the garden, Angel interrogates Tess as to why she is so burdened with 'sad imaginings', to which she cryptically replies that 'The trees have inquisitive eyes, haven't they? – that is, they seem to me as if they had. And the river says, – "Why do ye trouble me with your looks?"' (p. 163). Her feeling that she is being scrutinised, and that she is unwisely trespassing with her 'looks', gives shape to the hopeless feeling that Clare's curiosity produces in her. She feels that she can only prolong the relationship through evasion. And so it proves, since knowledge of her past makes Angel the ironic vehicle of social rejection. As much as *Jude*, then, though again with a difference, *Tess* is a novel about the failures of the face to face, and the ironic recoil of knowledge upon the illusions that cloud recognition. When Tess confesses her past to Angel on their wedding night, we read that '[E]ach diamond on her neck gave a sinister wink like a toad's' (p. 268), and that:

> ... the complexion even of external things seemed to suffer transmutation as her announcement progressed. The fire in the grate looked impish – demoniacally funny, as if it did not care in the least about her strait. The fender grinned idly, as if it did not care in the least about her strait. All material objects around announced their irresponsibility with terrible iteration. And yet nothing had changed since the moment when he had been kissing her; or rather, nothing in the substance of things. But the essence of things had changed. (p. 270)

It is a scene in which Tess and Angel appear to avoid looking at each other, though every object of the world appears to gaze eloquently at them. In the later scene Clare leaves, rising 'in the light of a dawn that was ashy and furtive', while 'the fireplace confronted him with its extinct embers' and 'the other articles of furniture' gave 'their eternal look of not being able to help it, their intolerable inquiry what was to be done?' (p. 279).

In closing, then, this discussion has sought to describe how Hardy's fiction in fundamental ways explores the nuances of looking and eye contact, and exploits their formative and catalytic powers for narrative. These modes of vision have been seen to offer a template for the kind of creativity that animates his work, since for him thought and self-expression are seen not as functions of reflexive subjectivity, but as functions of a physically mediated responsiveness by which the 'soul' recreates itself through its interactions with what is outside it – its environment and other people. Vision, for Hardy, is not a matter of seeing, as a static and objective recognition, but of looking, as a dynamic interaction, one in which the false unities of subjectivity and social personality are displaced, and hitherto undisclosed or forgotten possibilities of individual expression are released, for the narrator, character and reader.[34] Hardy himself found in such unstable moments an access to his own unconscious, physically conveyed, scenic and narrative powers. Finally, by implication, the reader also is introduced into this chain of looking and expression, as he or she becomes in turn reflected in the writing, as it draws out dormant or hidden feelings and desires.

notes

1. Virginia Woolf, extract from *A Writer's Diary*, reprinted in *Thomas Hardy: Interviews and Recollections*, ed. James Gibson (London, 1999), p. 223.
2. Ford Madox Ford, extract from *Mightier than the Sword*, in *Interviews and Recollections*, p. 30.
3. Rosamund Tomson, in *Interviews and Recollections*, p. 45.
4. Tony Tanner, 'Colour and Movement in *Tess of the d'Urbervilles*', reprinted in Graham Clarke, ed., *Thomas Hardy: Critical Assessments of Writers in English*, 4 vols (Mountfield, East Sussex, 1993), Vol. IV, p. 126.
5. J. B. Bullen, *The Expressive Eye: Fiction and Perception in the Work of Thomas Hardy* (Oxford, 1986), p. 2.
6. Thomas Hardy, *A Pair of Blue Eyes* (London, 1975), p. 55. Subsequent parenthetical references are to this edition.
7. I have argued this at length, in relation to Hardy's later reading and aesthetic reflections in chapter 5 of my book, *'Ecstatic Sound': Music and Individuality in the Work of Thomas Hardy* (Aldershot, 2001).

8. Richard Bowker, 'Thomas Hardy: The Dorset Novelist', in *Interviews and Recollections*, p. 14.
9. Tanner, 'Colour and Movement in *Tess*', p. 125.
10. Henry James, review in *The Nation* (December 1874), *Critical Heritage*, p. 28.
11. *Critical Assessments*, Vol. I, p. 47.
12. Thomas Hardy, *The Trumpet-Major* (London, 1974), p. 275.
13. John Bayley, *An Essay on Hardy* (Cambridge, 1978), p. 191.
14. Michael Irwin and Ian Gregor, 'Either Side of Wessex', in *Critical Assessments*, Vol. IV, p. 524. They refer to the 'impersonal' 'sense of being brought into direct contact with a certain sight or sound'.
15. Bayley, *An Essay on Hardy*, p. 206.
16. See for instance, John Goode, *Thomas Hardy: The Offensive Truth* (Oxford, 1988), Joe Fisher, *The Hidden Hardy* (London, 1992), and Peter Widdowson, *Late Essays and Earlier* (London, 1998).
17. Thomas Hardy, *Tess of the d'Urbervilles* (London, 1974), pp. 41–2. Subsequent parenthetical references are to this edition.
18. Thomas Hardy, *Jude the Obscure* (London, 1974), pp. 28–9. Subsequent parenthetical references are to this edition.
19. Thomas Hardy, *The Woodlanders* (London, 1974), p. 41. Subsequent parenthetical references are to this edition.
20. Phillip Mallett, '*Jude the Obscure*: A Farewell to Wessex', *Thomas Hardy Journal*, Vol. XI, no. 2 (October 1995), p. 50.
21. Thomas Hardy, *Under the Greenwood Tree* (London, 1974), p. 55.
22. Bullen, *The Expressive Eye*, pp. 47, 50.
23. Thomas Hardy, *The Return of the Native* (London, 1974), pp. 42, 44. Subsequent parenthetical references are to this edition.
24. Thomas Hardy, 'The Profitable Reading of Fiction', reprinted in Peter Widdowson, ed., *Thomas Hardy: Selected Poetry and Prose* (London, 1997), p. 34.
25. Barbara Hardy, from '*Under the Greenwood Tree*: A Novel about the Imagination', in *Critical Assessments*, Vol. IV, p. 6.
26. Thomas Hardy, *Desperate Remedies* (London, 1995), p. 137. Subsequent parenthetical references are to this edition.
27. Thomas Hardy, *The Well-Beloved* (Oxford, 1986), p. 88.
28. This description of the image of mind that is offered in Hardy's work does not exclude his sense of 'Our Old Friend Dualism', the idea that body and spirit exist as two ontologically distinct manifestations of the soul. However, it would be said to oppose rationalism totally, firstly by denying that spirit has a transcendence and priority over the body, and secondly in asserting that spirit and mind are nonetheless always *parallel* manifestations of the soul. There is no ghost and no machine in Hardy's non-rationalist version of the self, but a body that always expresses spirit or individuality, though with varying degrees of joy and sadness, dependent on the relationships it composes, and varying degrees of self-consciousness.
29. 'The Temporary the All'.
30. Thomas Hardy, *The Mayor of Casterbridge* (London, 1973), p. 274.
31. Thomas Hardy, *The Hand of Ethelberta* (London, 1975), p. 64.

32. Thomas Hardy, *Far from the Madding Crowd* (London, 1974), pp. 417–18. Subsequent parenthetical references are to this edition.
33. This is a formulation I've borrowed from Ludwig Wittgenstein, *Philosophical Investigations*, trans. G. E. M. Anscombe (Oxford, 1976), p. 135.
34. It would be interesting to ponder this distinction between 'seeing' and 'looking' further in relation to the distinction between 'stative' and 'dynamic' verbs drawn by Randolph Quirk, Sidney Greenbaum, Geoffrey Leech, and Jan Svartvik in their *Grammar of Contemporary English* (London, 1972), pp. 93–7.

11
hardy and nineteenth-century poetry and poetics

linda shires

Hardy's reputation continues to be based mainly on the 14 novels he penned between 1871 and 1895, including the most famous three: *Far from the Madding Crowd, Tess of the d'Urbervilles* and *Jude the Obscure.* Contemporary reviewers praised Hardy's fiction particularly for its reality effects, its memorable female characters, and for its creation of the half-real and the half-mythic Wessex. More recently, his fiction has been valuably reinterpreted through a literary criticism and theory relying less on traditional, realist-based assumptions than in the past. If he had composed no poetry at all, he would still be remembered as a key Victorian writer. Yet Thomas Hardy considered himself first and foremost a poet, just as he considered poetry the most important of literary genres.

Although his first volume *Wessex Poems* was not published until 1898, Thomas Hardy had been hearing, reading, and writing poetry for over 35 years. Early on, when composing *Far from the Madding Crowd*, he maintained that he 'did not care much for a reputation as a novelist in lieu of being able to follow the pursuit of poetry' (*Life*, p. 102). When he gave up novel writing, he turned almost full time to poetry. In all, Hardy wrote over 900 poems, invented numerous metrical and stanza forms, coined his own words, experimented with combining levels of diction such as archaic words or regional dialect with the King's English, and held a learned understanding of the English poetic tradition that most other poets then and today might envy. Still, criticism of his poetry has been less disseminated and less influential than that of his fiction, given the marginal position of poetry in our own society and culture. More importantly, it has been less self-questioning about traditional frames of interpretation.

The most substantial critical statements on Victorian poetry and poetics appearing in the last 50 years either omit Hardy or have almost nothing to say about him and his work. He is not included even marginally or by analogy in important books by Victorian poetry critics such as E. D. H. Johnson, Carol T. Christ or Robert Langbaum, who focus on Browning, Tennyson and Arnold, and by Anthony Harrison who looks at intertextuality among Romantics and Victorians. Important books written on his poetry by Samuel Hynes, Tom Paulin, James Richardson, Dennis Taylor and Donald Davie remain out of print and are not often enough cited. Hardy is mentioned in passing or as part of a coda in key books on Victorian poetics by W. David Shaw and Isobel Armstrong. Study of the poetry has continued, but either in highly specialised discussions, such as Taylor's on Hardy's literary language, or in new introductions to selected poems such as Tim Armstrong's, or buried in collections on wider topics, such as the 1993 essays by U. C. Knoepflmacher and Kerry McSweeney on Hardy's poetic antecedents.[1] The novelist of Wessex has not easily fitted into critical discussions of Victorian poetry and a revaluation is overdue. Each of the following sections aims to indicate areas of future work that might be profitably developed further than they have been in criticism on Hardy's poetry.

the broken key

In the early 1860s, at the same time he was first an articled architect in Dorchester, a draughtsman in London, and then an architect and church restorer in Dorset, Thomas Hardy began to write verses, both imitative and original. The context of Gothic architecture restoration is significant, as I will later argue, but Hardy's ability to draw, and his use of visuals as commentary in his fictional and poetic texts is also worth noting. When Hardy collected some of his earliest poetry in *Wessex Poems*, he included his line drawing of a broken key. More attention should be paid in criticism to his visuals. It is tantalising to imagine both what the key might have opened, why it is drawn as broken, and why Hardy chose it as part of his first published volume of poems, a volume significantly appearing at the tail-end of a century. I want to pause at this key because I think it illustrates an important relationship to nineteenth-century poetry, while the poem it illustrates clearly announces Hardy's metaphysical stance.

Of course we can't know definitively what Hardy may have intended by using this drawing alongside his poem 'Nature's Questioning'. The poem asks, in nature's voice, why we exist, who created us, and what we are. The key, and meanings it might unlock, lies snapped in half – seemingly irrevocably. Is Hardy suggesting, then, that answers offered in the past are now not forthcoming and the key to unlock them is now broken? Does this powerful symbol have multiple meanings? Could it be the key to a house or an entryway? Perhaps it is a key to wind a clock and thus, metaphorically, a key for interpreting the past, present or future? Is it a key to wind up a music box and does it thus also refer to lyrical measures we find in poetry? Its size is difficult to determine. It remains an emblem with multiple and suggestive meanings but no clear, single meaning. In the accompanying poem, Hardy's speaker announces somewhat ambiguously that either he does not know answers and/or that he will not tell answers to nature's queries.

Hardy is ambivalent about claims he is prepared to make in the role of 'answerer'. The 'Apology' to *Late Lyrics and Earlier* (1922), for example, seeks an alliance between religion and rationality by means of the 'interfusing effect of poetry', though at the same time he recognises that his may be an unrealisable hope. 'Nature's Questioning' though, while echoing the hard won humility about man's relationship to nature found in poems such as Arnold's 'In Utrumque Paratus', still suggests that we should not look to the poet for answers to fundamental questions because he does not have explanations: 'No answerer I … '. In 'Nature's Questioning,' Hardy exposes the narcissism of anthropocentrism. The key seems to serve as a commentary, then, on Hardy's own broken poetic relationship to the melodies, tones, times and assumed truths of the poetry that came before him. This is not to argue that he himself feels 'broken', but that he assumes a stance articulating a break with the past.

It seems no accident that the emblem of a key next to a poem refers not only to a lock, but also to music and thus to lyric. As his biographers note, and as Hardy himself illustrates through his texts, his early life was filled with music. The rural culture of Dorset was permeated with church hymns and country dances and labourers' songs. The rhythms and tunes of his father's fiddle and his mother's love of piano remained fresh in his imagination, so that some of his richest poetry plays with musical forms such as ballad or hymn. Hardy loved words as much as music. In using a key to illustrate a poem, letting each comment on the other, Hardy also calls up the many meanings and histories of the word *key*: a metal instrument by which the bolt of a lock is turned; something that provides an explanation or a solution; the lever of a keyboard, wind instrument vent, or brass instrument valve and of musical key as well as a metal instrument; a system of tones and harmonies generated from a scale. Music, we know, is scored in major or minor keys; yet Hardy's key is broken – a sign of disharmony and discordance. The snapped key, in terms of music, is important. It anticipates and helps explain arresting musical images, such as that from 'The Darkling Thrush' (1900), commemorating the new century, where he writes 'bine stems score the sky' like 'strings of broken lyres'. That poem speaks directly to distance between man and nature, but also between poet and muse (the bird being a central emblem for Romantic inspiration), as a new century dawns.

The broken key illustration also predicts the irregular beat, invented forms, original diction, and inventive poetic variations that prove to be the hallmark of Hardy's poetry for the next 30 years. Hardy's poetry can be seen productively as a response to important historical and social changes that would be recorded differently in modernism and post-modernism, but it should be seen, too, as an ambivalent echo, memorialising, adaptation, reversal and/or rejection of beliefs, ideologies and poetic strategies recorded in nineteenth-century poems he read. Hardy's grim irony and parodic comedy (as in 'Drummer Hodge' or 'Ah, Are You Digging On My Grave?'), his broken metres or invented ones (as in 'The Going'), his linguistic self-consciousness with diction and images ('Unknowing', 'Green Slates'), his refusals of generic expectations (whether in his exposé of rituals of mourning and the demands of sentimentalising human memory in 'Poems of 1912–13', or his frank explosion of history and hero worship in *The Dynasts*) do not shut out entirely the aspect of Romanticism that is positive and cheerful. It lives on in his poetry, like the song of a 'beruffled' thrush flung out against the gloom. It survives, he might say, at least in part as a satire of circumstance

Hardy is not alone among Victorian poets in challenging and revising what M. H. Abrams identified as 'The Greater Romantic Lyric', especially its handling of love, nature, transcendence or death. In this effort Hardy is very much like the witty Christina Rossetti, but whereas she decries humanist metaphysics and translates her attraction to Romanticism into High Anglican religious commitment, exposing Romantic secular ideologies as false or partial, Hardy altogether eschews any system of belief. If her treatment of erotic love demonstrates its basis in illusion, if her fascination with death is due to her trust in soul sleep and resurrection, and if her use of nature is largely typological, Hardy has lost the key to religious belief along with its emblems and does not support a theocentric universe any more than an anthropocentric one. He replaces God with a principle of chance he calls 'Hap', or overdetermined patterning 'Iron Necessity', or unintelligent randomness, the 'Unconscious Will of the Universe'. He introduces us to an even more severe secularism and refuses to offer definitive meanings or interpretations.

Hardy's poetry and poetics are closest to a radical tradition established by such authors as Robert Browning and William Thackeray, two of his favourite contemporary authors, and Christina Rossetti – a probing, questioning, critical, and ironic inquiry into the nature of being, time, and subjectivity. His radical aesthetic and politics also resembles what John Ruskin called the Gothic grotesque, to which I will return. These connections have not been made strongly enough. Hardy does not merely take up and rework the language or the tropes or metres of earlier poets, which would be easy enough to argue, but he intervenes in the very way we are allowed to think about the most substantive issues treated in poetry and makes us hyperconscious of how they are conveyed to us. Influenced by the new science (Lyell, Darwin, Huxley), new technologies of representation (movable type, photography, silent film), and by cultural criticism, Hardy exposes the inability of writing to capture verities. His poetry of 'impressions' unsettles the frames of interpretation and consolation on which even the most questioning of previous nineteenth-century poetry can be said to rest. The content of his poetry tests and questions nature worship, romance and love, religion, the cult of the dead, nationalism, war heroism and many other preoccupations of his time and ours.

It is important to place Hardy in relationship to the Romantic project, especially in regard to its philosophic and poetic treatment of subject and object, in order to note stark differences. Hardy's brand of secularism starts with a premise that undermines the Wordsworthian project entirely. If we recall Wordsworth's honouring of 'recollection in tranquillity' and the use of memory to fuse self and other into a moment of epiphanic union, or his development of such transcendent spots of time, as described and enacted in 'I Wandered Lonely as a Cloud' or 'Tintern Abbey', and if we then think, in comparison, of Hardy's handling of time, memory and self/other in such poems as 'The Self-Unseeing', 'The Voice' or 'During Wind and Rain', we must accept that Hardy's vision is radically different. For Hardy, fusion is not to be had between a speaker and a scene or a person, unless by accident. A moment in time might be selected to be remembered, but it is not to be recovered by the mind accurately (that is, as it once was experienced), nor is it to be elevated, not through memory or imagination or any other means. Likewise, seeing the past as it once was is impossible, and feeling it in the same way is out of the question, because layers of time and interpretation have intervened and the 'source' is no longer pure – if it ever was.

Moreover, Hardy's understanding of language – that over time it changes and grows archaic and then misunderstood – is directly related to how he also understands the human mind and its processes. In these conclusions, Hardy was aided by reading not only philosophers but also language theorists. Just as we are subject to a language whose history and cultural use frames us, but whose sources we can't know, so too the self is overdetermined or conditioned by its personal and cultural past. Nostalgia and curiosity make us try to unlock the self's causes and its origins, but any understanding we garner is also always already part of a process of self-deception, loss, and even obsolescence. We are broken not by our times, but by time and the nature of consciousness itself.

The best we can do, it seems, is to be aware of the cultural mythologies and ideologies that frame us, know that we live by them, realise that they are not equivalent either to material existence or to reality, and understand that they may not serve us if we call upon them.[2] On the one hand, Hardy's view of the self in time and circumstance is bleaker than the Romantic vision; on the other, being willing to stare at the worst merits more of our attention than we like to give it. What does staring at the worst really mean for Hardy – is it staring at death, at society, at contingency?

For Hardy, as Dennis Taylor puts it: 'Wordsworth's spot of time has become a frozen photographic frame.'[3] I want to develop this remark, to encourage more critical work on both Victorian technologies and Hardy and on Victorian theories of perception and Hardy. 'Neutral Tones', one of Hardy's earliest poems, can afford an entryway into the question of why photography and absence are so suggestive for thinking about his handling of relationship and representation. I will also note where Taylor's frame motif falls short in explanatory power. From there, I will discuss other areas fruitful for greater emphasis in Hardy studies generally: the Victorian double poem, Hardy's connections to and departures from the two main 'schools' of nineteenth-century poetry and poetics – those of Tennyson (a poetics of sensuous image, myth and questioning) and Browning (a poetics of dramatics and irony), and relationships between Hardy's poetry and what John Ruskin identifies as the (modern) Gothic grotesque.

'neutral tones'

When Taylor refers to a move from Wordsworth's epiphanic moments to a Hardyan photographic frame, he suggestively condenses a complex argument concerning philosophy, theories of visuality and imagination, time and poetics. As I have indicated, Wordsworth and Hardy share the valuing of a moment of meaningful experience and the retaining of it in memory. But there they part company. Wordsworth's poems offer metaphysical sureties that are absent in Hardy. Hardy does not trust that the self can reach out with good faith to the world and forge a connection. He does not assume that a poem about consciousness can produce a changed consciousness in the reader. Nor does he accept that re-evoked spots of time can exist as they were or function to transform.

It is true that in some of his poems, Wordsworth himself has a difficult time maintaining such sureties, as in poems such as 'Resolution and Independence' or the more sombre 'Elegiac Stanzas, Suggested by a Picture of Peele Castle'. Moreover, Coleridge, Shelley and Keats also demonstrate the limits and breakpoints of these sureties. However, they still remain a signature of the Wordsworthian and the Romantic, metaphysical and epistemological ideal. In place of such sureties, Hardy offers, as in the 1867 'Neutral Tones', a more real realism, a sceptical voice steeped in fragmentation and contingency:

We stood by a pond that winter day,
And the sun was white, as though chidden of God,
And a few leaves lay on the starving sod;
   – They had fallen from an ash, and were gray.

Your eyes on me were as eyes that rove
Over tedious riddles of years ago;
And some words played between us to and fro
   On which lost the more by our love.

The smile on your mouth was the deadest thing
Alive enough to have strength to die;
And a grin of bitterness swept thereby
   Like an ominous bird a-wing. ...

Since then, keen lessons that love deceives
And wrings with wrong, have shaped to me
Your face, and the God-curst sun, and a tree,
   And a pond edged with grayish leaves.

The situation is that a man and woman who have once been in love know that love has died, and in a later bitter meeting have nothing productive or kind to say to each other. From a longer temporal perspective, the speaker remembers their meeting by the pond and comments that time has afforded knowledge in the form of lessons he has learned. But the speaker is reserved. He tells us little about the relationship, what happened, or what he learned except that 'love deceives'. The landscape is equally silent, disengaged and unforgiving. Unlike a Wordsworth poem, this one is not about an active relation between a mind and a scene or about a speaker showing a reader how to gain a moment of epiphany and understanding. Nor is it just our encounter with a mind remembering.[4] Rather, it translates the speaker's stance of reserve, partial private knowledge, and public disengagement into a critique of Romanticism.

'Neutral Tones' illustrates perfectly what we might call Hardy's poetry of unknowing and of belated awareness. The speaker describes something that has happened to him in the past and, despite the pain of it, is now bitter but largely detached. He describes a time when he participated actively in a relationship but at the time of speaking the poem, he is an observer rather than a participant, an eye rather than an 'I'. Thus we have a double poem – a lyric expression and a commentary, a poem describing involvement but from a removed point of view. While the speaker conveys the authority of lived experience, the poet's authority comes from not being able or willing to explain more. The title refers to the colours of the scene, like a wash of grey, brown and white tones, but it also refers to the stance of disengagement that is forged through an emphasis on image and a grim acceptance.

In a typical Hardy poem memory can't serve us in a consolatory or redemptive fashion, either through an imaginative and metaphoric leap, linking time realms, or through a philosophical idea of unity across time and space, as in a typical Romantic poem. The Hardy poem, rather than enacting a process of present/past consciousness and self-making that a Romantic image can set into motion, 'sums up' retrospectively and serves as a commentary on a process of capturing experience. It indicates that our minds randomly choose certain images as metonymies of situations (parts represent a larger whole) and then, after the fact, 'shape' the situation through such parts and pieces: 'Your face, and the God-curst sun, and a tree, / And a pond edged with grayish leaves'. By extension, the poem suggests that at such moments of shaping, we may (or may not) see and understand most fully, even though we still see but partially. Hardy shows how a speaker shapes the scene, and the past and present, from contingency and fragments.

Hardy uses the passage of time not as a backdrop for an imaginative unifying of the self, as Wordsworth or Coleridge might, but to demonstrate divisions. He does so partly through diction and the exploitation of a series of double meanings, used to point to a doubleness of experience seen by the speaker, but only from the vantage point of the present. Victorian poetry, enlarging on tendencies we find markedly in poetry by Keats, although it is present in the work of other Romantics, draws attention to itself as representation or artefact. Hardy's poetry does so, not through comparison to art objects or by breaking the suspension of disbelief, but by drawing out ambiguity of meaning and thus a dialogic reading, where one meaning of a word or situation throws another into sharp relief.

The last stanza has been faulted for the cleverness of diction, but such criticism misses the point. Consider *keen*, *wrings*, and *wrong* from its first two lines: 'Since then, keen lessons that love deceives / And wrings with wrong'. The diction and phrasing itself, through double meanings, is being made to register the fall from idealism to realism – a larger point of the poem. 'Keen lessons' conveys the first meaning of *keen*: *eager*, as in a fresh new love (the speaker's past). Paired with *lessons*, *keen* simultaneously holds a second meaning of *sharp* and *painful*, the meaning it holds in a destructive or broken relationship (the speaker's present). *Lessons* contains the homonym *lessens*, indicating a falling away from love to disappointment. *Wrings* (the present) invokes its ghostly homonym *rings*, implying first an engagement ring or rings exchanged (the past). Gaining associations from the pond edge in the stanza, it also has the sense of *rings* as a shoreline or part of a circle. *Rings*, used spatially and emotionally in this context, indicates a mood of gloominess and deadness ringing them round. Moreover, it does so – in memory – for eternity, precisely because, as the poem tells us, the speaker's mind has chosen, consciously or unconsciously, these images and this scene to 'remember' and stand in for this situation. The double meaning of *keen* and the homonym *rings* merely reinforces *wrings* as in a twisting or squeezing. *Wrong* also carries a double meaning: *untruth* (as part of the speaker's view of what originally ended the relationship) and *injury* (the present sense of things). *Wrong* reinforces the sense of pain and estrangement.

Hardy described both his fiction and his poetry as 'impressions' or 'seemings', neither arguments nor philosophic statements. His imagination is primarily visual. He told two of his biographers that mental pictures preceded the formulation of his ideas in language.[5] The word *impression* is related in his mind to mental pictures and a general feeling conveyed to a viewer: 'We don't always remember as we should that in getting at the truth we get only at the true nature of the impression that an object, etc. produces on us, the true thing in itself being still beyond our knowledge, as Kant shows' (*Life*, pp. 261–2). Hardy's interest in impressions, and in ways to capture the singular mark of something through the senses, lead him to favour, with Ruskin, the late paintings of Turner which feature light, steam, mist, salt spray covering over the central 'thing' painted and firmly distorting it, whether it is a ship, a shoreline, a building, or a sky and horizon. Like the second-generation Romantics in particular, such as Shelley in 'Mont Blanc', and Victorian successors such as Arnold in 'Dover Beach' or 'The Buried Life', then, Hardy writes a poetry acknowledging that we are locked into our minds and to our perceptions of things, rather than having access to any 'truth' inherent in a thing, a scene, a relationship, or a situation. But he also maintains that things exist besides our perception of them – which is not to say that they don't exist through us for each other. Rather, he suggests that if we were all to pass away, then gravestones, lintels, shorelines, and so on, would still exist, even if they were no longer known to human consciousness or their natures expressed by human words.

Thinking about Hardy's poetry, in relation to photography, as Dennis Taylor does, is useful and should be developed. Taylor says Wordsworth's spot of time has become in Hardy a frozen photograph frame, not a photograph – the photo is gone. Taylor emphasises, if I read him correctly, that experience in any of its possible versions is gone; it is not recoverable as is a Romantic poet's spot of time, not even as a photo with its fidelity to the real. All that is left is the framing of what was. In 'Neutral Tones', all that is left is the edge of the pond, sun, tree, face – the ringing of the experience through a few key images.

But photography is double itself – both in its fidelity and its infidelity to the real. Hardy was influenced by nineteenth-century changes in ways of seeing, knowing and representing and in technologies of observing, photography among them. Photographs signify promises of presence and possession, but also mark an absence. If we had a person with us we would not need a photograph to 'remind' us or 'bring back' a face or figure. And to put this quite differently, as Hardy does in his poem 'The Photograph', the destruction of a portrait photograph is like, *but not the same as*, destroying the subject of it. In fact though, the photograph itself, a print of a negative, marks the absence of the subject, so that destroying it is a double destruction. In other words, photos are iconic signs, pointing to another reality. They come in different types, aesthetic styles, and are used to different ends; perhaps even more to the point, they garner different interpretations, different views and perceptions from those who look at them. But they all have a relation to death and absence, or as Barthes says: 'a photograph asserts that a corpse is alive as *corpse*: it is the living image of a dead thing'.[6]

Photography from its beginnings was associated both with magic and idealism, with illusion: photography dwells partly in an area of make believe. A photograph presents a past that was once a present; it makes the past present; and it opens up the gap between origins and retrospection.[7] But photography was also associated with positivism and with fact: with the photograph as a cultural policing mechanism as in mug shots or racial stereotyping, and as a conveyer of fact as in pictures of distant lands or battles. It was likewise associated with its method: the precision of chemistry, angle, long temporal pose, and light. Most importantly, it was associated with a reality effect, which is why photography is so important to the development of the Victorian novel.[8] Fascinated by what is authentically visible, but also by what is not, Hardy explored the photograph and its meanings of presence and absence, of fact and of ghostliness, in his stories, in poems such as 'The Photograph', in *Desperate Remedies*, *A Laodicean* and in *Jude the Obscure*, where photography figures in larger themes of reproducibility, identity and materiality.[9]

However, it is the doubleness of the photograph itself – its material presence and its iconicity to a past that no longer exists – that makes it an interesting analogue for a Hardy poem. A photograph seems to make one moment of the act of recording and the referent, but the gap always exists, just as Hardy's poems frequently open a gap between present and past or between reality and illusion. Hardy is aware of what Eduardo Cadava, citing Baudelaire and Walter Benjamin, has called the 'inability of the photograph to represent'.[10] The photograph is crucial, and successful, precisely because it does not faithfully reflect nature accurately. Hardy's poems are peculiarly modern in their registering of instability and dislocation.

Hardy's special achievement in nineteenth-century poetry, drawing out tendencies from his predecessors and contemporaries, is to explore the paradoxes and contradictions of sign/icon and referent. Moreover, he uses the multiple interactions of time, representation, and subjectivity as a way to critique not only the poetics he inherited but also the society in which he lived, by throwing into question all 'verities' as human, and thus contingent, constructions. Hardy's emphasis on chance, his distrust of easy sentiment or common sense – from romantic codes to institutionalised religion – his understanding of the relativity of time as it interacts with the human subject, his remarkable feel for outworn forms of words or genres and their sedimentary layers of meaning, all contribute to a poetry that is startlingly modern in its content. The politics of its aesthetics, however, is perhaps even more radical than has been noted.

double poems

Various critics have, over the years, talked about a split – two voices of, or two sides in – marking Hardy the man, a self-division that they then attribute to his writings. In reverse, some locate divisions in the writing and explain them in terms of the man's personality. Critics have explained this split in different ways: in terms of class origins versus class rise, in terms of gendering, in terms of artistic control and loss of control, in terms of intention and result, in terms of high intellect versus the natural or simple, in terms of conscious and unconscious.[11] I want to suggest that the divisions are in the poems for a historical, political, and aesthetic and not a biographical or psychological reason. As I will show, Hardy inherits and takes from two Victorian traditions which are aesthetically innovative in their use of dialogism in poetry, but which also proffer political, social change through poetry. What Hardy does with those traditions is unique and various, and worth further investigation, but it seems short-sighted to locate divisions in Hardy the man when they permeate Victorian poetry.

Many of Hardy's poems, like those of other Victorians, illustrate Arthur Henry Hallam's 1831 notion that the spirit of modern poetry is to be found in the 'return of the mind upon itself', or Matthew Arnold's 1853 idea that Victorian poetry is best described as 'the dialogue of the mind with itself'.[12] These astute assessments refer to an inwardness, loneliness and self-analytic solipsism. Arnold diagnosed nineteenth-century men as leading buried lives – forced to function on the surface through polite codes, rarely communing deeply with another, turned in upon themselves. With this kind of description, we might expect a tortured poetry of lyrical expression, hysteria and obsession. And there are certainly moments when Victorian poetry reads that way. But if we take Hallam's and Arnold's phrases structurally and programmatically, as Isobel Armstrong does, we can imagine a dialectical kind of poetry, featuring debate, questions and analysis. The Victorian double poem in its dramatic monologue form is an original and a powerful development of the Romantic genre the 'conversation poem' (such as Coleridge's 'Frost at Midnight' or Wordsworth's 'Tintern Abbey'). But not all double poems are dramatic monologues. Most importantly, Victorian poetry is not just a display of self-consciousness or split subjectivity, but a formal investigation into the status of the 'I' and its utterance. The result is both analysis of the failure of a transcendent ego and acknowledgement of the revelation and destruction of self through the very process of voicing.

In Armstrong's words, the dialogic nature of Victorian poetry afforded 'a way of exploring and interrogating the grounds of its representation'. With a poem housing both a lyric expression and a critical look at the very same lyric expression, as if the 'I' were both subject and object, 'the Victorian poet achieved … quite often literally two concurrent poems in the same words'.[13] Sometimes this comes through ambiguity of meaning with the same words; more often it comes through ironic distance established in various ways poetically. Although critics of Hardy have not much availed themselves of Armstrong's book, since she treats only his epic *The Dynasts* and that in a 'Postscript' alongside other poems, her work is some of the most suggestive we have on how and where we can place Hardy in this period and in this tradition. In her explanations of double poems as sceptical forms, Armstrong uses examples by Browning, Tennyson and others to show how the dramatic monologue, the premier and original Victorian poetic genre, is related to framed narrative poems, dream poems, dialogues and parodies, all of which enable poets to explore utterance as both a subject and an object, not a transparent statement.

Reordering lyric as drama, as in the dramatic monologue – Browning's 'My Last Duchess', Tennyson's 'St. Simeon Stylites', Swinburne's 'Itylus' – opens up a gap for analysis. Many other double poems, such as Barrett's 'Lord Walter's Wife', Arnold's 'Dover Beach', Christina Rossetti's 'Winter: My Secret' or Morris's 'The Haystack in the Floods', offer ways for readers to hear the lyric expression containing a counter-voice to itself. The dramatic element internalises an element of critique, pitting, as it were, one version or view or reading against another. As Armstrong notes: 'Epistemological and hermeneutic problems are built into its very form, for interpretation, and what the act of interpretation involves, are questioned in the very existence of the double model.'[14] However such doubleness, with utterance exposed as representation, can be found in many poetic genres, even if achieved differently.

By way of a Hardy example, 'During Wind and Rain' establishes an internal 'conversation' by use of refrain. However, it is important to reiterate clearly that doubleness is not mere conversation or dialogism in which sides of a debate are presented and face each other. Rather, problems of representation and struggles of interpretation are foregrounded by a debate in which an expressive statement is set in relief as representation, not mere transparent utterance, thus refining the terms of the debate as it proceeds and as we read. The content of each side critiques the other, so that expressive and phenomenological reinterpret each other and new questions arise.[15]

> They sing their dearest songs –
> He, she, all of them – yea,
> Treble and tenor and bass,
>   And one to play;
> With the candles mooning each face ...
>   Ah, no; the years O!
> How the sick leaves reel down in throngs!
>
> They clear the creeping moss –
> Elders and juniors – aye,
> Making the pathways neat
>   And the garden gay;
> And they build a shady seat ...
>   Ah, no; the years, the years;
> See, the white storm-birds wing across!
>
> They are blithely breakfasting all –
> Men and maidens – yea,
> Under the summer tree,
>   With a glimpse of the bay,
> While pet fowl come to the knee ...
>   Ah, no; the years O!
> And the rotten rose is ript from the wall.
>
> They change to a high new house,
> He, she, all of them – aye,
> Clocks, and carpets and chairs
>   On the lawn all day,
> And brightest things that are theirs ...
>   Ah, no; the years, the years;
> Down their carved names the rain-drop ploughs.

Hardy sets up this poem as a dialogue. It is separated into four stanzas with each stanza itself composed of two sections: five lines of narrative summary followed by two lines of refrain, 'Ah, no', and a statement which reads as commentary. One set of propositions is affirmative, one negative. The opening of each stanza is spoken from the point of view of an observer of those making music and moving house, while the refrain is spoken from a wider, more omniscient point of view that seems a commentary – the opposition is marked by *yea* or *aye* and by *no*. The struggle between observer's utterance and commentator is apparently over the power of the human versus the power of nature.

However, the poem is not quite so simple as it appears. As in a dramatic monologue statements which appear to be descriptive and matter of fact reveal more. There is, in fact, an internal critique of the point of view presented within each first five lines. The first stanza critique is most evident in *mooning*; the second in *creeping*; the third in *blithely*, the fourth in *brightest*. Light's *mooning* refers, one imagines, to a semicircular or circular light from candle flames brightening the faces of those singing and playing songs. It may be in a photograph; it may be a distant memory. It is unclear. However *mooning*, taken out of the context of an image of light, also means to spend time idling in reverie, and relates to the use of *blithely* in stanza three. The people may be singing their dearest songs, making their garden gay, enjoying their breakfast, happily moving up to a high house with bright possessions, but they do so in a kind of happy oblivion which is not only a forgetting but an absence and perhaps even a repression, reinforced by strong caesurae, by white spaces and by ellipses. *Blithely* means not only light-heartedly but also lacking due thought or consideration. The world view represented here is similar to that of 'The Self-Unseeing' which documents a family scene, music-making and enjoyment with a qualification: 'But we were looking away.' 'During Wind and Rain' is also similar to the vanity of human wishes represented by Hardy, through irony, diction, rhyme and line lengths, in 'The Convergence of the Twain'.

The fact that there are four stanzas is significant. Each may represent a season; each seems also to represent a person (of whom there are four). Though the poem insists on 'they' – the collective – at the start of each stanza, the force of the single 'rotten rose ript from the wall' is a reminder of the capriciousness of death. In addition, the powerful single rain-drop ploughing down each name, on what we must presume is a family cemetery stone, indicates just how vulnerable the *they* and the *theirs* may be. Individuals make up a *they* and as roses rot and chairs and walls fall down, so individuals die off, one by one at different times. Diction alone is not the only strategy for critique: for instance, the rhyming of *chairs* with *theirs* indicates just what is considered 'brightest' in this middle to upper class, which harbours a materialistic and unself-reflective world view. Neatness and gayness may be privileged, but what is sick here is not only the leaves in throngs but also the vanity of humans.

The fact that there is no person named, no consciousness entered, no distinction among 'characters' in the first five lines of each stanza, except generically by sex, is crucially important. The poem both enacts the erasure of consciousness it speaks about, comments on a lack of self-consciousness and refuses itself to make connections for the reader. Reverie may try to halt time and tame nature, changing houses may seem to postpone a final resting place, but time and nature continue *creeping* on.

However, this is not the whole story. In a Victorian dialogic poem, the initial statement pressures any counterstatement as well. Thus the refrain is critiqued by the first voice's existence and utterances. For it can be argued that the 'they' of the first five lines of each stanza is, in fact, not just a they that consumes obliviously. *They* are representative of optimism, of some of the greatest forces of civilisation (building, making, relating to the animal world, music), of light (candles, brightest), of unity (all), and of joy, love and affection (dearest, pet). They are like Hardy's darkling thrush who throws his voice and song against the gloom and, in this sense, they are heroic in the face of death. The voice of the refrain, in comparison, is mired in an unattractive, repetitive pessimism, paralysed, suspended, as it watches or imagines rain erase (their) names carved in stone. The poem's reverse critique opens questions that must be answered by a reader, since they are posed but not answered by the poem: What is the point of life? What relationship do things have to nature and to emotions? What is the relationship between the individual and the plural? The first word of each stanza's last line articulates the problematic of the poem: How / See / And / Down. How are we to see life in the face of the inevitable movement down (of the fall, of the rain, of death)?

'During Wind and Rain' is also clearly in conversation itself with many prior poems. There is no space here to explore this facet of its extended dialogism, but note that the 'they' who 'sing their dearest songs' in the first line may also refer to many of the great lyricists before Hardy. For the poem is hardly shy in its intertextual revisions of many prior lyrics of mutability and loss. A few such examples include the poem which stands behind this one most directly, Shelley's 'Ode to the West Wind', but also Gray's 'Elegy in a Country Churchyard', Blake's 'The Sick Rose' and 'The Garden of Love', Keats's 'To Autumn', Coleridge's 'The Ancient Mariner' and Tennyson's lyrics about family and garden from *In Memoriam* and *Maud*.

'During Wind and Rain', through its refrain and its double point of view, as well as through its internal critique and through its extended debate with prior poems, supports the view of Isobel Armstrong that double poems draw attention to epistemology and the cultural conditions in which subjectivities are formed. This Hardy poem exposes the cultural conditioning which promotes an easy nostalgia, mindlessness, materialism and quest to rise in status. At the same time, it proposes that self-consciousness is not self-sufficient. 'Ah, no' of the refrain sounds too close to 'I know' to be an accident. Hardy does not let his 'knower'/commentator rest easy either. Hardy's contribution to this historically situated poetics and literary politics is much greater than has been accepted and requires further exploration.

the poetics of image and myth; the poetics of dramatic irony and critique

From this far side of the nineteenth century, with some distance on the modernists, who (except for Ezra Pound) often disowned connections to Victorian writers, it is possible to see two traditions within poetry manifesting themselves in the work of Tennyson and Browning. To be sure, a poetry of sensation and one of dramatic irony do not originate or end with these two authors or their circles and followers. But each tradition, as well as later merging of their poetic strategies in various combinations, affects Hardy's poetics and aesthetic politics. Both traditions aim to be subversive of the way readers see and understand the world and their society. Each tries to shake up presuppositions about reading and meaning. The more difficult poetics to understand as cultural analysis is that proposed by the Cambridge Apostles, a group of intellectuals who banded together while at university in the 1830s, and exemplified in the poems of their best poet, Tennyson. The poetry may seem so imagistic, fantastic, affecting, and mythological that one questions if it harbours ideas at all. Yet Arthur Hallam's review of Tennyson's work elevates his poetry of sensation, arguing that it directly appeals to the heart of man to do its work.[16]

The Cambridge Apostles put forth a fairly conservative programme, aiming for individual change as a means to social and national change.

Armstrong calls them subversive conservatives. The poetry expresses but also analyses the sensations, then, of living lives of oppression ('The Lotos Eaters') or a romantic waiting in solipsism ('Mariana') or other states of mind including sensations of states of unconsciousness ('The Kraken'), or of mourning and melancholia (*In Memoriam*), or of hysteria (*Maud: A Monodrama*) or of types of desire and types of mental or spiritual labour set into highly emblematic narrative vignettes (*The Princess* or *Idylls of the King*). This poetry 'shows' the condition and the obsessions of the modern mind in order to rouse us out of self-consuming private consciousness and, perhaps more radically, to question the controlling abilities of that consciousness in a world becoming always more fragmented and confusing.

One of its most important aspects is the handling of myth. The Apostles read British mythographers and claimed that it was through myth, and national myth (such as that of King Arthur or a composite of traditions which would produce a figure such as the Kraken), that they might both expose and heal the fractured subjectivities and societies of their time. According to the Apostles, myths carry great power to console, to establish historical continuities, and to transform a society and a nation, whether one dealing with agricultural riots, wars or conquests of empire. Yet they also foreground, among poetic elements, the aural and the texture of verse. A lost organic unity, in other words could be remade or its parts re-fused, by re-educating readers' feelings through a process of associations and through the elemental sound of the poetry. We find such aims expressed in poems as diverse as 'The Lady of Shalott' and 'Crossing the Bar', where an appeal to the reader is made on the basis of sound as much as of sense. Hallam's commendation of Tennyson's verse for its metrics and sound, even in the group of early 'lady' poems that are almost nothing but sound, is significantly part of a programme for change and not merely a comment on style or aesthetics. It would be useful in future Hardy criticism to understand his complicated relationship to this poetic tradition. Hardy's strong interest in telling stories and his unlulling metric irregularity means that he is not easily linked with a tradition featuring anti-narrative narratives and a musical line aimed at evoking emotion and not idea. However, his belief that we understand reality through impressions (as in Impressionism), his fondness for the later Turner, and his interest in going deep to get at the emotional 'essence' of a thing also makes his poetry a cousin, if a distant cousin, of Tennyson's poetry of sensation.

The second grouping of poets works within the Benthamite aesthetic of the 1830s, articulated by William Johnson Fox, editor of the *Monthly Repository*, that influences Robert Browning. This movement of dramatic irony and critique is even more germane as a context for examining Hardy's literary practices, both in the novel and in poetry. There are various links that can be made. However, most importantly, Fox believes that literary texts should analyse and enact 'modern' states of mind, projecting and exploring associative processes as they are formed in different environments and in different time schemes. This kind of programme does not support notions of straightforward historical continuity (teleology) or accurate memory. It does not support unquestioned ideologies or cultural myths by which people live out their lives. It overtly questions identity, agency and any sort of monological or centric construction, including theocentrism and androcentrism.

Fox would have supported, for example, Hardy's conception of history as a wayward stream, his demythologisation of romance codes (as in 'The Waterfall'), or of war heroism (as in *The Dynasts*), or of arrogant claims to greatness (as in 'The Convergence of the Twain' on the sinking of the *Titanic*), and his subtle understanding of the byways and overlapping of memory and desire and death (as in 'During Wind and Rain' or 'Thoughts of Phena' or 'The Photograph'). Likewise, Hardy's overhauling of genres such as ballad, epic, elegy, bird poem, war poem and nature lyric is in the service of making new hermeneutical demands on readers.

For this group of poets and thinkers, though, analysing states of minds means more than just showing a mind in action. The poem also has to enact that modern state of disjunction and dissociation, of critique and questioning. For Hardy, who, like Hopkins, takes language practices to the extreme, the poem itself has to force the reader to unpack parts of words and phrases, as we have seen earlier with 'ring' in the poem 'Neutral Tone'. In what way does an engagement ring 'ring' us? 'wring' us? 'wrong' us? Language itself must be moulded, reshaped and unshaped, if necessary, to shake the reader in order that he or she may question the cultural clichés in which he or she finds him- or herself embedded. A future criticism will explicate more fully the demands Hardy makes on his readers.

The aesthetic put forward by Fox features dramatic projection, dialogism and a role for the reader that demands intellectual labour to read and interpret. This aesthetic was adopted and crafted anew by Browning, and in a different way by Barrett, Christina Rossetti, Greenwell, Levy and other women poets, and yet again differently by D. G. Rossetti and Morris and Hopkins. Poems like the dramatic monologue or linked monologues such as *The Ring and the Book* or long linked sonnets such as Christina Rossetti's 'Monna Innominata' show how mental events can be externalised and objectified through dramatic presentation.

This kind of Victorian projection is clear in a poem such as Browning's 'Porphyria's Lover' where we may be seduced or shocked into listening to the rhetoric of the speaker as he tells how he strangled Porphyria, but we can also hear through associations – fire, warmth, party, rosiness, hair – her beauty, grace and charm, and so we look carefully at the mind that speaks of her and we ask questions about that voice and representation. Regardless of who a nineteenth-century poem's speaker may be – madman, saint, prostitute, Renaissance artist or Duke, Greek mythic figure, Victorian wife or spinster, lesbian lover or world-weary man – we are bound to find double frames of reference commenting on each other and calling each other into question. We have, then, untrustworthy voices, multiple points of view, multiple geographic spaces and various time frames intermingling or in dialogue. How does this work in Hardy's poetry?

The radical aesthetic did not influence Hardy only through a line of Fox and Browning. Other intellectuals and cultural critics, such as Carlyle in 'Signs of the Times' and *Sartor Resartus* and Ruskin in *Stones of Venice*, influenced Victorians in many disciplines to think further about mechanised society and fractured or alienated consciousness, which they termed 'modern', and which Hardy referred in *Tess of the d'Urbervilles* as the 'ache' of modernism. Ruskin directly addressed the aesthetics and politics of alienation through his examination of the Gothic grotesque. He believed that a modern consciousness can only embody itself through distortion and fracture; and that a resulting unstable art or artefact that addresses such fracture always demands hard labour to interpret or appreciate and may not be unified in conventional ways. This aesthetic intervenes to stop rote reading and rote thinking, exposing, as the Benthamites do, cultural ideologies taken as truths. Ruskin's remarks on Gothic grotesque are particularly pertinent as a context in which to examine Hardy's verse.

hardy's gothic grotesque

The relationship of Hardy to theorists of the Gothic in culture and in art and architecture has still to be analysed in detail. But the Gothic aesthetic, as Dennis Taylor, Tom Paulin, Tim Armstrong and Isobel Armstrong have suggested, was very important to Hardy not merely because of his work as a restorer of Gothic churches. Rather, it was a paradigm he drew on as useful to explain his poetry as he neared the end of his career. When he dictated his ghost-written biography to his second wife Florence, he detailed the connection:

> He knew that in architecture cunning irregularity is of enormous worth, and it is obvious that he carried on into his verse, perhaps unconsciously, the Gothic art-principle in which he had been trained – the principle of spontaneity, found in mouldings, tracery, and such-like – resulting in the 'unforeseen' (as it has been called) character of his metres and stanzas – that of stress rather than of syllable, poetic texture rather than poetic veneer. (*Life*, p. 323)

In *The Stones of Venice*, Ruskin counterpoises the Gothic artist or stoneworker, who fashioned individual gargoyles and traceries independently, to a modern worker who is crippled by the routine slavery of cutting identical glass pieces. Ruskin identifies the properties of the Gothic as: savageness or energy, changefulness or refusal of order, naturalism or fecundity, rigidity or assertion of will, redundancy or excess. Although modern artists and workers do not usually have freedom because of the division of labour, Ruskin claims that it should be possible in the age of Victoria to create an art in the individualistic spirit of Gothic, one where the worker can have some amount of freedom to effect highly individual touches, while also working as part of a social unit.[17]

While Taylor and Paulin trace how visual patterns of Ruskin's Gothic are related to imaginative patterns and to the use of structures, shaping, and architecture in theme and form of Hardy's poetry, I'd like to suggest a wider application. Hardy achieves a special convergence of the two main streams of Victorian poetry, but with an emphasis, through the Gothic grotesque, on questioning and critique. Poems influenced by a grotesque aesthetic and politics don't concern themselves with work or class issues per se, though Hardy's own interest is very much in a community of labour that is class-based. But these poems are primarily kinds of commentaries on consciousness; sometimes a classed or gendered consciousness, sometimes not. They attempt to 'be' the form in which modern consciousness sees, experiences and desires, while also critiquing the very ideologies and forces that make it exist as it is.

Hardy may be said to blend the two strains I have discussed above in a particularly interesting way. Certainly he is much closer to Fox's reading of Bentham and the programme exemplified by Browning than to the programme of the Cambridge Apostles and Tennyson. Hardy demythologises myths and ideologies, works with heavy irony, and dramatises relationships, as Browning does. Still, like the Apostles, he also relies on image, what I have referred to previously as his interest in impressions and how they affect memory and mind, and in some ways – think of the end of 'Neutral Tones' – he can be seen as a forerunner of twentieth-century Imagism. Moreover, like Tennyson through King Arthur, he creates a myth of place, class and Englishness for a region of England when he 'founds' Wessex, becoming identified with it and its reputed values.

At the same time that he dramatises encounters between self and other in nature, as in 'The Darkling Thrush' or 'To Outer Nature', or among various others, as in 'Channel Firing', or among the self and a larger principle of the universe, as in 'Hap' or 'New Year's Eve', Hardy writes a poetry in which self confronts the self. More criticism should attend to this subset of his work. Such a confrontation takes various forms: sometimes the self meets or sees its ghost, or its ghost takes over the speaking, as in some of the poems for Emma written in 1912–13, or in such poems as 'Lost Love' or 'The Dead Man Walking'. This dialogue with ghosts recalls poems by Christina Rossetti where she observes her own corpse or her sleeping soul after death, but Hardy casts his death poems into a wholly secular context. At other times, the Hardy speaker conducts a dialogue between a man and a woman or between gendered parts of the self ('The Waterfall', 'After a Journey'). Sometimes Hardy's speaker performs a self-analysis within the poem, as in 'Conjecture' or 'The Self-Unseeing' or 'In a Former Resort After Many Years'.

Although the tone and diction are very different, these poems still recall the intensity of self-inspection or self-obsession we find in *In Memoriam* or *Maud*. But usually Hardy's speakers are neither religious nor mad. They don't seek transcendence of any kind. As Tim Armstrong has suggested, Hardy's poems obtain their power by eschewing traditional authority. Hardy replaces the 'I's authority with one based in observation from afar, whether in time or space or level of consciousness. It is a state of disembodiment or of posthumousness or of self-repression – reproducing the temporal and spatial gap we see when we look at a photograph.

Lately, fine critics of Hardy's novels have suggested that satire or parody is the mode through which we should approach them, not tragedy or classic realism or irony. This suggestive idea needs further testing and developing with regard to the poetry alone and through examination of the poetry with the fiction.

In the tradition of creators of the Victorian double poem and the Gothic grotesque, Hardy throws away the key to old poetic formulas and old foundations of belief. His poems, like his novels, expose the comfortable rationalisations we rely upon continually, in private and public life, to prop our most significant constructions, those of identity: gender, class, region and nation; those of hierarchies: God, man, nature; and those of temporal and spatial co-ordinates. Such constructions allow us to claim both selves and meaning. How and why Hardy intervenes to overturn cultural fictions through particular poems at certain historical moments should be the work for critics of the twenty-first century.

notes

1. Tim Armstrong, 'Introduction', *Selected Poems* by Thomas Hardy (London, 1993), pp. 1–42; Kerry McSweeney, 'Hardy's Poetic Antecedents', and U. C. Knoepflmacher, 'The Return of a Native Singer: Keats in Hardy's Dorset', both in *Influence and Resistance in Nineteenth-Century English Poetry*, eds G. Kim Blank and Margot K. Louis (London, 1993).
2. This sentence is indebted to a reading of Dennis Taylor's *Hardy's Literary Language and Victorian Philology* (Oxford, 1993), specifically to p. 251.
3. Dennis Taylor, 'Hardy as a Nineteenth-Century Poet', in *Cambridge Companion to Thomas Hardy*, ed. Dale Kramer (Cambridge, 1999), p. 189.
4. J. Hillis Miller has suggested rightly that Hardy's writing is a 'sustained encounter with the past', and that he is interested in conveying 'what it is like to be someone who remembers'. In other words, Hardy's speaker's stance is that of the observing eye and the self-observing eye, a mode of non-participation or analysis. He lets us watch his speakers watch. J. Hillis Miller, *Thomas Hardy, Distance and Desire* (New York, 1970), p. 29.
5. Ernest Brennecke, Jr, *The Life of Thomas Hardy*, pp. 113–14, and Clive Holland, *Thomas Hardy, O.M.*, p. 60, both quoted in J. B. Bullen, *Thomas Hardy: The Expressive Eye* (Oxford, 1986), p. 2.
6. Roland Barthes, *Camera Lucida: Reflections on Photography*, trans. Richard Howard (New York, 1981), p. 79.
7. My discussion of photography is influenced by Walter Benjamin's 'A Little History of Photography', in *Selected Writings, Volume 2, 1927–1934*, trans. Rodney Livingstone and others; eds Michael W. Jennings, Howard Eiland and Gary Smith (Cambridge, MA, 1999), pp. 507–30. I'm also indebted to Lindsay Smith, *The Politics of Focus: Women, Children and Nineteenth Century Photography* (New York, 1998), pp. 2–5 and Eduardo Cadava, *Words of Light: Theses on the Photography of History* (Princeton, 1997).
8. Nancy Armstrong, *Fiction in the Age of Photography* (Cambridge, MA, 1999). I'm not convinced by some of Armstrong's historical and theoretical claims

concerning realism and photography, but the readings of novels are invariably interesting.

9. Jennifer Green-Lewis, *Framing the Victorians: Photography and the Culture of Realism* (Ithaca, 1996), pp. 79–88, explores Hardy's attitudes to photography in his fictions. She notes Hillis Miller's phrase about Hardy's narrators being 'optically detached'.

10. Cadava, *Words of Light*, p. 14.

11. See my earlier noting of this point with regard to Thomas Hardy the man versus the voices in his novels: Linda M. Shires, 'The Radical Aesthetic of *Tess of the d'Urbervilles*', in *Cambridge Companion to Thomas Hardy*, pp. 146–7.

12. Arthur Henry Hallam, 'On Some of the Characteristics of Modern Poetry and on the Lyrical Poems of Alfred Tennyson', reprinted in *Victorian Poetry and Poetics*, eds Walter E. Houghton and G. Robert Stange (Boston, 1968), p. 852; originally published in *The Englishman's Magazine*, August 1831. Matthew Arnold, Preface to *Poems 1853*, *The Poems of Matthew Arnold*, ed. Kenneth Allott (London, 1965), p. 591.

13. Isobel Armstrong, *Victorian Poetry, Poetics, and Politics* (New York, 1993), p. 12.

14. Armstrong, *Victorian Poetry*, p. 13.

15. See Armstrong, *Victorian Poetry*, pp. 14–15, and her discussion of 'Mariana', which bears upon this analysis.

16. Hallam, 'Characteristics of Modern Poetry', p. 853.

17. Ruskin's 'The Nature of Gothic', in Volume II of *The Stones of Venice* (1851–53), was also published as a separate pamphlet in 1854. See E. T. Cook and Alexander Wedderburn, eds, *Works of John Ruskin*, 39 vols (London, 1903–12), X, p. 190.

12
hardy's aesthetics and twentieth-century poetry

Thomas Hardy once said that 'the whole secret of a living style ... lies in not having too much style – being, in fact, a little careless, or rather seeming to be, here and there. It brings wonderful life into the writing.' He expands this interestingly: '[This view] is, of course, simply a carrying into prose the knowledge I have acquired in poetry – that inexact rhymes and rhythms now and then are far more pleasing than correct ones' (*Life*, p. 108). It seems then that he saw his prose as coming out of his poetry, rather than the reverse as chronology might have suggested; and since the passage just cited is from 1875 – twenty years before *Wessex Poems*, his first collection, was published – we can hardly see these remarks as poetically defensive.

Allusions to aesthetic imperfection, overt or implied, are common in Hardy's comments. 'Art is a disproportioning – (i.e., distorting, throwing out of proportion) – of realities' (*Life*, p. 239). On paintings: 'I am more interested in the high ideas of a feeble executant than in the high execution of a feeble thinker' (*Life*, p. 333). In 1912, before formulating his later principle of 'exhumed memory', he wrote that 'our imperfect memories insensibly formalize the fresh originality of living fact'.[1] Hardy referred repeatedly to the 'idiosyncrasy' (*Life*, p. 158) of the individual artist as the key to his/her uniqueness. In his own successive volumes of poetry he saw a 'miscellaneous collection', a 'sense of disconnection' and 'a very mixed collection indeed', in all of them 'mere impressions of the moment', while one of the earliest, *Poems of the Past and the Present*, possessed 'little cohesion of thought or harmony of colouring. I do not greatly regret this.'[2] That last touch of firmness well shows that, for Hardy, neither awkward style nor uncohesiveness call for apology. Rather those stem from a general view of the world, and the aesthetic approach follows. In reaction to Romanticism, Nature herself is now seen as defective: 'So, then, if Nature's defects must be looked in the face and transcribed, whence arises the *art* in poetry and novel-writing? ... I think the art lies in making these defects the basis of a hitherto unperceived beauty' (*Life*, p. 118).

The nineteenth-century debate about aesthetic perfection was associated with the figures of Walter Pater, John Stuart Mill and John Ruskin. Hardy was fully aware of Ruskin's work, not least of course because they were both architects. So Ruskin's famous essay 'The Nature of Gothic' (1852), the *locus classicus* of the notion of imperfection as a valid aesthetic criterion, is relevant here.[3] Ruskin aimed to characterise the vigour and variety of Gothic architecture. This energy is achieved through the freedom allowed to the unlettered medieval craftsmen who created its huge and various features – carvings, decorated stones, statues, gargoyles, and so forth. Ruskin summarises the Gothic provenance under six headings: savageness, changefulness, naturalism, grotesqueness, rigidity and redundance. But only via a more general principle, namely imperfection, can these six characteristics be achieved. Ruskin's conclusion is as follows, and the italics are his own: 'Accurately speaking, no good work whatever can be perfect, and *the demand for perfection is always a sign of a misunderstanding of the ends of art.*'[4]

Earlier Ruskin has suggested how this seemingly paradoxical principle is reached. The architect can't build the cathedral by himself, so unless he treats his workmen as slaves he 'must take [them] as he finds them, and let them show their weaknesses together with their strength, which will involve the Gothic imperfection, but render the whole work as noble as the intellect of the age can make it'. Maybe patronising to us now, but Ruskin turns out to be seeing imperfection as larger and grander than its opposite. For it is 'ignoble ... to prefer the perfectness of the lower nature to the imperfection of the higher'. Finally Ruskin generalises the matter into an overall metaphysic. 'No great man ever stops working till he has reached his point of failure'; and this Browningesque maxim is followed by the even more universal observation – where, perhaps, we approach Hardy – that 'imperfection is in some sort essential to all that we know of life'.[5]

We cannot be certain how far Ruskin's ideas on culture and society – his opening up of art to ordinary people, and his strong if somewhat unorthodox socialism – affected Hardy, although it seems likely. But a counter-argument to the imperfection thesis came from John Stuart Mill.[6] In an address to the University of St Andrews in 1867 – 15 years after *The Stones of Venice* appeared – Mill attempted a survey of the whole gamut of areas of human knowledge, including mathematics, science, philosophy, politics, religion, history and the arts. On the last, Mill reverses the direction of the artist's and craftsman's aspirations. For by its

> conception of an ideal Beauty, to be eternally aimed at, though surpassing what can be actually attained … [art] trains us never to be completely satisfied with imperfection in what we ourselves do and are: to idealize, as much as possible, every work we do, and most of all, our own characters and lives.[7]

That is to say, the good painting or poem doesn't embody merely a perfect landscape, image or even abstract form. It puts us in mind of perfection itself. And, even in acknowledging that this ideal beauty will always 'surpass what can be actually attained', Mill affirms his position as the opposite of Ruskin's. For both writers perfection is not attainable in this world. But for Mill you must still go on trying, lest the aspiration itself falls away from you. For Ruskin, the imperfection is both inherent and desirable.

Everything we know of Hardy shows that he sided with Ruskin. His endless experiments with poetic forms evince the changefulness Ruskin saw as a chief criterion of the Gothic.[8] A passage in the *Life* comments directly on the issue:

> Between [architecture] and … poetry he had discovered … a close and curious parallel … He knew that in architecture cunning irregularity is of enormous worth, and it is obvious that he carried on into his verse, perhaps unconsciously, the Gothic art-principle in which he had been trained – the principle of spontaneity found in mouldings, tracery and such-like – resulting in the 'unforeseen' (as it has been called) character of his metres and stanzas, that of stress rather than of syllable, poetic texture rather than poetic veneer; the latter kind of thing, under the name of 'constructed ornament', being what he, in common with every Gothic student, had been taught to avoid as the plague. He shaped his poetry accordingly, introducing metrical pauses, and reversed beats; and found for his trouble that some particular line of a poem exemplifying this principle was greeted … with a would-be jocular remark that such a line 'did not make for immortality' … The

same critic might have gone to one of our cathedrals (to follow up the analogy of architecture), and ... have declared with equally merry conviction, 'This does not make for immortality.' (*Life*, p. 323)[9]

The emphasis of this long passage lies precisely in the space Hardy was willing to give to it. The parallel with Gothic is obvious, as is the importance Hardy attached to the issue. His architectural expertise defends him against critical ridicule of his verse. This is germane as to how far Hardy saw this as also a social issue, as Ruskin – if slightly differently – seems to have done; how far, that is, this identification with Gothic imperfection ties in with a liberal/democratic recognition in Hardy that ordinary people are necessarily imperfect and have never claimed otherwise. On this basis an aesthetic for the whole of society might emerge, counter to the traditional elitist (I would prefer to say aristocratic) notions of aesthetic to which Mill's formulation seems related. My own view is that Hardy profoundly valued both – the social *and* the aesthetic.

For Hardy's sense of imperfection goes wider than his own chosen modes of poetic writing. A key group of poems suggest that creation itself is imperfect, constructed so by a careless God. These include 'Nature's Questioning', 'The Absolute Explains', 'God's Education' and, most of all, 'God-Forgotten'. In this last, a human visitor to heaven tries to enlist God's interest in the human plight. At first God replies 'I have no remembrance of such place'. When reminded of it he makes excuses, feigns ignorance and blames others: 'It lost my interest from the first' ... 'not a cry / Of aught it bears do I now hear' ... 'All other orbs have kept in touch'. God even says he has better things to do, framing 'shining spheres of flawless stuff'. When he finally relents he acts quickly: 'Hence, Messengers! And straightway put an end / To what men undergo.' But it is too late, for these messengers to earth never appear. The poem is important for our theme in that, despite those 'shining spheres of flawless stuff', God's imperfection is not merely poor craftsmanship. He is dilatory and irresponsible. The point turns out to underline a range of ways in which Hardy sees 'imperfection' in the world around him: in himself for a start, for certain passages ruefully see himself as a generally ineffectual influence, even on the smaller members of the natural world. 'In Tenebris II' is the theme-poem of this kind, but 'A Commonplace Day' (precursor to Larkin's 'I Remember, I Remember') is an allegory of a commonplace life or person, seemingly Thomas Hardy. And, in 'I Am The One', in his final collection:

I am the one whom ringdoves see
  Through chinks in boughs
  When they do not rouse
  In sudden dread
But stay on cooing, as if they said:
  'Oh; it's only he.'

One can discern various aspects of this imperfection theme in Hardy's poetry. First there is 'falling-short'. This can be related to Donald Davie's contention, that Hardy 'sold the [poetic] vocation short, tacitly surrendering the proudest claims traditionally made for the act of the poetic imagination'. Hardy was '"the honest journeyman," highly skilled indeed but disablingly modest in his aims'; his poems seem to say '"Take it or leave it" ... or, even more permissively, "Take what you want, and leave the rest".'[10] This last touches a chord, for Hardy's offhand sadnesses, his melancholy-in-passing, resonate deep within his poetic voice. But Davie surely misses his own point. Hardy's seemingly modest aims embody a stance toward not just his social-cultural reference group – critics, friends, peers and family – but to the cosmos generally, which locus of our fortunes he found so saddening. Davie's misunderstanding can be tied to his faulty rating of many of the poems he discusses.[11] I would suggest that 'falling-short' is one of the motifs of imperfection which Hardy, consciously or not, espoused.

The poem 'Overlooking the River Stour' has the poet staring intently at the river, its currents and eddies, and the birds splashing on its surface. In the last stanza we learn that something more poignant and more human has been going on 'behind my back' to which, alas, 'never I turned'. Davie's view of this poem is that it 'confesses, guiltily, that its composition did not engage the full attention of its author. It thus proclaims its own minor or marginal status.' This is because 'its precision is more apparent than real. The poem raises issues which in the end it does not resolve nor account for.' This view seems far too limited.[12] If we compare it with another poem, 'On the Esplanade', we see that both are built the same way, and that both turn out to belong to a wider group of poems which evince the 'falling-short' motif. As in 'Overlooking the River Stour' and, to some extent, its companion piece 'On Sturminster Foot-Bridge', the poem 'On the Esplanade' has the poet looking at a stretch of water while, behind his back, something more fateful is occurring. The structure is slightly different in the esplanade poem, but the wider inference is the same.

In the bay in 'On the Esplanade' the poet sees the moon, a pathway going to the shore, 'the lamps of the Bay', the tideline, the sea wall as 'a constant mile of curve', and indeed the horizon itself. But, rather than going on out, he follows his mind *back* to 'a window, open, with undrawn blind', music, and a lady dancing. A typical Hardy story of lost love; but the wider inference is his lack of interest in the sea as the scene of infinity. Hardy's seashore poems, such as they are, always have this lack. They do not move outward, but turn back inland. As such they suggest deeper ideas of falling-short than Davie's 'selling short' suggests. 'At Lulworth Cove' is about Keats's departure to Rome; 'The Harbour Bridge' a rather sourly failed liaison; 'The Souls of the Slain' ends with the spirits – not the bemused poet – disappearing out to sea; and the various seashore poems of 1912–13 ('The Phantom Horsewoman', 'Beeny Cliff', 'At Castle Boterel', 'Where the Picnic Was') never look out to the sea as any kind of domain parallel to where his dead wife may now be residing. Much Romantic and Victorian poetry took the sea-coast as exactly that symbol of boundlessness – Wordsworth's 'children sport[ing] upon the shore', Arnold's 'Dover Beach' and his classic-conventional close to 'Sohrab and Rustum', Tennyson's 'Break, Break, Break', even little Paul at his death in *Dombey and Son*. The railways brought the sea close to the Victorian consciousness; but Hardy, who lived near it, used it differently.

This 'falling-short' is thus the formula for Hardy's aesthetic of imperfection. Other observable modes are the 'too late' theme, the 'not knowing' theme, the impotent kiss theme, and the range of technical failings which so many critics have lit upon but which, as already suggested, Hardy's own comments show that he intended, and that he spent long hours working on.

The 'too late' theme has been examined by Dennis Taylor in *Hardy's Poetry 1860–1928* (1981). Taylor suggests that many of Hardy's short lyrics reveal interruption leading to recapitulation; a sudden incident of today presents an inference for feelings and events many years gone by. For Taylor this process culminates in the death of Emma Hardy, which led to the 'Poems of 1912–13'. In these poems Hardy – but too late – learns that his life has been a sad journey up to this irreversible moment. This leads Taylor into a wider view of Hardy's poetic development. Critics have been divided on that issue, but the 'too late' notion certainly drifts through many of Hardy's poems more locally. It is overt of course in such poems as 'A Trampwoman's Tragedy', where the woman realises, tragically too late, her folly in teasing her true love. More cryptically the ruined maid, in the poem of that name, seems proud of but irreversibly numbed by her new comforts and position, and what she did to get them. In the God-poems already considered God learns 'too late' what a mess he has made of the creation. In a long poem 'The Revisitation' past lovers chance to meet at night on a hillside decades later. By dawn she has left and the man sadly ruminates that 'love is lame at fifty years'. Illegitimate children, unsurprisingly, are frequently tokens of too-late quarrels or regrets. Everywhere the owl of Minerva flies out at dusk.

Metaphysically speaking, all human knowledge comes 'too late' by its nature. For clearly, nothing can be known until it has first come into existence. But – and this is a third aspect of the matter – Hardy's poetry is saturated with 'not knowing' generally. People half-know, never know, remain bewilderedly unaware, or die in unwitting ignorance. It is seldom that they don't *want* to know; a wistful, sometimes half-hearted search can also be present. In 'Ah, Are You Digging On My Grave?', a dead and buried woman hopes the noises overhead mean her loved ones are mourning her. She is always wrong, and even her dog has only come to retrieve its bone. In 'In the Cemetery' two bereaved mothers squabble over which grave (containing their dead infants) is which, unaware that the small bodies were moved elsewhere anyway when new drains were installed in the graveyard. The people of Stratford had no idea who their famous son was – 'ah, one of the tradesman's sons, I now recall ... / Witty, I've heard ... / We did not know him' ('To Shakespeare') – and it is typical of Hardy to cast an otherwise formal eulogy in this fashion, as he did equally in 'At Lulworth Cove'. There are degrees of ignorance. In 'The Wind's Prophecy' the lover on his train journey doesn't know that he will transfer allegiance from the woman he has come from to the one he is going to; but the sounds of wind and rain seem to tell him. In some poems one person knows what another doesn't, as in 'The Husband's View'; the husband has known all along that his wife's pregnancy was caused by another man, but with the national need 'for sons for soldiering' he forgives her. One senses Hardy feeling his position – along with most others of his time – as 'No answerer I' ('Nature's Questioning'), despite his wide reading within the general agnosticism of the post-Darwin years in the late nineteenth century. Like God and humans, Nature too shares this ignorance, as implied in the beautiful ambiguity of the final line of 'An August Midnight', where the poet has watched tiny insects gathering on his book: 'They know Earth-secrets that know not I.'

Finally the 'impotent kiss' marks out the corporeal frame as another terrain where falling-short occurs, this time sexual. The kiss is often as far as the liaison gets. In 'In the Days of Crinoline' a vicar's wife goes out wearing a dowdy hat, to her husband's secret relief. On her way to meet her lover she switches to a more glamorous hat concealed under her dress. When she returns home her not-knowing husband 'kissed her on the cheek'. Only on the cheek; the pre-Freudian symbolism of the hats is patent to the reader. In 'On The Departure Platform' the farewell kiss begins the poem, but the lady then walks away to her train, getting smaller and smaller, her inviting body thus visibly receding. Similarly in 'A Hurried Meeting' illicit lovers 'passively kiss' at the start, but then only discuss what to do about the lady's pregnancy before they part for ever. And in *Tess of the d'Urbervilles*, the milkmaids longingly but in vain kiss Angel Clare's shadow where it briefly hovers on the wall nearby. There are other examples.

It appears then that Davie's 'selling short of his vocation' is, at best, a single strand in a much wider tendency which Hardy's poetry evinces in countless long narratives, small parables, fleeting incidents and, in his own recurring term, impressions of what happens to happen. All are modes of or angles on cosmic, natural and human imperfection. Davie faults Hardy for not fully expressing in his poetry what he clearly possesses; namely, 'the one poetic imagination of the first magnitude in the present century who writes out of, and embodies in his poems, political and social attitudes which a social democrat recognises as "Liberal".[13] My own view is that Hardy's stance toward the social-democratic is encased in a much wider apprehension of the human condition, socially, cosmically, and in nature. But if we are to relate this social-democratic stance to Hardy's aesthetic of imperfection, we must first look at this aesthetic more analytically. What is Hardy's aesthetic? What is the 'aesthetic' at all?

Here I must briefly introduce my own approach to the aesthetic. I have elaborated this elsewhere;[14] what follows now has to be somewhat generalised but I hope may be useful in looking at Hardy's poems. I take the aesthetic to be a mode of cognition, one of seven such human modes which can be discerned. The seven, in this deliberate order, are mathematical/logical, empirical/scientific, hermeneutic, philosophical, moral, aesthetic and religious. Mathematical/logical cognition is cognition of the relations between things without regard to their content: in multiplying 18 by 73 we don't need to know whether these are 18 lemons, childbirths, galaxies or anything else. Empirical or scientific cognition is cognition of physical matter via our five senses. In formal science our senses are extended by microscopes, telescopes, cloud-track chambers and the rest, but still in the mode of sensual recognition.

Hermeneutic cognition is cognition of these first two modes, but now insofar as the observed object signals something meaningful beyond itself. On seeing the sign 'No Smoking' I don't consider whether the notice is made of plastic or is six inches long: I read the intention of whoever put it up there. Philosophical cognition extends this area of intended meaning to generality: not what someone meant on some occasion, but how far such statements are permanently meaningful and regardless of who is saying them – for example statements like 'all is flux' or 'I think therefore I am'. Moral cognition is cognition of a single and different pressurising consciousness; namely, that what I do I am to be held responsible for. Putting by aesthetic cognition for the moment, religious cognition is cognition of whatever is left over beyond these other six modes. It is cognition of the limits of human cognition and therefore of what conceivably lies beyond it.

These seven modes of cognition (the aesthetic still to be adduced) have certain characteristics, some of them important here. One is that none of the seven can be cognitively used in terms of any other. They may be combined in practice – for example, historians look at physical material for evidence of the past, and philosophers use logic to reach general human meaning – but no empirical evidence can finally prove to us what we morally ought to do. I will never know if a painting is beautiful by being told its title or the painter's supposed purpose, nor anyone's views on religion solely from knowing they are philosophers. And so on. Another key feature is diminishing order of certitude. Mathematical/ logical cognitions are tautologically true and cannot be untrue. Empirical/ scientific cognitions are virtually always reliable once the first hypothesis has been established. Hermeneutic cognitions are more often faulty, but they must still be generally reliable or everyday life would be literally unliveable. Philosophical cognitions are more unstable still, but their general region is objectively acceptable. In the three remaining cognitions the material cognised is itself in doubt. The real-life occasion of morality, of 'what I ought to do or resist', bar maybe a very few exceptions, is almost never reliable as a pointer to correct moral response. Exceptional circumstances can usually be imagined when otherwise reprehensible actions might be allowable or even desirable; for example, theft from the rich if my infant child is starving. On the aesthetic we will, for a moment, just say that the artwork is never predictable in either quality or substance; while religion deals with entities which a sizeable number of humans don't believe exist.

We can now try to locate and define the aesthetic. I suggest that aesthetic works are fictions. Clearly this can't mean just lies, because one can lie within any cognition. So the definition of artworks should perhaps enlarge to 'known fictions with which the spectator is complicit'. This definition lets us see the aesthetic as an independent mode of cognition, for under such a definition the aesthetic can't be confused with any other mode. Other modes of cognition will occasionally use fiction as passing example, but this must be seldom or serious truth-claims in those domains would be endangered. This definition also accounts for the position of the aesthetic low down in the ranking of certitude, between the moral and the religious. Justifying that ranking would take considerable further discussion; but we can see, from it, that an aesthetic of imperfection may not be a contradiction in terms.

The artist and poet make fictions, are 'imaginatively creative', as a way of apprehending elusive truth, or expressing an embryonic but otherwise unattainable sense of cognition from within fictions themselves. But such fictions – again as opposed to lies – can only come into existence gratuitously. Gratuity is the wider terrain of the aesthetic. This view sees artworks as, in part, things that wouldn't have been there in the ordinary course of events, and therefore arrived by non-instrumental means. No other human cognition is of this kind. Artworks then are analogous to the universe itself which, as Stephen Hawking has put it, is the ultimate free lunch. Of course the artwork can be instrumental indirectly, for example to celebrate an event – as with Hardy's 'The Convergence of the Twain' – or indeed in some general sense simply to entertain. The point is made most strongly in light of those works of art – characteristically modern – which at first sight may not seem fictional at all. These include blank canvases, lumps of stone, ordinary items like a cow but sawn in half, or indeed much music, which might seem just sequences of sounds. Briefly, and this too can't be developed here, I would call these items impossibilities. They can only come into existence *as* works of art, gratuitously, to 'make them in order to make them', to see what they are like. But they can therefore be seen as closely allied to the fictional, for they are fiction-type examples of how anything in the natural and material world comes into existence.

So far, then, we have seen the aesthetic as cognising those items – artworks – which (a) are fictional, (b) come into existence gratuitously. Why then would anyone be interested in them? The answer lies in the two other aspects of the aesthetic to be introduced here, on the way to examining Hardy's poetry of imperfection more closely. The work of art must compel our attention, and it must survive to do so. 'Pleasure' is the common term for the emotional experience aesthetic cognition gives us, because ordinarily no one is obliged to encounter any one work of art. This is precisely because in its gratuity the work of art serves no previous instrumental purpose. We witness it because, whatever the circumstances, we want to and like doing so. But 'pleasure' hardly describes our feelings on encountering the great tragic works: it is more like a satisfactory resolution, whether open-ended or not, of whatever it has put before us earlier. A sentimental story of unthreatened courtship and church-bells marriage may be compelling, as might a dead body riddled with bullets and worms, but neither can be said to offer a satisfactory resolution we would recognise as truly aesthetic.

Finally, it is clear that if the work of art is to give this pleasure or compulsion, it must be constructed to retain our interest long-term; that is to say, to survive. The work is a gratuitous fiction. It contains no organic life, like a bird or a fruit; it has no tool-like function; and it is not, as such, a work of perception which could be applied directly as a problem-solving item, by for example teachers or psychiatrists. So the work must ensure its ongoing existence within its very makeup. The required component I suggest is tension. The parts of a lasting work of art relate to each other such that an inner equilibrium is attained. The pressures which make for this inner self-relation then radiate to the viewer, listener or reader. Clearly such oft-noted items as contrast, anticipation and timing contribute to the overall tension a compelling work of art secretes.

These characteristics then are what the aesthetic cognition typically apprehends. The work of art embodies fiction, gratuitous origin, pleasure (or compulsion), and tension. Four-point schemes aren't popular in current theorising, but I hope I have shown how these four seminal features arise naturally out of each other and belong with each other. We now need to consider Hardy's poetry in the light of these ideas.

Both in and outside his poetry Hardy records a sense that the universe itself is flawed. His God-poems repeatedly suggest this, as we saw. That being so, any person, any poet, must be flawed too; and the aesthetic of imperfection comes from the ways things just are. From all angles this both promises and threatens the idea of a successful aesthetic, an art that works. To be consonant with reality itself the aspects of gratuity, fiction, pleasure-compulsion and tension must also be flawed; yet those flaws would seem to make any resulting poem a failure. But maybe Hardy so cunningly works his imperfections into his poems that aesthetic achievement does come.

Behind the gratuity we have distinguished there might hover Hardy's profound sense of fate. If we all live at the hands or whim of fate then we are 'imperfect' to that degree; as a species we haven't evolved a self-sufficiency that would free us from this subjection. Take the poem 'A Woman's Fancy'. A friendless woman arrives at a house to take up lodgings. She is mistakenly thought to be the wife of a man who lived there and has just died. She protests that she is someone quite different but everyone thinks she is rambling. They address her as the dead man's wife so much, and for so long afterwards while she lives there, that 'his past form and fame / Grew on her, till she pitied his sorrow / As if she truly had been the cause'. She wonders what he was like and, to their surprise, inquires about him: '"But *you* know, surely, Ma'am?" they would answer, / Much in perplexity'. Then she visits his grave, sees there is no headstone, and sets one up herself. She dreams about him. When years later she too is dying, she begs them to bury her in his grave alongside him and, finally, to call herself by the dead man's name on the headstone.

Hardy ends this remarkable poem with unusual absence of comment. He merely notes:

> And so it became there
>   That, by the strength of a tender whim,
> The stranger was she who bore his name there
>   Not she who wedded him.

Such an extraordinary story is theoretically possible in real life. But what comes over is that the 'woman's fancy' of the title is also the gratuitous fancy of the poet. The story is so unlikely that it only makes sense if we think of the woman as somehow drawn fatefully forward into the events that follow. It could of course be interpreted in more everyday ways. Maybe the woman was never loved and so is frustrated, and this was lifelong. But the weird atmosphere of the poem takes us beyond this. The story gradually seals itself into itself, so the movement toward the final death and burial feels impossible and inevitable at once. This combination is itself gratuitous and the resulting poem – the story over and finished – is left as a fated event in that the poet imposes no other concluding interpretation.

This brings us to fiction. If we pass our lives imperfectly under the aegis of (gratuitous) fate, then art's fictionalising of this is likely to bear the same mark. But, unsurprisingly for a Victorian novelist, Hardy's poetic fictions are commonly overt. They are often clear and lengthy narratives with beginnings, developments, outcomes and – usually ironic – denouements. Such are 'The Paphian Ball', 'The Dance at the Phoenix', 'The Contretemps', 'The Chapel-Organist', 'The Two Wives', 'A Sound in the Night' and many others. There are variants of course. Often the poem is short, narrating one brief incident or observation; or it is a monologue from the mouth of a universal entity (God, fate, Nature) by which a thesis can be questioned, or weigh heavily on its hearers. But a common feature, central to Hardy's aesthetic especially in the fuller narratives, lies in the frequent ironic symmetry of the conclusion. Again and again the agonising result somehow gives, yes, pleasure, and we can only account for this by a sense that since loose ends have been tied up, however grievously, at least a position has been cleared.

In 'The Two Wives', for example, two women go boating. A third woman enters, mistress of the poem's speaker (one of the two men). News then comes that one of the boating women has been drowned. When they learn that the victim is the non-speaker's wife the speaker is frustrated, for his own wife's death would have released him to his mistress fully. But she disillusions him, for the bereaved husband, she says, was her lover too. So, in aesthetic balance, either wife's death would have had the same result. The reader's feeling is curiously assuaged. Equally in 'The Paphian Ball', less tragically but more ominously, the Mellstock choir sets out one night to go carol singing. On the way they are accosted by a mysterious figure who invites them to perform at a ball instead. He promises better money than carol singing would offer, but they must agree to go blindfolded. They find themselves in a magnificent mansion with sumptuous decor, but also 'half-naked women' and men who 'swore strange oaths'. When the tiring choir inadvertently sings a carol the ballroom vanishes; they are unpaid and it is nearly dawn. They go shamefacedly home, but are greeted with cheers from the churchgoers for their performance of the previous night. Never before, apparently, had they sung so well. Again there is a symmetry. The sense of evil is relieved by the fact that all was, seemingly, just a bad dream – or, if we prefer, that happy outcome is compromised by the scary memory of the powers of darkness the choir have seemingly encountered. This balance of good and evil makes for an aesthetic harmony which, however, leaves us in the hands of fate as surely as ever.

In Hardy's narratives, too, the dead often speak. Since in the normal way of things this is impossible, it sits naturally in the realm of fiction. The dead speak in 'The Coronation', 'Friends Beyond', 'Channel Firing', 'Voices from Things Growing in a Churchyard' and a number of others. Speech from the dead, it would seem, is imperfect, 'too late' virtually by definition. Direct speech in all these poems, however – regardless of speaker – is a further aspect of the overtness of Hardy's narrative fiction. For even if a poem retells an old story perhaps once true enough, the dialogue itself has to be invented. Hardy often does this in 'imperfect' fashion in a way that is 'pleasurable' in the sense suggested above.

What one might call the humdrum remark, directly reported, figures frequently in Hardy's poetry. We can almost hear them being said. They underline that 'poetic diction', formal, high-flown or indeed fully achieved (Miltonic), is no part of Hardy's aesthetic. This offers an interesting addition to what is commonly suggested about Hardy's neologisms, 'clumsiness', and so on. We have already cited the villagers' response to the lady in 'A Woman's Fancy': '"But *you* know, surely, Ma'am?" they would answer, / Much in perplexity'; and the ringdoves cooing 'Oh; it's only he' in 'I Am The One'. In 'The Contretemps' the speaker and a girl embrace on a bridge only to find they have each picked the wrong person, and others soon become involved. 'And next the lover: "Little I knew, / Madam, you had a third!"' It works because any of these snatches, as of overheard phrases, vividly embodies the life told in the poem's story.

In 'The Harbour Bridge' the humdrum phrase is rather touching, as the deserted woman tries to tempt her man back when he has left her for another woman:

At last: 'Won't you come home?' She moves still nigher:
"Tis comfortable, with a fire.'

The supposedly awkward rhyme 'nigher/fire' doesn't make us – or me at least – think it forced. Rather, Hardy is happy to let his craft as poet merge with the humdrum words of his characters. In 'The Inscription' a widow refuses offerings of love because her husband's tomb bears a brass inscription which leaves room for her own when she too dies. After years of rejection, her suitor gives her till midsummer night to change her mind. Her stress grows, she compulsively looks at the brass in the church, and on midsummer night disappears. The servants and villagers are alarmed. '"The church!" they whispered with qualms; "where often she sits".' Again the truncated phrase (no main verb) and the bizarre

Hardy construction ('with qualms') fits in with the so-recognisable utterance by which the bystanders express their impulsive fear. In 'In a London Flat' it is the ghosts who speak this way. A lady teases her husband that he looks like a widower: '"Let's get him made so – just for a whim!" / Said the Phantom Ironic.' The Sprite of the Pities replies, '"O pray not! ... she said it in fun!"' The everyday direct speech is matched by the down-to-earth setting, the 'folding-doors' and the traffic outside – 'a cab-hack's wheeze, and the clap of its feet / In its breathless pace on the smooth wet street' – as well as Hardy's throwaway response to why the lady did soon die: 'But so it befell, whatever the cause, / That what she had called him he next year was'.

In fictive narrative then, unlike in history (pure hermeneutic cognition), the poet is free to invent his characters' speeches; and if his aesthetic aspires to imperfection, the humdrum mode is one way of achieving it. Another remarkable feature emerges here. Poetry's necessary fiction in Hardy's imperfection turns out to be fated, yet its form is one of robust narratives and speech directly rendered. But the same turns out to be true of Hardy's deeper tensions, noted above as another inherent feature of the aesthetic generally. They too are often equally firm, equally robust, just like that of the fated fictions. This is surprising, for it has often been thought of as the opposite.

I'm referring here to what J. Hillis Miller called Hardy's 'double vision', his frequent centring of a poem on opposed points of view with no closing resolution.[15] A poem will evoke two people's contrary emotions; an imagined but then real outcome; time then and time now; rich and poor; what he/she knows while he/she doesn't; what is against what could have been, and numerous other dualities. In each case the pairing is left free-hanging, with only an irony or twist to accompany it. It is robust, though, because the two sides of the picture always have a strong profile, and their separation is clear. The double-vision is usually found in shorter poems, less often a full narrative because their double character is a formal structure. Such would include 'A Thought in Two Moods', 'In Church', 'The Wind's Prophecy', 'Life and Death at Sunrise', 'In the Days of Crinoline', 'A Thunderstorm in Town', 'Throwing a Tree', 'The Curate's Kindness', 'Near Lanivet, 1872', 'The Children and Sir Nameless', 'Afternoon Service at Mellstock', 'The Walk', 'The Lament', 'The Convergence of the Twain', and many more.[16] This poetic irresolution too can be classed, tentatively, as one more aspect of the Hardyesque imperfection.

This points to a discussion in a recent study of aesthetics and literature, by Isobel Armstrong in *The Radical Aesthetic*. In chapter 2 she examines post-modernist ideas of the aesthetic, particularly using work of the late Gillian Rose, the political theorist and sociologist. The title of the relevant work, Rose's *The Broken Middle* (1992), may point to the connections we will suggest as to this group of Hardy's poems. My brief account here conflates the views of Armstrong and Rose, I hope doing no disservice to either. If debate has no middle, no mediation, then it is binary. Such discourse 'refuses to countenance a thinking through of contradiction and the anxiety of the middle'. It may also be *immediate*, but there the second term is still invisibly present, having been suppressed by (for example) the 'law', as imposed by Lacanian psychoanalysis, or the ideas of such as De Man, Lyotard and Foucault. All of these offer some kind of theory of coercion or imposed single-track cognition as a way out of our predicaments. Always the post-modern world posits binaries: consumerism and ecology, town planning and freewheeling capitalism, conservatism and socialism, developed and developing countries, 'utopia and dystopia, love and violence … sign and simulacra, individual and panoptical power'. In such a context the middle is 'rended not mended' – as it might also seem to be in Hardy's 'double-vision' or, as one might see them, broken-backed poems.[17]

For Gillian Rose however the 'middle' enables the Hegelian syllogism. It is the locus of growth and creation. It is the seat of anxiety, but one which accepts no easy solutions, nor prematurely takes sides. Rather it is 'a pivot of the movement forwards'. This anxiety thinks through contradiction to a new conclusion or new start. It is essentially creative, for it alone in the post-modern world is where it is possible, in Rose's words, 'to know, to misknow, and yet to grow'. It is exactly as though Hardy's double-vision poems never reach this creative ground. The double-vision poems, it seems, take no position forwards, but leave their protagonists hanging on two sides of a cleft. In 'Near Lanivet, 1872', for example, both the poet and his lady notice that as she leans wearily against a signpost she looks like a crucifix; but all they can say is 'alas, alas'. At the end of 'Throwing a Tree', about chopping a tree down, we find only the two aspects futilely contrasted: 'two hundred years' steady growth has been ended in less than two hours'. Yet such a view might seem to pitch us back into Davie's position: these poems offer the tension essential to any work of art, but they do so, as Davie said, too resignedly.

Yet I suggest that Hardy's poems of this kind leave the middle ground wide open for the reader's own entry. In each case the tension set up by the poems' two parts allows the ultimate pleasure of an open space in which new things are possible. As Armstrong says, Rose's conclusion is that middle-ground anxiety accrues precisely because 'a struggle with breaks and difficulty, not an unproblematical resolution, is [the] true Hegelian response, a mode of understanding'. Hardy's lifelong grappling with philosophy, science, religion and the arts squares him with this view, as Armstrong further expresses it, that 'mediation creates a space for *coming to know and knowing about that coming to know*, a space inevitably of fracture rather than connection, agonistic, but a space all the same'.[18]

This brief discussion of Armstrong's and Rose's ideas returns us to our list of the main human modes of cognition, and the distinction of the aesthetic from the others, just as they are also distinct from each other. The Hardyesque 'not knowing' is thus a major aspect of his aesthetic of imperfection. The power of the aesthetic to leave spaces productively open, and to open up such spaces in the first place, is matched by no other cognitive power except perhaps the moral, whose space lies only in the field of our right actions. Even the moral gives us no scientific or historical facts, or even religious truths, but the aesthetic can enter all these and other fields. Hardy's 'imperfections', I have tried to suggest, work at all levels. Human inadequacy in the face of fate; the humdrum-ness of everyday talk; Hardy's own accepted or even deliberate awkwardnesses of expression and unconcealed problem-solutions (like obvious rhyme words); the near-ubiquity of amorous inadequacy; the facing of experiences too late – all these are incorporated. I suggest that these are what give us whatever is aesthetically 'pleasurable' or compelling in Hardy's poetry. I suggest too that these concerns are as large for Hardy as are the undeniable pains brought about by social division. For the greater sadness lies in the sense that we are all, no matter our positions in the world, necessarily imperfect, and that most people never claim otherwise.

Finally the issue arises of what all this led to. The premise behind Donald Davie's study of Hardy and others left no doubt about Davie's answer: 'In British poetry of the last fifty years (as not in American) the most far-reaching influence, for good or ill, has been not Yeats, still less Eliot or Pound, not Lawrence, but *Hardy*.'[19] The 'last fifty years' here is approximately 1920–70. Our final question then, if Davie's contention is true, is how far and in what ways it has been so in light of Hardy's aesthetic of imperfection and its social and/or fateful corollaries.

The leading First World War poets who died in battle did so when half of Hardy's poetic output was still to appear. Yet where their responses to

Hardy have survived they are relevant to the matter. Siegfried Sassoon probably persuaded his friend Wilfred Owen to read Hardy's poetry, but we don't know what Owen thought of it, or did with it. At the time Sassoon himself rated Hardy more highly than any other current poet, and frequently visited him at Max Gate in later years; but Sassoon left no major criticism. The more important figure is Edward Thomas, whose stock rose in Britain in the 1970s and 1980s, and whose reviews of Hardy remain interesting. In summary, Thomas found Hardy's sadness and pessimism 'almost perverse' but thought very highly of Hardy's talent. Thomas's astute perceptions give us confidence on both points. Often Hardy's characters 'are or ought to be happy, but there is an inexplicable sigh'. Hardy has obsession, even superstition; but 'only a very great talent could have rescued anything uninjured from the weight of it'.[20] In the confused mix of opinions that were to appear as to Hardy's awkwardnesses, 'clumsiness' (the commonest term) and general poetic incompetence, it is noteworthy that the poets usually seemed to realise what he was doing, and achieving. Thomas was among the first to do so.

In our context of imperfection the responses of the standardly labelled right-wing group of Eliot, Pound and Yeats must be unusually significant. Yeats gave Hardy little house-room in his *Oxford Book of Modern Verse*. Loyalty fluctuated later for Auden and Larkin as between Yeats and Hardy, so the fact that Yeats hardly noticed Hardy is striking. But one of Yeats's few comments on his poetry has a characteristic finality and firmness: 'Thomas Hardy, though his work lacked technical accomplishment, made the necessary correction through his mastery of the impersonal objective scene.'[21] The close is cryptic, but 'making the necessary correction' sounds as if Yeats did recognise a writerly discipline carefully at work. The other two poets, given their political positions, are surprisingly supportive of Hardy. Of course Eliot took little notice, but his well-known comment squares with what was said by more sympathetic critics: 'At times [Hardy's] style touches sublimity without ever having passed through the stage of being good.'[22] At a minimum that is intriguing. F R. Leavis, Virginia Woolf and Katherine Ann Porter expressed the same paradox in more complimentary vein. Ezra Pound's responses were the most positive. He greatly valued Hardy's comments on his own work; he noted one or two poems for special praise; most of all there is the much-quoted comment on the pervasive Hardy mode: 'Now there is a clarity. There is the harvest of having written 20 novels first.'[23] Pound, in particular, saw in Hardy what he was striving for in others and himself: the choice of exact word is all, even if it jars awkwardly with its neighbours; that imperfection doesn't matter if what is thereby expressed is a precise truth. From a different political viewpoint Edmund Blunden saw the same thing. Picking on Hardy's 'oddities' and 'stuffed-owl simplicities', Blunden still concludes that Hardy 'risks all that. He goes his road in the manner of expression, unworried by grinning faces, and in this spirit he arrives at numberless decisive ways of putting things, offered him and accepted from an open love of life.'[24]

The way is now cleared for the theme we meet often from then on. Hardy had a general influence rather than a particular one. Auden twice listed half-a-dozen major influences on his work, Hardy's name being the only one common to both groups. Auden had briefly adopted Eliot's mode but soon found it was not for him. But earlier still, the year before Blunden wrote his own remarks (in 1924), Auden had come across Hardy in an anthology edited by Walter de la Mare. Auden valued Hardy for not being overtly modernistic and sophisticated. 'I was fortunate indeed in finding the only poet who wrote of my world ... For more than a year I read no one else.'[25] Later Auden expanded this.

> [Hardy] was a good poet, perhaps a great one, but not *too* good. Much as I loved him, even I could see that his diction was often clumsy and that a lot of his poems were plain bad. This gave me hope where a flawless poet might have made me despair. His world and sensibility were close enough to mine ... so that, in imitating him, I was being led toward not away from myself.[26]

The only other influences Auden mentions here are Hardy's adherence to regular forms and his firm rebuttal of free verse.

Read in context, the passage is respectful but a touch distant. It is from Auden's inaugural lecture as Professor of Poetry at Oxford in 1956; Auden has gone careful, detached and suave, and he isn't going to commit himself too fully to a poet he has long since put aside for other influences. But this makes our point the more strongly. Auden's use of the standard bad word 'clumsy' here makes us ask all the more what he saw in his early master. The answer has just been given. The *general* ethos raised by Blunden and others, namely, Hardy's overwhelmingly convincing sincerity and clarity, gave Auden and later poets a 'hope' for themselves, in that if such results could be achieved the local manner didn't much matter. Auden's verse scarcely suggests that he 'imitated' Hardy. Rather, in espousing him Auden 'was being led toward not away from myself'. That is to say, although distinctions such as personality, background and even class might still hold, Hardy's example really enabled each poet he influenced to find his own voice, h.s own manner and subject-matter and style – and that, surely, is a general move toward the democratic. Hardy's espoused imperfection, furthermore, is part of the point, for no young poet need feel weighed down ɔy him as by a guru from a higher order – like Milton, or Eliot – and so take aboard a manner or formal poetic diction within an accepted and perhaps over-tight canon. The many newly prominent poets influenced by Auden himself in the 1980s, when the trends toward nationalism and/or nature poetry (Ted Hughes, Peter Redgrove, Geoffrey Hill and R. S. Thomas) were superseded, were thus freed to give fuller attention to a plural, urban and increasingly cosmopolitan or global scene. Such were James Fenton, Michael Hoffmann, Sean O'Brien, Peter Porter and others.

One highly influential poet remained Hardy's champ on throughout. This of course was Philip Larkin. But Larkin's loyalty is especially notable as to how he answered that vexed question of which Hardy's poems are central and which, as many thought, should be discarded. Larkin was uncompromising: 'May I trumpet the assurance that one reader at least would not wish Hardy's *Collected Poems* a single page shorter, and regard it as many times over the best body of poetic work this century so far has to show?'[27] 'So far' was 1966. Actually one feels Larkin was a touch possessive about Hardy. He savagely attacked G. D. Klingopoulos for using, again, the word 'clumsiness'; the context was Barnes but Larkin's animus seems general. Klingopoulos actually said this feature 'seems a guarantee of integrity' in Hardy, and that Hardy 'evolved a sensitive verse style by sheer genuineness of character, a native incorruptibility'. Hardy was, without reservation, 'the most considerable poet ɔetween the time of Hopkins and the First World War'.[28] Unfortunately, this is 'not, of course, to see Hardy as the contemporary equal of Yeats, Lawrence and Eliot', a qualification no doubt adding to Larkin's ire. But the inference is still clear; despite his repeated endorsement Larkin's poetry does not imitate Hardy's.

The debt was comparable to Auden's, though more career-shifting. Larkin first came under the influence of Yeats, probably through his friend Vernon Watkins, who saw Yeats as the century's pre-eminent poet. Larkin then discovered Hardy, and later famously described his effect on him: 'When I came to Hardy it was with a sense of relief that I didn't have to try and jack myself up to a concept of poetry that lay outside my own life ... One could simply relapse into one's own life and write from it.'[29] Yeats had had the reverse effect. In the same passage Larkin names many contemporary poets equally influenced. He listed John Betjeman, C. Day Lewis, and even Dylan Thomas, who (Watkins had told him) regarded Yeats as supreme but Hardy as his favourite.[30] Larkin's comment runs the same note. 'I rather think they may have found what I found, that Hardy gave them confidence to feel in their own way.'

It isn't always underlined how far Larkin's own poetry exemplifies the point. Hardy's influence was a release, not in general a model. Larkin's poetry has virtually no dialogue, narrative or characters. Andrew Motion's *Philip Larkin* (1982) has suggested that the Yeatsian influence never entirely disappears. The 'strong unhindered moon' in 'Dockery and Son', the snow falling 'undated' in 'An Arundel Tomb', and the flight of arrows at the end of 'The Whitsun Weddings', all allow a residual embryonic symbolism to survive. Many of Larkin's exact landscape descriptions, like the evocations of road, supermarket and then beach in 'Here', seem more perfectly worked than Hardy's throwaway, or thrown-to-the-reader, pictures. Both 'Church Going' and 'Dockery and Son' end with firm, tight-knit closing statements, positions achieved and not again to be discarded. As Larkin himself observed, 'there are no successful imitators of Hardy'. He didn't try to become the exception.

In the last three decades of the twentieth century, it might seem, on the one hand, that Hardy's influence has, if not declined, certainly become pervasive or got lost in the crowd. On the other, he has become a cultural monument. This is through the huge allegiance his novels as well as his poetry have attracted, and the sense of an identifiable place – Wessex – which people, tourists and lovers of an older England eagerly explore. But English poetry today is both more urban and more global. Al Alvarez's famous Preface to his 1962 anthology, *The New Poetry*, gave scant attention to Hardy, listing him with the more regrettable forces behind the continuing British regard for what Alvarez called the 'gentility principle'. After that, but also including (despite its title) Michael Horovitz's anthology *Children of Albion* in 1969, the spread has been outward. Increasingly American, Asian and African poets, more and more women poets, poets of little formal education and/or sense of any need to preserve, or even recognise, a British tradition, enter anthologies, win awards and receive wide publication. Blake Morrison and Andrew Motion, in their introduction to the successor-anthology *The Penguin Book of Contemporary British Poetry*, call this 'extending the poetic franchise'. This isn't adduced here as either a good outcome or a bad one. Rather it demonstrates that Hardy's general influence of enablement may have been so successful that it is no longer needed. The trend is irreversible.

The pointedly titled anthology *The New Poetry* of 1993 describes its poets (55 against 20 each in the previous two anthologies) as fresh, risk-taking and plural.[31] The margins have gone to the centre. It may be that the 'loss of the sense of the canon has weakened British poetry' which is 'above all *sceptical*' (editors' emphasis). But the eminent poet Glyn Maxwell can remind us that 'language is always debased currency', while Simon Armitage, also highly rated, is 'loath to stray too far from the semi-literate'.

There is a third inference, from the realms of science. Since the 1960s, as the cognitive basis for many of our chief orientations and decisions, the social sciences have largely been superseded by chaos theory, biology and genetics. The view that we might change human nature via social organisation has been replaced by the view that there are possibly unpalatable truths about our natures and the cosmos which we can observe, possibly locally modify, but not change. This takes us back to the Darwinism which so influenced Hardy in his youth. As it has recently been expressed, Darwin challenged Paley's argument from design, with its stress on formal fixity, replacing this with 'a set of unstable forms that slip into new forms even as they are being named and represented'.[32] Hardy, staying with Darwin, is nearer the post-modern world which today's poets inhabit. All the more then is 'imperfection' in the aesthetic established, for poetry too is 'unstable', and no one now can really say what perfection in poetry ever is. Maybe we conclude where we began, with the imperfection aesthetic of Hardy and Ruskin. Hardy's influence on poetry is now a silent one, but it is still with us.

notes

1. See *Thomas Hardy's Personal Writings*, ed. Harold Orel (London, 1967), p. 22.
2. *The Complete Poems of Thomas Hardy*, ed. James Gibson (London, 1976), pp. 6, 190, 556, 84.
3. Davie suggests that Hardy 'took for granted' the texts of Pugin and Ruskin when he 'talked about the aesthetic of Gothic architecture'; it seems highly likely: Donald Davie, *Thomas Hardy and British Poetry* (London, 1973), p. 14.
4. *The Genius of John Ruskin*, ed. John D. Rosenberg (London, 1964), p. 183.
5. Rosenberg, *The Genius of John Ruskin*, pp. 182–3, 177, 183–4.
6. Hardy's notebooks reveal Mill, along with Darwin, Huxley, Spencer, Comte, Arnold and others, as the most frequent sources among his early reading; but, of Mill, it was probably the social and libertarian ideas that proved most influential.

7. John Stuart Mill, in *James and John Stuart Mill on Education*, ed. F. A. Cavenagh (Westpoint, 1931/1979), p. 196.

8. Hardy is said to have attempted a new form, however slight the difference, in all his 940-plus published poems.

9. The pure aestheticism – real or attributed – of Walter Pater and his followers reaches out into a different area. In his earlier work Pater treated art and life as separate and desirably so, although he did later protest that his aesthetics did not compromise the importance of right morals in either society or art. His first view may or may not be 'elitist', though it would commonly be thought so today. Intriguingly, on their first meeting Hardy described Pater as one 'whose manner is that of carrying weighty ideas without spilling them' (Michael Millgate, *Thomas Hardy: A Biography* (Oxford, 1982), p. 273). This nicely suggests the Paterian fastidiousness by which art is to be viewed; but it also contrasts the 'clumsiness' which the majority of earlier critics saw in Hardy's own verse.

10. Davie, *Thomas Hardy and British Poetry*, pp. 62, 36, 28.

11. My argument for this would focus on Davie's notion of Hardy as 'engineer'. Claude Lévi-Strauss once distinguished between the engineer and the bricoleur; Hardy seems to me to have been the latter. See Lévi-Strauss, *The Savage Mind* (London, 1966), esp. pp. 16–21.

12. Davie, *Thomas Hardy and British Poetry*, pp. 48, 23. Davie sees the poem, even so, as 'a much better piece' than 'The Wind's Prophecy' (p. 22), thereby assigning the latter poem a very low rank indeed. I can only demur, seeing 'The Wind's Prophecy' as a strong and clear example of what Hillis Miller describes in *Thomas Hardy: Distance and Desire* (Oxford, 1970) as the broken-backed or 'double-vision' poem.

13. Davie, *Thomas Hardy and British Poetry*, p. 6.

14. John Powell Ward, 'The Aesthetic and Literature', *Critical Survey*, 13(1) (2001), pp. 1–17.

15. Discussed in Hillis Miller's terms, more lengthily than possible here, in John Powell Ward, *The English Line: Poetry of the Unpoetic from Wordsworth to Larkin* (London, 1991), esp. pp. 109–12.

16. Clearly many of these dual tensions may match gender tensions. U. C. Knoepflmacher has seen 'Hardy's recovery of the feminine [as] the propelling force behind many of his finest lyrics'. To Rosemarie Morgan, reviewing Knoepflmacher, this was 'Hardy's empowerment of the female voice'. That being so, while retaining his own maleness, the cleft between the two equal visions was set up. U. C. Knoepflmacher, 'Hardy Ruins: Female Spaces and Male Designs', in Margaret R. Higgonet, ed., *The Sense of Sex: Feminist Perspectives on Hardy* (Urbana and Chicago, 1993), reviewed by Rosemarie Morgan in *Thomas Hardy Journal*, X, May 1994, pp. 73–5.

17. Isobel Armstrong, *The Radical Aesthetic* (Oxford, 2000), pp. 63–5.

18. Armstrong, *The Radical Aesthetic*, pp. 62–3; emphasis in the original.

19. Davie, *Thomas Hardy and British Poetry*, p. 3; emphasis in the original.

20. Edward Thomas, *A Language Not To Be Betrayed: Selected Prose*, ed. Edna Longley (Manchester, 1981). On the perversity: Thomas especially cited the double-vision poem 'The Curate's Kindness' in this regard. In the terms used above, Thomas perhaps saw that poem as a case of the 'facetiousness [or] kind of

agonistic comedy rather than irony' to which Armstrong referred as the provenance of the 'broken middle'. See pp. 71, 73, 68.

21. W. B. Yeats, *Selected Criticism and Prose*, ed. A. Norman Jeffares (London, 1980), p. 218.
22. Quoted from Ralph W. V. Elliott, *Thomas Hardy's English* (Oxford, 1984), p. 15.
23. *The Letters of Ezra Pound*, ed. D. D. Paige (New York, 1950), p. 294; Pound's emphasis.
24. Quoted from Elliott, *Thomas Hardy's English*, p. 17.
25. Humphrey Carpenter, *W. H. Auden: A Biography* (London, 1981), p. 35.
26. W. H. Auden, *The Dyer's Hand & Other Essays* (London, 1963), p. 38.
27. Philip Larkin, *Required Writing: Miscellaneous Pieces 1955–1982* (London, 1983), p. 174.
28. *Selected Letters of Philip Larkin, 1940–1985*, ed. Anthony Thwaite (London, 1992); G. D. Klingopoulos, 'The Literary Scene' in *From Dickens to Hardy*, ed. Boris Ford (Harmondsworth, 1958), pp. 85, 69, 97.
29. Larkin, *Required Writing*, p. 175.
30. Passages in Dylan Thomas's poems, evincing his compulsion to select words very exactly, sometimes ring closely of some of Hardy's. An extended study of this might be profitable.
31. *The New Poetry*, eds Michael Hulse, David Kennedy and David Morley (Newcastle-upon-Tyne, 1993).
32. Roger Ebbaston, reviewing James Krasner's *The Entangled Eye*, *Thomas Hardy Journal*, XIII, May 1997, p. 85. The words of the internal quotation are Krasner's.

select bibliography

bibliographies

Davis, W. Eugene, and Helmut E. Gerber. *Thomas Hardy: An Annotated Bibliography of Writings about Him*. De Kalb, Ill.: Northern Illinois University Press, 1973
Davis, W. Eugene, and Helmut E. Gerber. *Thomas Hardy: An Annotated Bibliography of Writings about Him, Vol II: 1970–1978 and Supplement for 1871–1969*. De Kalb, Ill.: Northern Illinois University Press, 1983
Draper, Ronald P., and Martin S. Ray. *An Annotated Critical Bibliography of Thomas Hardy*. London and New York: Macmillan, 1989
Millgate, Michael. 'Thomas Hardy'. *Victorian Fiction: A Second Guide to Research*, ed. George H. Ford. New York: Modern Language Association of America, 1978
Purdy, Richard Little. *Thomas Hardy: A Bibliographical Study*. Oxford: Clarendon Press, 1954

biographies

Brennecke, Ernest. *The Life of Thomas Hardy*. New York: Greenpoint Press, 1925
Gibson, James. *Thomas Hardy: A Literary Life*. London: Macmillan, 1996
Gibson, James, ed. *Thomas Hardy: Interviews and Recollections*. London: Macmillan, 1999
Gittings, Robert. *Young Thomas Hardy*. London: Heinemann, 1975
Gittings, Robert. *The Older Thomas Hardy*. London: Heinemann, 1978
Hands, Timothy. *A Hardy Chronology*. London: Macmillan, 1992
Hardy, Evelyn. *Thomas Hardy: A Critical Biography*. London: Hogarth Press, 1954
Millgate, Michael. *Thomas Hardy: A Biography*. New York: Random House, 1982
O'Sullivan, Timothy. *Thomas Hardy: An Illustrated Biography*. London: Macmillan, 1975
Seymour-Smith, Martin. *Hardy*. London: Bloomsbury, 1994
Stewart, J. I. M. *Thomas Hardy: A Critical Biography*. Harlow: Longman, 1971
Turner, Paul. *The Life of Thomas Hardy*. Oxford: Blackwell, 1998
Weber, Carl. *Hardy of Wessex: His Life and Literary Career*. New York: Columbia University Press, 1940; reprinted 1966

life, letters, and notebooks

Beatty, C. J. P., ed. *The Architectural Notebook of Thomas Hardy*. Dorchester: Dorset Natural History and Archaeological Society, 1966

Björk, Lennart A., ed. *The Literary Notebooks of Thomas Hardy*. 2 vols. London: Macmillan, 1985
Millgate, Michael, ed. *The Life and Work of Thomas Hardy, by Thomas Hardy*. London: Macmillan, 1984
Millgate, Michael, ed. *Thomas Hardy's Public Voice; The Essays, Speeches, and Miscellaneous Prose*. Oxford: Clarendon Press, 2001
Orel, Harold, ed. *Thomas Hardy's Personal Writings*. New York: St. Martin's Press, 1990
Purdy, Richard Little, and Michael Millgate, eds. *The Collected Letters of Thomas Hardy*. 7 vols. Oxford: Clarendon Press, 1978–88
Taylor, Richard H., ed. *The Personal Notebooks of Thomas Hardy*. London: Macmillan, 1979

general criticism

Abercrombie, Lascelles. *Thomas Hardy: A Critical Study*. London: Secker, 1912
Bailey, J. O. *The Poetry of Thomas Hardy: A Handbook and Commentary*. Chapel Hill: University of North Carolina Press, 1970
Bayley, John. *An Essay on Hardy*. Cambridge: Cambridge University Press, 1978
Beach, Joseph Warren. *The Technique of Thomas Hardy*. Chicago, Ill.: University of Chicago Press, 1922; reprinted New York: Russell & Russell, 1962
Beer, Gillian. *Darwin's Plots: Evolutionary Narrative in Darwin, George Eliot and Ninteenth-Century Fiction*. Cambridge: Cambridge University Press, 1983, 2nd edition 2000
Berger, Sheila. *Thomas Hardy and Visual Structures: Framing, Disruption, Process*. New York: New York University Press, 1990
Bloom, Harold, ed. *Modern Critical Interpretations of Thomas Hardy*. New York: Chelsea, 1987
Blunden, Edmund. *Thomas Hardy*. London: Macmillan, 1967
Boumelha, Penny. *Thomas Hardy and Women: Sexual Ideology and Narrative Form*. Brighton: Harvester, 1982
Brady, Kristin. *The Short Stories of Thomas Hardy*. London: Macmillan, 1982
Brooks, Jean R. *Thomas Hardy: The Poetic Structure*. London: Elek Books, 1971
Brown, Douglas. *Thomas Hardy*. London: Longmans, Green, 1954; revised edition 1961
Buckler, William. *The Poetry of Thomas Hardy: A Study in Art and Ideas*. New York: New York University Press, 1983
Bullen, J. B. *The Expressive Eye: Fiction and Perception in the Works of Thomas Hardy*. Oxford: Clarendon Press, 1986
Butler, Lance St J., ed. *Thomas Hardy After Fifty Years*. London: Macmillan, 1977
Butler, Lance St J., ed. *Alternative Hardy*. London: Macmillan, 1989
Carpenter, Richard C. *Thomas Hardy*. New York: Twayne, 1964
Casagrande, Peter. *Unity in Hardy's Novels: 'Repetitive Symmetries'*. London: Macmillan, 1982
Chapman, Raymond. *The Language of Thomas Hardy*. London: Macmillan, 1990
Clarke, Graham, ed. *Thomas Hardy: Critical Assessments of Writers in English*. 4 vols. Mountfield, East Sussex: Helm Information, 1993

Clements, Patricia, and Grindle, Juliet, eds. *The Poetry of Thomas Hardy*. New York: Barnes and Noble, 1980

Collins, Deborah L. *Thomas Hardy and His God: A Liturgy of Unbelief*. London: Macmillan, 1990

Cox, R. G., ed. *Thomas Hardy: The Critical Heritage*. London: Routledge & Kegan Paul, 1970

Daleski, H. M. *Thomas Hardy and Paradoxes of Love*. Columbia and London: University of Missouri Press, 1997

Davie, Donald. *Thomas Hardy and British Poetry*. London: Routledge & Kegan Paul, 1973

Draper, Ronald P., ed. *Hardy: The Tragic Novels*. London: Macmillan, 1975; revised edition 1991

Ebbatson, Roger. *The Evolutionary Self: Hardy, Forster, Lawrence*. Brighton: Harvester, 1982

Ebbatson, Roger. *Hardy: The Margin of the Unexpressed*. Sheffield: Sheffield Academic Press, 1993

Elliott, Ralph W. V. *Thomas Hardy's English*. Oxford: Basil Blackwell, 1984

Elvy, Margaret. *Sexing Hardy: Thomas Hardy and Feminism*. London: Crescent Moon, 1998

Enstice, Andrew. *Thomas Hardy: Landscapes of the Mind*. London: Macmillan, 1979

Federico, Annette. *Masculine Identity in Hardy and Gissing*, London and Toronto: Associated University Presses, 1991

Firor, Ruth. *Folkways in Thomas Hardy*. Philadelphia: University of Pennsylvania Press, 1931

Fisher, Joe. *The Hidden Hardy*. London: Macmillan, 1992

Garson, Marjorie. *Hardy's Fables of Integrity: Woman, Body, Text*. Oxford: Clarendon Press, 1991

Gatrell, Simon. *Hardy the Creator: A Textual Biography*. Oxford: Clarendon Press, 1988

Gatrell, Simon. *Thomas Hardy and the Proper Study of Mankind*. London: Macmillan, 1993

Gibson, James, and Johnson, Trevor, eds. *Thomas Hardy: Poems*. London: Macmillan, 1979; 1991

Goode, John. *Thomas Hardy: The Offensive Truth*. Oxford: Blackwell, 1988

Green, Brian. *Hardy's Lyrics: Pearls of Pity*. London: Macmillan, 1996

Greenslade, William. *Degeneration, Culture and the Novel 1880–1940*. Cambridge: Cambridge University Press, 1994

Gregor, Ian. *The Great Web: The Form of Hardy's Major Fiction*. London: Faber and Faber, 1974

Grundy, Joan. *Hardy and the Sister Arts*. London: Macmillan, 1979

Guerard, Albert J. *Thomas Hardy: The Novels and Stories*. Cambridge, Mass.: Harvard University Press, 1949; revised edition, London: New Directions, 1964

Hands, Timothy. *Thomas Hardy: Distracted Preacher? Hardy's Religious Biography and its Influence on his Novels*. London: Macmillan, 1989

Hands, Timothy. *Thomas Hardy*. London: Macmillan, 1995

Hardy, Barbara. *Thomas Hardy: Imagining Imagination: Hardy's Poetry and Fiction*. London: Athlone Press, 2000

Higonnet, Margaret R., ed. *The Sense of Sex: Feminist Perspectives on Thomas Hardy*. Urbana: University of Illinois Press, 1993

Howe, Irving. *Thomas Hardy*. New York: Macmillan, 1967

Hughes, John. *'Ecstatic Sound': Music and Individuality in the Work of Thomas Hardy*. Aldershot: Ashgate, 2001

Ingham, Patricia. *Thomas Hardy: A Feminist Reading*. Hemel Hempstead: Harvester, 1989

Irwin, Michael. *Reading Hardy's Landscapes*. London: Palgrave Macmillan, 2000

Jedzerewski, Jan. *Thomas Hardy and the Church*. London: Macmillan, 1996

Johnson, Trevor. *A Critical Introduction to the Poems of Thomas Hardy*. London: Macmillan, 1991

Kay-Robinson, Denis. *Hardy's Wessex Reappraised*. Newton Abbott: David and Charles, 1971

King, Jeanette. *Tragedy in the Victorian Novel: Theory and Practice in the Novels of George Eliot, Thomas Hardy and Henry James*. Cambridge: Cambridge University Press, 1978

Kramer, Dale. *Thomas Hardy: The Forms of Tragedy*. Detroit: Wayne State University Press, 1975

Kramer, Dale, ed. *Critical Approaches to the Fiction of Thomas Hardy*. London: Macmillan, 1979

Kramer, Dale, ed. *The Cambridge Companion to Thomas Hardy*. Cambridge: Cambridge University Press, 1999

Laird, John Tudor. *The Shaping of 'Tess of the d'Urbervilles'*. Oxford: Oxford University Press, 1975

Langbaum, Robert. *Thomas Hardy in Our Time*. London: Macmillan, 1995

Lawrence, D. H. *Study of Thomas Hardy and Other Essays*, ed. Bruce Steele. Cambridge: Cambridge University Press, 1985

Lerner, Laurence, and John Holmstrom, eds. *Thomas Hardy and His Readers: A Selection of Contemporary Reviews*. London: Bodley Head, 1968

Lucas, John. *The Literature of Change: Studies in the Nineteenth-Century Provincial Novel*. Brighton: Harvester, 1977

Lucas, John. *Modern English Poetry from Hardy to Hughes*. London: Batsford, 1986

Mallett, Phillip, ed. *The Achievement of Thomas Hardy*. London: Macmillan, 2000.

Mallett, Phillip, ed. *Thomas Hardy: Texts and Contexts*. London: Macmillan, 2002.

Mallett, Phillip V., and Ronald P. Draper, eds. *A Spacious Vision: Essays on Thomas Hardy*. Penzance: Patten Press, 1994

Meisel, Perry. *Thomas Hardy: The Return of the Repressed*. New Haven: Yale University Press, 1972

Miller, J. Hillis. *Thomas Hardy: Distance and Desire*. Cambridge, Mass.: Harvard University Press, 1970

Miller, J. Hillis. *Fiction and Repetition: Seven English Novels*. Cambridge, Mass.: Harvard University Press, 1982

Millgate, Michael. *Thomas Hardy: His Career as a Novelist*. London: Bodley Head, 1971

Moore, Kevin Z. *The Descent of the Imagination: Postromantic Culture in the Later Novels of Thomas Hardy*. New York: New York University Press, 1990

Morgan, Rosemarie. *Women and Sexuality in the Novels of Thomas Hardy*. London: Routledge, 1988

Morgan, Rosemarie. *Cancelled Words: Rediscovering Thomas Hardy*. London: Routledge, 1992

Morrell, Roy. *Thomas Hardy: The Will and the Way*. Kuala Lumpur: University of Malaysia Press, 1965

Orel, Harold. *The Final Years of Thomas Hardy, 1912–1928*. London: Macmillan, 1976

Orel, Harold, ed. *Critical Essays on Thomas Hardy's Poetry*. New York: G. K. Hall, 1995

Page, Norman. *Thomas Hardy*. London: Routledge & Kegan Paul, 1977

Page, Norman, ed. *Thomas Hardy: The Writer and His Background*. London: Bell and Hyman, 1980

Page, Norman, ed. *Oxford Reader's Companion to Thomas Hardy*. Oxford: Oxford University Press, 2000

Paterson, John. *The Making of 'The Return of the Native'*. Berkeley: University of California Press, 1960

Paulin, Tom. *Thomas Hardy: The Poetry of Perception*. London: Macmillan, 1975

Pettit, Charles P. C., ed. *New Perspectives on Thomas Hardy*. London: Macmillan, 1994

Pettit, Charles P. C., ed. *Reading Thomas Hardy*. London: Macmillan, 1998

Pinion, F. B. *A Hardy Companion*. London: Macmillan, 1968

Pite, Ralph. *Hardy's Geography: Wessex and the Regional Novel*. London: Palgrave Macmillan, 2002

Ray, Martin. *Thomas Hardy: A Textual Study of the Short Stories*. Aldershot: Ashgate, 1997

Rutland, William R. *Thomas Hardy: A Study of His Writings and Their Background*. Oxford: Basil Blackwell, 1938

Smith, Anne, ed. *The Novels of Thomas Hardy*. New York: Barnes and Noble, 1979

Southerington, F. R. *Hardy's Vision of Man*. London: Chatto and Windus, 1971

Springer, Marlene. *Hardy's Art of Allusion*. London: Macmillan, 1983

Sumner, Rosemary. *Thomas Hardy: Psychological Novelist*. London: Macmillan, 1981

Taylor, Dennis. *Hardy's Poetry, 1860–1928*. London: Macmillan, 1981; 1989

Taylor, Dennis. *Hardy's Metres and Victorian Prosody*. Oxford: Clarendon Press, 1988

Taylor, Dennis. *Hardy's Literary Language and Victorian Philology*. Oxford: Clarendon Press, 1993

Taylor, Richard H. *The Neglected Hardy: Thomas Hardy's Lesser Novels*. London: Macmillan, 1982

Thomas, Jane. *Thomas Hardy, Femininity and Dissent: Reassessing the 'Minor' Novels*. London: Macmillan, 1999

Vigar, Penelope. *The Novels of Thomas Hardy: Illusion and Reality*. London: Athlone Press, 1974

White, R. J. *Thomas Hardy and History*. New York: Harper and Row, 1974

Widdowson, Peter. *Hardy in History: A Study in Literary Sociology*. London and New York: Routledge, 1989

Widdowson, Peter. *On Thomas Hardy: Late Essays and Earlier*. London: Macmillan, 1998

Williams, Merryn. *Thomas Hardy and Rural England*. London: Macmillan, 1972

Wing, George. *Thomas Hardy*. Edinburgh: Oliver and Boyd, 1953

Wotton, George. *Thomas Hardy: Towards a Materialist Criticsin*. Dublin: Gill & Macmillan, 1985

Wright, T. R. *Hardy and the Erotic*. London: Macmillan, 1989

Wright, Walter. *The Shaping of 'The Dynasts'*. Lincoln: University of Nebraska Press, 1967

Zietlow, Paul. *Moments of Vision: The Poetry of Thomas Hardy*. Cambridge, Mass.: Harvard University Press, 1974

index.